Radiation Protection in Nuclear Medicine and Pathology

THE INSTITUTE OF
PHYSICAL SCIENCES
IN MEDICINE

Radiation Protection in Nuclear Medicine and Pathology

Edited by
K E Goldstone, P C Jackson, M J Myers and A E Simpson

Report No. 63

Published by the Institute of Physical Sciences in Medicine
P.O. Box 303, York YO1 2WR, England

Printed by Stephen Austin & Sons Ltd., Hertford

CONTENTS

PREFACE

Over the years and in response to increasing public awareness of the potential hazards of ionising radiations, the United Kingdom Parliament has introduced legislation and regulations controlling the use of radioactive substances. Many of the Statutory Instruments have encompassed the use of radiation in both industry and hospitals and the regulations have influenced greatly the working practices of many professions associated with the use of unsealed radionuclides. In particular, legislation has been concerned with the proper and safe use, transport and disposal of unsealed radionuclides, and the administration to patients of radioactive substances. In practice, the regulations governing the hospital use of unsealed radionuclides have been implemented under the auspices of the Health and Safety Executive (HSE), the Department of the Environment (DoE) and the Administration of Radioactive Substances Advisory Committee (ARSAC). Further legislation has required the professions concerned to include a demonstrable, practical knowledge of radiation safety with unsealed radionuclides in training and professional examinations.

The Institute of Physical Sciences in Medicine (IPSM) has instigated, through its Radionuclide and Radiation Protection Topic Groups, a working committee to produce this handbook that enables both experienced radiation physicists and others in the field to obtain an up-to-date knowledge of the legislation and be able to fulfill relevant regulations in practice. Personnel experienced both in the day to day handling of unsealed radionuclides and in the interpretation of the regulations were asked to write the relevant chapters, and the committee is grateful to all the authors who have made contributions.

The committee has sought throughout this book to produce self-contained chapters on specialist topics, which highlight the relevant features of practical radionuclide safety and allow rapid assimilation of information. For this reason, the reader may become aware of recurring themes throughout the book which are given emphasis according to the requirements of the speciality. A glossary of terminology has been included. Should the reader require more information, a bibliography is included in the current edition of the Guidance Notes (see Chapter 1, reference 11). Later chapters provide expert knowledge and practical advice on topics necessary to all specialities. The information and data, particularly relating to dose limits, have been extracted from legislation current at the time of going to press. It is important to appreciate that estimates of the amount, effects and allowed limits of exposure of the population to ionising radiation are constantly being reviewed and the reader should refer always to current legislation to ensure compliance.

The working committee are grateful for the assistance received from colleagues in the preparation of this book, particularly members of the Radiation Protection and Radionuclide Topic Groups, and the Scientific and Publications Committees of the IPSM. We are, of course, indebted to the authors for their enthusiasm and dedication in producing manuscripts. The editors acknowledge the great loss to the scientific community of the untimely death of Trevor Godden and thank his wife and family for allowing his manuscript (Chapter 2) to be published.

The editors wish to thank in particular Miss Louise Lovejoy and Mrs Janet Fish for typing the manuscript.

K E Goldstone	M J Myers
P C Jackson	A E Simpson

CONTRIBUTORS

Mr C B Clayton BSc,
Royal Victoria Infirmary, Queen Victoria Road, Newcastle upon Tyne NE1 4LP

Dr M Frier BPharm, MRPharmS, PhD,
Medical Physics Department, Queen's Medical Centre, Nottingham NG7 2UH

Mr T J Godden, BSc, FIPSM, (deceased)
Department of Medical Physics and Bioengineering, Bristol Radiotherapy and
Oncology Centre, Horfield Road, Bristol BS2 8ED

Mrs K E Goldstone, BSc, MSc, FIPSM,
East Anglian Regional Radiation Protection Service, Addenbrooke's Hospital,
Hills Road, Cambridge CB2 2QQ

Dr S R Hesslewood, BPharm, PhD, MRPharmS, MCPP,
Department of Physics & Nuclear Medicine, Dudley Road Hospital, Dudley
Road, Birmingham B18 7QH

Dr P C Jackson, BSc, PhD, CPhys, FInstP, FIPSM,
Department of Medical Physics & Bioengineering, Bristol General Hospital,
Guinea Street, Bristol BS1 6SY

Dr P J Mountford, BSc, MSc, PhD, CPhys, FInstP, FIPSM,
Department of Medical Physics, Kent & Canterbury Hospital, Ethelbert Road,
Canterbury CT1 3NG

Dr M J Myers, BSc, PhD, ARCS, MIPSM,
Department of Medical Physics, Hammersmith Hospital, DuCane Road, London
W12 0HS

Ms E M Pitcher, BSc, MSc, MIPSM,
Department of Medical Physics and Bioengineering, Bristol General Hospital,
Guinea Street, Bristol BS1 6SY

Dr P J Roberts, BSc, MSc, PhD, FIPSM,
Regional Radiation Physics and Protection Service, Queen Elizabeth Medical
Centre, Edgbaston, Birmingham B15 2TH
present address:
Regional Medical Physics Department, Southampton General Hospital, Tremona
Road, Shirley, Southampton SO9 4XY

Dr A E Simpson, MA, PhD, CPhys, MInstP, MIPSM,
Regional Medical Physics Department, Newcastle General Hospital, Westgate
Road, Newcastle upon Tyne NE4 6BE

Dr E D Williams, MA, MSc, PhD, CPhys, FInstP, FIPSM,
Regional Medical Physics Department, Sunderland District General Hospital,
Kayll Road, Sunderland SR4 7TP

GLOSSARY

This glossary gives operational rather than strict definitions and should not be read in isolation from other texts.

Absorbed dose The energy imparted per unit mass of material by ionising radiation. The SI unit of absorbed dose is the Gray (Gy) which is equivalent to $1 \, J \, kg^{-1}$.

Activity concentration The ratio of the activity of a radioactive substance to the total mass of the solution or mixture. The units will generally be $Bq \, g^{-1}$. This is sometimes, incorrectly, called the **specific activity**.

ALARA as low as reasonably achievable—the general principle applied to radiation exposures.

Annual limit on intake (ALI) The quantity of a radionuclide which, when introduced into the body, results in a **Committed Effective Dose Equivalent** or individual organ dose equal to the appropriate annual **dose limit**.

ARSAC Administration of Radioactive Substances Advisory Committee, which provides advice to the Secretary of State for Health on guidance concerning this subject, and certification of doctors to administer radioactivity to humans.

Becquerel (Bq) The SI unit of radioactivity equal to 1 nuclear disintegration per second. This supercedes the old unit of radioactivity, the Curie (Ci), which is equivalent to $37 \times 10^9 \, Bq$.

Bremsstrahlung is penetrating radiation (photons) emitted when a charged particle such as an electron is slowed or stopped in matter.

Classified person An employee who has been designated, in accordance with the Ionising Radiations Regulations (Reg 9(1)), as likely to receive a dose which exceeds 3/10 of any relevant dose limit. Such workers receive special monitoring and medical surveillance.

Committed effective dose equivalent (CEDE) The effective dose equivalent summed over a period of 50 years following the intake of one or more radionuclides into the body.

Controlled area An area, designated in accordance with the Ionising Radiations Regulations (Regs 8(1) or (3)), inside which doses from ionising radiation are likely to exceed 3/10 of any dose limit for employees aged 18 years or over. A detailed explanation is given in Chapter 1.

Derived limit (DL) A measurable unit, which will ensure that an exposed person will not exceed the appropriate **dose limit**. The **Annual Limit on Intake** is one such derived limit. Others include Derived Air Concentration (DAC), Derived Water Concentration (DWC) and Derived Levels of Surface Contamination.

Dose equivalent The dose equivalent, commonly referred to simply as 'dose', is the product of the **absorbed dose** and the **quality factor** (Q). The SI unit of dose equivalent is the **Sievert** (Sv) which is equivalent to $1 \, J \, kg^{-1}$. For X and gamma radiation ($Q = 1$), the dose equivalent in Sv is numerically equal to the absorbed dose in Gy.

Dose limits The limits of radiation dose to employees and trainees, and **members of the public**, excluding the doses resulting from natural background radiation and any **medical exposure**. Whole body dose limits apply to the sum of the **EDE** received from external exposure and the **CEDE** resulting from the intake of **radionuclides** during the same period. There are further limits on the individual dose to certain specified organs (e.g. the lens of the eye).

Dose rate Commonly, and interchangeably, used to refer to the rate of exposure to ionising radiation in terms of either **absorbed dose** or **dose equivalent**, and expressed in units of $Gy\,h^{-1}$ or $Sv\,h^{-1}$ respectively.

Effective dose (equivalent) (EDE) The sum of the products of **dose equivalent** and risk weighting factor for individual organs, and is related to the **dose equivalent** from uniform whole body exposure. The risk weighting factor reflects the relative risk of fatal malignancy and genetic defects due to exposure to ionising radiation of the individual organ. The SI unit of EDE is the **Sievert** (Sv) which is equivalent to $1\,J\,kg^{-1}$.

Gray (Gy) The SI unit of absorbed dose equal to $1\,J\,kg^{-1}$. The obsolete unit of absorbed dose is the rad, which is equivalent to $10\,mGy$.

ICRP International Commission on Radiological Protection—an international body founded in 1928, which provides general guidance on radiation protection.

Instantaneous dose rate The **dose rate** averaged over one minute at a particular location (as defined in the Ionising Radiations Regulations 1985).

Intervention level A value of an actual or derived dose quantity which, when exceeded, will initiate an investigation, contingency or emergency plan.

Isomer An alternative name for a metastable **radionuclide** (e.g. Tc-99m is an isomer of Tc-99).

Isotope Refers to **nuclides** of the same chemical element (i.e. same atomic number) but differing mass numbers. If the isotope is unstable (i.e. a **radionuclide**) it is termed a **radioisotope**.

Linear energy transfer (LET) The energy transferred to the medium as ionising radiation traverses a small distance within the medium. The unit of LET is $keV\,\mu m^{-1}$.

Medical exposure The intentional irradiation of a person, either externally or internally, for the purpose of his or her *own* medical treatment or diagnosis or as the subject of medical research. It does not include the incidental exposure of others.

Members of the public Individuals in the general population, but excluding occupationally exposed workers or trainees during their working hours or patients or volunteers while undergoing a medical exposure.

NRPB The National Radiological Protection Board (NRPB) was established by the Radiological Protection Act 1970. It is the national point of authoritative reference in radiological protection. Its principal duties are to advance the acquisition of knowledge on protecting mankind from radiation hazards and to provide information and advice to persons (including Government Departments) with responsibilities in the United Kingdom for protecting the community as a whole or particular sections of it from radiation hazards.

Nuclide A species of atom, characterised by its elemental chemical form (atomic number), its nuclear mass (mass number) and nuclear energy state. If the nuclide is unstable, it will change to a more stable form by radioactive decay, and is termed a **radionuclide**. (See also **isotope**.)

Qualified person A person, appointed in accordance with the Ionising Radiations Regulations (Regs 24(3) and 10(7)), who is competent to examine and test radiation monitoring equipment.

Quality factor (Q) A dimensionless number used to weight absorbed doses according to the effectiveness of the radiation in damaging tissue, and is a function of **LET**; e.g. currently the quality factor for X and gamma reays is 1, whereas for alpha particles it is 20.

Radiation Protection Supervisor (RPS) A competent employee appointed by the employer, in accordance with the Ionising Radiations Regulations 1985 (Reg 11), to secure compliance with the requirements of the Regulations covering work with ionising radiations.

Radiation Protection Adviser (RPA) A qualified and experienced person, generally an expert radiation physicist, appointed, in accordance with the Ionising Radiations Regulations (Reg 10), to advise an employer on compliance with the Regulations and on other radiation safety matters.

Radioisotope A radioactive **isotope**, having the same chemical properties as the stable isotopes of the same element but being physically distinguishable by its radioiactive emissions.

Radionuclide A radioactive nuclide. The term is in practice often used interchangeably with **radioisotope**.

Sievert (Sv) The SI unit of **dose equivalent** (or the related dose quantities **EDE** and **CEDE**) equal to $1 \, J \, kg^{-1}$. The obsolete unit of dose equivalent is the rem, which is equivalent to $10 \, mSv$.

Specific activity The ratio of the activity of a radiolabelled compound to the mass of that *same compound* (unlabelled) present in a solution or mixture. The units will generally be $Bq \, g^{-1}$. This is sometimes incorrectly used to refer to **activity concentration**.

Specific gamma ray constant The exposure rate at a point 1 metre from a 1 Curie source measured in $rad \, hour^{-1}$.

Supervised area An area, other than a controlled area, designated in accordance with the Ionising Radiations Regulations 1985 (Regs 8(2) or (3)), inside which doses of ionising radiation are likely to exceed 1/10 of any dose limit for employees aged 18 or over. (A detailed explanation is given in Chapter 1.)

Tenth value layer The thickness of a material necessary to reduce the transmission of gamma photons to one tenth of the initial value.

Time averaged dose rate The dose rate averaged over any 8 hour working period at a particular location, as defined in the Ionising Radiation Regulations 1985.

CHAPTER 1

Legal and Administrative Framework

P J Roberts

1.1 Introduction

Radiation protection legislation is concerned with the protection of people both individually and in general against detrimental effects of exposure to radiation, while still allowing the various beneficial uses from which radiation exposure arises. The detrimental effects are either *stochastic*, for which the probability of occurrence is a function of the dose received, or *non-stochastic* (*deterministic*), for which the severity of the effect depends on the radiation dose received but for which there is no known effect below a certain threshold. Possible hereditary effects and carcinogenesis are of prime concern in the case of stochastic effects while cataracts and skin ulcerations are examples of non-stochastic effects.

The Ionising Radiations Regulations (1985)[1] have been made under the **Health and Safety at Work etc Act (1974)**[2] to provide mandatory safe conditions which will ensure that doses from ionising radiation are kept at or below an acceptable level so that non-stochastic effects will not occur during the lifetime of an employee and the probability of any stochastic effects is extremely low. The dose limits specified are based on the best available international evidence on radiation exposure and associated risks. They are, however, currently under review.

The largest contribution to the radiation dose to the population is from the natural background radiation, discussion of which is outside the scope of this book. The majority of hospital employees working with ionising radiation do not increase their radiation exposure by more than the variation in natural background over the UK because of the required safe working practices which are implicit in the legislation. The largest man-made source of radiation exposure to the population is from the medical use of ionising radiation and legislation regarding the protection for patients aims at the lowest possible exposure for the benefit expected.

This chapter identifies the administrative requirements which must be satisfied by any employer undertaking work which uses radioactive materials. Heads of departments using radioactive materials, Radiation Protection Advisers and Supervisors, and any others directly involved in radiation protection should be familiar with the legal background. Duties and responsibilities imposed on employers and employees through legislation must be rigorously upheld.

1.2 Legal Background

The legal foundation for practical health and safety in hospitals is the **Health and Safety at Work etc Act (1974)**[2] (HSW Act). Relevant statutory provisions which predate this have been incorporated by reference in Schedule 1 of the HSW Act with the stated objective that they will, in due course, be replaced. Meanwhile, the enforcement provisions of the Act apply to all relevant statutory provisions. Regulations which have been made subsequent to the Act refer back to the Act, being made under powers embodied within the Act, so the basic provisions and

1

philosophy of this Act are fundamental to all present and future safety practices. There is no Crown Immunity for Health Authorities from any regulations formed under the Act **[National Health Service (Amendment) Act (1986)]**[3].

The HSW Act was passed by Parliament in 1974 to establish a cohesive foundation for the health, safety and welfare of all employees while at work (see Section 1.5). Additionally, the European Community has issued Directives[4-7] relating to safety of workers and the public which the UK has incorporated into regulations made under the Act.

The regulations which have been made in the UK under the HSW Act as a direct result of these Directives are **The Ionising Radiations Regulations (1985) (IRR)**[1]. **The Ionising Radiation (Protection of Persons undergoing Medical Examination or Treatment) Regulations (1988) (POPUMET)**[8] have been made to comply with European legislation. These two sets of regulations embrace all the legal requirements for the safe use of unsealed radioactive substances in medicine; they establish the basic safety standards for the protection of workers and the general public, including patients, against the risks of ionising radiation. They cover every use of ionising radiation from radioimmunoassay kits to nuclear fuel reprocessing, and are therefore expressed in very general terms which are subject to different interpretations depending on the specific application.

To assist in determining the requirements, there are various Codes and Guidance Notes[9-14], some approved in a legal sense by the Health and Safety Executive (HSE) (e.g. **Approved Code of Practice: the protection of persons against ionising radiation arising from any work activity (1985) (ACOP)**[14]). Approved Codes of Practice should be followed unless equally satisfactory alternative methods of implementing the law can be substantiated. Approved Codes would always be cited as evidence in any legal proceedings in the same way as the Highway Code. Codes of Practice which have not been approved and Guidance Notes (e.g. **Guidance Notes for the protection of persons against ionising radiations arising from medical and dental use (1988) (Guidance Notes)**[11]), have no strict legal status and are simply advisory but do provide useful practical advice.

1.3 Legislation: Radioactive Substances Act (1960)[15]

The keeping and use of radioactive material together with the accumulation and disposal of radioactive waste are regulated by the **Radioactive Substances Act (1960)**[15] which is enforced in England by the Radiochemical Inspectorate, now part of HM Inspectorate of Pollution in the Department of the Environment. Through this Act, the control of and accounting for radioactive materials and waste are exercised for the purpose of protecting people and the environment.

1.3.1 Registration

All users of radioactive material have to be registered with the Department of the Environment under this Act unless any of the various exemptions apply. Hospitals using small amounts of radioactivity are exempt from this form of registration.[16]

1.3.2 Waste

All disposals and accumulations of radioactive waste in hospitals have to be authorised, except those which are covered by **The Radioactive Substances (Hospitals) Exemption Order (1990)**[16]. Such exemptions still require notification but apply only for hospitals with relatively small usage of radioactive materials such as in pathology departments; nuclear medicine departments will invariably require authorisation. However, even when exemptions do apply, there are administrative requirements which must be followed, such as maintaining records of the date, activity and route of every disposal, all of which must be available for inspection. Other exemption orders cover items such as smoke detectors, gaseous tritium light devices, luminous articles, uranium and thorium, thorium-X, and closed sources which have become waste.

Radioactive waste may be hazardous for reasons in addition to its radioactivity. If it has other dangerous properties, these must be dealt with under **The Control of Pollution (Special Waste) Regulations (1980)**[19]. Consignment notes may have to be used when dealing with material which can cause death or serious damage on ingestion, inhalation or through skin or eye contact. However, dispensations from prior notification of every such consignment may be applicable for regular scheduled disposals.

Further details of radioactive waste disposal requirements are covered in Chapter 9.

1.3.3 Transport

Transport of radioactive materials is governed by the **Radioactive Substances Act (1948)**[20]. **The Ionising Radiation Regulations (1985)**[1] also cover movement and transport of radioactive materials by any means.

Road transport is the concern of **The Radioactive Substances (Carriage by Road) (Great Britain) Regulations (1974)**[21] which have been amended to incorporate SI units together with the latest guidance from the International Atomic Energy Agency (IAEA) in **The Radioactive Substances (Carriage by Road) (Great Britain) (Amendment) Regulations (1985)**[22]. The IAEA has produced comprehensive guidelines in their **Regulations for the Safe Transport of Radioactive Material (1985)**[23] which must be read in conjunction with the Supplement (1988)[24]. Special delivery firms, taxis, private cars and hospital transport may all be used for the transport of radioactive materials by road under the appropriate parts of the Regulations. **The Code of Practice for the Carriage of Radioactive Materials by Road (1986)**[25] currently provides detailed guidance on compliance with Regulations but will be revised by the Department of Transport as an Approved Code in due course.

British Rail and the Post Office have their own rules covering carriage of radioactive material[26,27]. Regulations covering transport by air and sea are listed at the end of the chapter[28-31]. The situation is extremely complex and full details covering the movement and transport of radioactive materials can be found in Chapter 10.

1.4 Legislation: Medicines Act 1968

In 1978, to comply with the **Euratom Directive (76/579)**[4], the application of specified provisions of the **Medicines Act (1968)**[32] was extended by **The Medicines (Radioactive Substances) Order (1978)**[33] to include certain articles and substances that 'contain, generate or are radioactive substances'. Radiopharmaceuticals used for diagnosis and treatment were effectively included at this stage. These provisions enabled regulations to be made prohibiting the sale, supply or administration of medicinal products specified in the regulations except to or by practitioners holding a certificate issued for the specific purpose.

1.4.1 Administration to patients

The Medicines (Administration of Radioactive Substances) Regulations (1978)[34] prohibit the administration of radioactive medicinal products except by doctors or dentists holding a certificate issued by the Health Ministers in respect of radioactive medicinal products, or by persons acting under the directions of such a doctor or dentist. The implementation of CEC Directive (76/579)[4] requires a system of prior authorisation. The regulations also include provisions as to the grant, duration, renewal, suspension, variation and revocation of certificates and provide for the appointment of a committee to advise the Health Ministers. This committee is known as ARSAC (Administration of Radioactive Substances Advisory Committee) and is responsible for issuing the certificates that authorise the administration of radioactive substances to both patients and volunteers.

Persons applying for an ARSAC Certificate must have the knowledge, experience, competence and skill necessary to administer radioactive medicinal products. Evidence of competence has to be recorded by the employing authority (see Section 1.7). In addition, the applicant must have available suitable equipment and facilities to enable all administrations to be made safely. Certificate applications require the signature of the Radiation Protection Adviser (RPA) and of the person responsible for the associated scientific services. Notes for guidance have been produced by **ARSAC (1988)**[13] to assist applicants.

Chapters 2 and 3 give detailed guidance on the administration of radioactive substances to patients.

1.4.2 Infection

When administering radioactive substances to patients, there is a possibility of infection both to and from the patient. Appropriate sterile procedures should always be used; Chapter 6 gives details on the preparation of radiopharmaceuticals. There is a **Code of Practice for the the Prevention of Infection in Clinical Laboratories and Post-mortem Rooms (1978)**[35], popularly known as the 'Howie Code' (currently under revision). More recent guidance concerns HIV and hepatitis viruses[17] and hazardous substances generally[18], which may include pathogenic material.

Clinical waste will also arise in hospital departments and guidance on the safe handling, transport and disposal of clinical waste is given in **The Safe Disposal of Clinical Waste (1982)**[36] published by the Health and Safety Commission.

1.5 Legislation: Health and Safety at Work etc Act (1974)[1]

This Act is concerned with the health, safety and welfare at work of all employees. The onus falls on both the employer and employee to ensure that working conditions are satisfactory. In the NHS, the employer is understood to be the Health Authority or equivalent. Responsibilities under the Act include:

a) The provision and maintenance of plant and systems of work that are, as far as reasonably practicable, safe and without risks to health.

b) Arrangements for ensuring, as far as reasonably practicable, safety and absence of risks to health in connection with the use, handling, storage and transport of articles and substances.

c) The provision of all necessary information, instruction, training and supervision to ensure, as far as reasonably practicable, the health and safety at work of employees.

d) The maintenance of any place of work under the employer's control in a condition that is safe and without health risks and the provision and maintenance of entrances and exits that are safe and without health risks.

e) The provision and maintenance of a working environment for employees that is safe, without risks to health, and with adequate facilities and arrangements for welfare.

Enforcement of the Act in general is the responsibility of the Health and Safety Executive which operates through a network of local inspectors. The powers of the inspectorate include serving improvement notices on employers to improve their standards so as to bring them into line with the legal requirements. The inspectorate can also issue a prohibition notice. This means that operations to which the notice relates, which carry a risk of serious personal injury, cannot lawfully be continued until the breach of the law is dealt with satisfactorily. As a consequence of the **National Health Service (Amendment) Act (1986)**[3], the full range of instruments and penalties under the HSW Act, including prosecution, are available to the inspectorate.

Employing authorities must have a written safety policy to cover all aspects of the HSW Act. They are legally obliged to establish safety committees if requested to do so by safety representatives appointed by trade unions under the Act. Such committees do not, however, fulfil the managerial role of the radiation protection committee referred to later in Section 1.8

1.6 Legislation: The Ionising Radiations Regulations (1985)[1]

Under the HSW Act, the specific regulations made to minimise radiation exposure of employees are the **Ionising Radiations Regulations (1985)** (IRR)[1]. These regulations embody the three principles of the International Commission for Radiological Protection (ICRP) specified in ICRP 26[37] which are:

a) no practice shall be adopted unless its introduction produces a positive net benefit;

b) all exposures should be as low as reasonably achievable, economic and social factors being taken into account (the ALARA principle) and

c) the dose equivalent to individuals shall not exceed the limits recommended for the appropriate circumstances by the Commission.

To conform with the wording of the HSW Act and virtually all UK safety legislation, reference is made to ALARP (as low as reasonably *practicable*) rather than ALARA but the meaning is equivalent in the regulations for all practical purposes.

The regulations impose duties on employers to protect employees and other persons against risks arising from work with ionising radiation. They also impose duties on employees which arise from the HSW Act itself (see Section 1.8). The regulations are divided into nine sections and the remaining chapters of this book describe their detailed application in relation to the hospital use of unsealed radionuclides.

A brief summary is given here of the contents of the regulations, with the most relevant headings.

1.6.1 Notification

Regulations 1–5 define the terms used in the regulations and require each employing authority to notify the HSE of work with ionising radiation. *Note that this is separate from the Registration required under the Radioactive Substances Act (see Section 1.3.1).* They also require co-operation between employers, for example where the employee of one health authority is working in the hospitals of another, or where a manufacturer is installing equipment in a radiation area.

1.6.2 Dose limitation

Regulations 6–7 require every employing authority to take all necessary steps to restrict, so far as is reasonably practicable, the extent to which employees and other persons are exposed to ionising radiation, and impose limits (*table 1.1*) on the doses of ionising radiation which employees and other persons may receive in any calendar year. Dose reviews need to be made every 13 weeks for female classified persons (see Section 1.6.3). The dose limits are based on the recommendations of the ICRP (ICRP 26)[37] and are currently under review.

Table 1.1   IRR (1985) Dose limits

These are the legal limits at the time of going to press

	Classified Staff	Trainees (and non-Classified Staff)	Members of the Public
Whole Body[1] Annual	50 mSv	15 mSv	5 mSv
Individual[2] Organs Annual	500 mSv	150 mSv	50 mSv
Lens of [2] the Eye Annual	150 mSv	45 mSv	15 mSv
Female[3] Abdomen 3-month	13 mSv	13 mSv	5 mSv
Pregnant[3] Abdomen (declared term)	10 mSv	10 mSv	5 mSv

Notes
1   Sum of effective (external) and committed effective (internal) dose equivalents.
2   Sum of external and committed (internal) dose equivalents.
3   Dose equivalent limits for external radiation only, averaged over abdomen.

Every employee, whether appointed in a special capacity or not, must follow all local rules set up under the IRR and is responsible for his or her own actions. Under Regulation 6(4), reasonable care must be taken by all employees not to expose anyone to ionising radiation unnecessarily, protective clothing as provided must be used and any equipment defects must be reported immediately.

1.6.3 Controlled areas, RPAs & staff classification

Regulations 8–12 require that areas in which persons are likely to receive more than specified doses of ionising radiation be designated as controlled or supervised and entry into controlled areas is restricted to specified persons and circumstances. The simple definition of a controlled area is where the instantaneous dose-rate exceeds 7.5 μSv h^{-1} due to the presence of radionuclides. However, Schedule 6 takes various factors into account including the risks from internal contamination. All these are shown in a decision tree in Appendix I.

In nuclear medicine, controlled areas are likely to be needed for radio-pharmacies, radionuclide laboratories, waste stores, injection rooms and perhaps patient waiting areas. Controlled areas are likely to exist around thyroid cancer patients who have been treated using radioiodine. Further details are given in subsequent chapters. Pathology laboratories are unlikely to need to be controlled unless large amounts of radioiodine are handled, (e.g. for protein iodination); they are more likely to be supervised areas (see Chapter 5).

Employees who are likely to receive doses of ionising radiation greater than specified levels are required to be designated as classified persons. If suitable working practices are used, particularly to reduce doses to the hands of staff working with radionuclides, it is unlikely that staff will require classification.

The regulations also require employers to appoint radiation protection advisers (RPA)[38] and supervisors (RPS). The ACOP[14] details in paragraph 71 the requirements of an RPA and in paragraph 75 the matters over which an RPA should be consulted. Paragraphs 81 and 83 relate to the RPS. Employers must also make local rules for the conduct of work with ionising radiation, ensure that such work is properly supervised and that adequate information, instruction and training are given to employees and other persons.

1.6.4 Dose assessment

Regulations 13–17 require that doses of ionising radiation received by classifed and certain other specified persons are assessed by one or more dosimetry services approved by the HSE and that records of such doses are made and kept for each such person. A central index of dose information (CIDI) is maintained which contains dose records for all classified persons in Great Britain. The index is run by the National Radiological Protection Board for the Health and Safety Executive. It maintains complete dose records and provides information in the form of transfer records. The regulations require classified persons to be subject to special medical surveillance and provide for the HSE to require employers to make approved arrangements for the protection of the health of any individual employee. Personal monitoring of staff is covered in detail in Chapter 7.

1.6.5 Control of radioactive substances

Regulations 18–23 require that where a radioactive substance is used, it should, whenever reasonably practicable, be in the form of a sealed source and that any articles embodying or containing radioactive substances are suitably designed, constructed, maintained and tested. The regulations also cover the accounting, keeping and transport of all radioactive substances and require in certain cases the provision of washing and changing facilities. All personal protective equipment must be regularly examined and properly maintained.

1.6.6 Monitoring

Regulation 24 requires radiation levels to be monitored in and around controlled and supervised areas and provides for the maintenance and testing of monitoring equipment. Further details of the requirements are given in Chapter 7.

1.6.7 Hazard assessments

Regulations 25–31 require every employer who undertakes work with ionising radiation to make an assessment of the hazards that are likely to arise from that work and, in cases where more than specified quantities of radioactive substances are involved in the work, to send an assessment report to the HSE. The regulations require employers to make contingency plans for dealing with forseeable incidents and in certain circumstances to submit them to the HSE.

Investigations of personal exposures should be made where any employee is exposed above three-tenths of the annual limit for the first time or exceeds 75 mSv to the whole body in five years[42]. The purpose of investigation is to determine whether all necessary steps to restrict exposure are being taken. If an employee or any other person is suspected to have received an overexposure (i.e. a relevant dose limit has been exceeded), the circumstances must be investigated and, if **not disproved**, notified to the HSE. Overexposures may arise from a single incident or because the total of doses received by the person during the period in question exceeds any dose limit for that period. For example a female employee who receives an abdominal dose greater than 13 mSv in a 13 week period has been overexposed. If a suspected overexposure of an employee is **not disproved** following an investigation, the Employing Authority must notify an Employment Medical Adviser. An additional notification should be made to the Appointed Doctor if one is in post. Modified dose limits may be applied for employees who have received an overexposure. These particular regulations also require that incidents in which more than specified quantities of radioactive substances escape or are lost or stolen be notified to the HSE. Such notification is separate from the similar requirement to notify the DoE under certain circumstances of uncontrolled dispersal. Procedures to be carried out in practice when an incident occurs are detailed in Chapter 8.

1.6.8 Equipment safety

Regulations 32–34 impose duties on manufacturers and installers of articles for use in work with ionising radiation to ensure that such articles are designed, constructed and installed so as to restrict, so far as is reasonably practicable, exposure to ionising radiation. Similar responsibilities are imposed on employers in relation to equipment used for medical exposures. Employers are also required to investigate any defect in medical equipment which may have resulted in a patient, or other person undergoing a medical exposure, receiving a much greater dose of ionising radiation than was intended. The HSE must be notified of a confirmed incident. Misuse of sources of ionising radiation is prohibited. Further legislation covering patient safety from ionising radiation is mentioned in Section 1.7.

1.6.9 Modifications to the legislation

Regulations 35–41 provide for defence on contravention, exemptions, transitional arrangements and other incidental provisions. The reference to the payment of fees to the HSE (in Reg 38) in respect of medical surveillance has already been revoked.

1.7 Legislation: The Protection of Patients undergoing Medical Examination or Treatment Regulations (1988)[8]

Protection of the patient is provided by **The Ionising Radiation (Protection of Persons Undergoing Medical Examination or Treatment) Regulations (1988)** (POPUMET)[8]. Five articles of the CEC Directive (84/466/Euratom)[7] have been translated into twelve regulations. This has been the subject of an explanatory Health Circular HC(88)29[39], and further guidance is given in HC(89)18[41].

The regulations require every exposure of a person to ionising radiation for a diagnostic or therapeutic purpose to be carried out under the responsibility of a person who is clinically directing such an exposure and in accordance with accepted practice (Regulation 4). Only persons who have received adequate training may carry out medical exposures (Regulations 5 and 6). Guidance is given as to the training required. Employers are under an obligation to ensure compliance with the training requirements and must keep a record of the particulars of training of persons they employ (Regulations 7 and 8). They must also keep a record of radiation equipment (Regulation 9). Expert advice from a physicist experienced in the application of physics to diagnostic and therapeutic uses of radioactive medicinal products must be available to staff clinically or physically directing an exposure (Regulation 10). This expert advice is covered for practical purposes for the use of radionuclides by the requirement for a medical physicist to be available under the ARSAC provisions.

The application and interpretation of these regulations has been generally anticipated in the medical and dental Guidance Notes (1988)[11]. The regulations came into force in 1988 and enforcement is by the HSE except in respect of Regulation 4 which is enforceable by the Secretary of State for Health.

1.8 Administrative Requirements

The employer is ultimately responsible for ensuring compliance with all regulations. To assist in this task, a Radiation Protection Committee may be established. The functions of this Committee would include consideration of the reports of the RPA, consideration of staff dosimetry assessments, informing the employing authority at least once every twelve months of the state of protection arrangements and recommending any further protection measures which may be necessary. The DHSS has published guidance on the management arrangements for implementing the IRR in **Health Circular HC(85)31**[40].

A typical organisational structure is suggested by the Guidance Notes and is given in *figure 1.1* although this may vary widely according to local circumstances. Heads of departments using unsealed radionuclides are directly responsible to the employing authority and are responsible for the safety of their staff. Since there will be controlled areas in X-ray departments and nuclear medicine departments, even if not always in pathology departments, in practice all employing (health) authorities are required by the IRR to appoint a RPA. Appointments of RPAs must be made in writing by the employer and notified to the local office of the HSE. The RPA is appointed to advise on all matters of radiation safety and must be provided with appropriate support facilities. There should be good liaison with heads of departments and all others with responsibility for radiation safety. The RPA should be a member of the Radiation Protection Committee, where one exists.

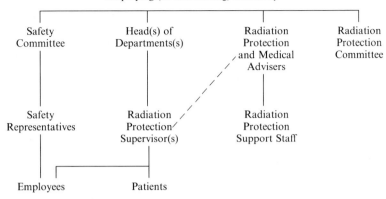

Employing (or Contracting) Authority

Safety Committee — Head(s) of Departments(s) — Radiation Protection and Medical Advisers — Radiation Protection Committee

Safety Representatives — Radiation Protection Supervisor(s) — Radiation Protection Support Staff

Employees — Patients

Figure 1.1   An example of a possible management arrangement for radiation protection in hospitals

Radiation protection supervisors (RPS) must also be appointed in writing by the employing authority and should be local to the department where the radioactive work is being performed and preferably in a position of line management for the relevant staff. The RPS has the duty locally to ensure that all staff comply with written systems of work which cover entry into controlled areas, and that local rules are followed. RPSs may be members of the Radiation Protection Committee.

When an employing authority designates classified persons, it must have made arrangements whereby such employees are under adequate medical surveillance by an Appointed Doctor, who has been appointed in writing by the HSE. Requests for appointment should be directed to the appropriate regional Senior Employment Medical Adviser. Such requests from an employing authority to appoint a particular individual are normally complied with provided that the doctor concerned has relevant experience in occupational medicine and/or supervision of the health of radiation workers. In health authorities where there are no classified persons, there is no legal requirement to have these arrangements. In the event of any overexposure of an employee, the procedure in Section 1.6.7 applies. In cases where there is no hospital Appointed Doctor and where it is felt useful to have medical advice on radiation exposure available, the employing authority may appoint its own medical adviser. This person would, however, have no legal status under the IRR.

This chapter has defined the legislative framework under which unsealed radionuclides may be used safely in hospitals. The following chapters specify the methods and techniques which may be adopted in practice to comply with the numerous regulations whilst maintaining clinical efficacy.

References

1 *The Ionising Radiations Regulations 1985* (SI 1985 No 1333) (HMSO, London)
2 *Health and Safety at Work etc Act 1974* (HMSO, London)
3 *National Health Service (Amendment) Act 1986* (HMSO, London)
4 Commission of the European Communities 1976 CEC Directive 76/579/Euratom, *Official Journal of the EC* **19** No L187 12.7.76, (CEC, Luxembourg)
5 Commission of the European Communities 1980 CEC Directive 80/836/Euratom, *Official Journal of the EC* **23** No L246 17.9.80, (CEC, Luxembourg)
6 Commission of the European Communities 1984 CEC Directive 84/467/Euratom, *Official Journal of the EC* **27** No L265 5.10.84, (CEC, Luxembourg)
7 Commission of the European Communities 1984 CEC Directive 84/466/Euratom, *Official Journal of the EC* **27** No L265 5.10.84, (CEC, Luxembourg)
8 *The Ionising Radiation (Protection of Persons Undergoing Medical Examination or Treatment) Regulations 1988* (SI 1988 No 778) (HMSO, London)
9 HSE 1985 *Guidance Notes for Appointed Doctors* (HSE, Bootle)
10 HSE 1986 *Guidance Notes for Approved Dosimetry Services Parts 1–3* (HSE, Bootle)
11 *Guidance Notes for the protection of persons against ionising radiations arising from medical and dental use 1988* (HMSO, London)
12 *A Guide to Radiation Protection in the use of X-ray Optics Equipment 1986*, Occupational Hygiene Monograph No 15 (Science Reviews Ltd, Leeds)
13 ARSAC 1988 *Notes for Guidance on the administration of radioactive substances to persons for purposes of diagnosis, treatment or research* (DHSS (ARSAC), London)
14 Health and Safety Commission 1985 *Approved Code of Practice. The protection of persons against ionising radiation arising from any work activity* (HMSO, London)
15 *Radioactive Substances Act 1960* (HMSO, London)
16 The Radioactive Substances (Hospitals) Exemption Order 1990 (SI 1990 No 2512) (HMSO, London)
17 Department of Health 1990 *Guidance for Clinical Health Care Workers: Protection against infection with HIV and hepatitis viruses* (HMSO, London)
18 Department of Health 1989 *The Control of Substances Hazardous to Health: Guidance for the Initial Assessment in Hospitals* (HMSO, London)
19 *The Control of Pollution (Special Waste) Regulations 1980* (SI 1980 No 1709) (HMSO, London)
20 *Radioactive Substances Act 1948* (HMSO, London)
21 *Radioactive Substances (Carriage by Road) (Great Britain) Regulations (1974)* (SI 1974 No 1735) (HMSO, London)
22 *The Radioactive Substances (Carriage by Road) (Great Britain) (Amendment) Regulations 1985* (SI 1985 No 1729) (HMSO, London)
23 *IAEA Regulations for the Safe Transport of Radioactive Material 1985*, No 6 Safety Standards Series (IAEA, Vienna)
24 *IAEA Regulations for the Safe Transport of Radioactive Material 1988*, No 6-Supplement, Safety Standards Series (IAEA, Vienna)
25 *Code of Practice for the Carriage of Radioactive Materials by Road 1986* (HMSO, London)
26 *Dangerous Goods by Freight Train and by Passenger Train or similar service. List of dangerous Goods and Conditions of Acceptance* BR 22426 1977 revision (British Rail, London)
27 *Post Office Guide*, current edition (Post Office, London)
28 *The Merchant Shipping (Dangerous Goods) Rules 1978* (SI 1978 No 1543) (HMSO, London)
29 *The Air Navigation Order 1976* (SI 1976 No 1783) (HMSO, London)
30 *Code of Practice for the Storage of Radioactive Material in Transit 1975* (HMSO, London)
31 *Code of Practice for the Carriage of Radioactive Materials through Ports 1975* (HMSO, London)
32 *The Medicines Act 1968* (HMSO, London)

11

33   *The Medicines (Radioactive Substances) Order 1978* (SI 1978 No 1004) (HMSO, London)
34   *The Medicines (Administration of Radioactive Substances) Regulations 1978* (SI 1978 No 1006) (HMSO, London)
35   *Code of Practice for the Prevention of Infection in Clinical Laboratories and Post-mortem Rooms* 1978 (HMSO, London)
36   Health and Safety Commission 1982 *The Safe Disposal of Clinical Waste* (HMSO, London)
37   International Commission on Radiological Protection 1977 *Recommendations of the International Commission on Radiological Protection* Publication 26 (ICRP Publications, Pergamon Press, London)
38   *The role of the medical physicist as radiation protection adviser in the use of ionising radiations in health care* (1986) (HPA, London).
39   HC (88) 29 Health Services Management *Implementation of Ionising Radiation (Protection of Persons undergoing Medical Examination or Treatment) Regulations 1988* (DHSS, London)
40   HC (85) 31 Health Services Management *Ionising Radiations Regulations 1985* (DHSS, London)
41   HC(89)18 Health Services Management *Health Service Use of Ionising Radiations* (DoH, London)
42   Health and Safety Commission 1991 *Dose limitation—restriction of exposure. Approved Code of Practice Part 4* (HMSO, London).

CHAPTER 2

Therapeutic Uses of Unsealed Radionuclides

T J Godden

2.1 Introduction

Unsealed radionuclides or radiopharmaceuticals have been used as therapeutic agents for over 60 years. Irradiation of a target organ for therapy may be achieved either by using the normal physiological functions of the body to localise the radionuclide, (e.g. I-131 in the treatment of thyroid disorders) or by introducing the radiopharmaceutical directly into a body cavity, (e.g. Y-90 for radiation synovectomies). Although beta ray emitting radionuclides are preferred for unsealed source therapy, in practice the radionuclides used may also emit gamma radiation.

When considering the radiation protection aspects of unsealed source therapy the main concerns are to prevent the accidental dispersal of the radionuclide (through spillage, leakage, vomit or incontinence) and to devise means of keeping the absorbed dose to staff to a minimum. In deriving safe working practices for unsealed source therapy, methods of preparing and administering the radio-nuclides and nursing patients containing radionuclides must be reviewed. Since radiation protection is a major consideration with those radionuclides used in radiotherapy, a summary of their physical characteristics and application is given in sections 2.2.1 to 2.2.5.

2.2 Clinical Techniques

2.2.1 Iodine-131

Iodine-131 is the most important unsealed therapeutic radionuclide. For many years this nuclide has been administered orally as sodium iodide for the treatment of thyroid disease. The specific localisation of iodide within the thyroid allows high doses to be delivered to the gland with low whole body doses. The radionuclide emits gamma rays, with a principal energy of 0.364 MeV and beta particles of average energy 0.246 MeV. The energy of the beta particles results in a maximum range in tissue of approximately 3 mm. The physical half life of the radionuclide is 8 days.

There are two levels of activity used for treatment. In the management of hyperthyroidism, where it is necessary to prevent the thyroid producing excessive thyroid hormones, activities administered are generally in the range of 100–500 MBq depending on the size of the gland and its ability to take up the sodium iodide. About 90% of the absorbed dose to the normal-sized thyroid is due to the beta rays and 10% from the gamma rays. Higher activities of I-131 are used in the treatment of well-differentiated thyroid tumours. For treatment to be effective, activities of I-131 in the range 3–8 GBq are given to ablate the normal thyroid gland and to treat metastases. These doses may be repeated at intervals of 4–6 months until there is no clinical evidence of residual functioning thyroid tissue or metastases.

In recent years I-131 has also been used to label radiopharmaceuticals which are known to concentrate in malignant lesions. Two particular techniques using radiopharmaceuticals have been developed. Firstly monoclonal antibodies, chosen because they target particular types of tumour (e.g. ovarian cancers, CNS leukaemia), labelled with 1–4 GBq of I-131 have been injected or infused into the patient. The other technique is used in the treatment of some adrenergic tumours, such as malignant phaeochromocytoma, and involves injecting the radio-pharmaceutical meta-[I-131]-iodobenzylguanidine (I-131 MIBG) intra-venously over 90 minutes. Activities typically used are in the range 2–16 GBq and each patient may receive several such treatments.

In treatments using I-131 most of the radioactive iodine is excreted in the urine although it may also be excreted in the saliva, sweat and faeces. These modes of excretion must be taken into account when considering radiation protection.

2.2.2 Gold-198

The intracavitary application of Au-198 for palliative treatment of malignant effusions began in the mid 1940s. The radionuclide has a physical half-life of 2.7 days and emits gamma rays with a principal energy of 0.412 MeV and beta particles of average energy 0.391 MeV. These beta particles have a maximum range in tissue of approximately 4 mm. The radionuclide is used in the form of a colloidal suspension of metallic gold. For the treatment of malignant pleural effusions activities of 1–4 GBq are injected into the pleural cavity, whilst for treatment of malignant ascites in the abdomen activities in the range 2–8 GBq are injected into the peritoneal cavity. In these techniques the potential sources of contamination are associated with leakage of the fluid from the cavity at the site of the injection. The presence of energetic gamma rays in the spectrum of Au-198 creates an external irradiation problem as well as a contamination problem; for this reason Au-198 is no longer the agent of choice of intracavitary therapy.

2.2.3 Yttrium-90

The pure beta emitter, Y-90, in the form of colloidal yttrium silicate in aqueous solution, is now widely used. This radionuclide, which has a physical half-life of 64.2 hours, emits beta particles with an average energy 0.923 MeV and a maximum range in tissue of 10 mm. At this beta energy the possibility of bremsstrahlung radiation causing an exposure hazard should be considered although this is usually minimal for the activities handled.

Treatments using this radionuclide involve injecting activities in the range (a) 1 to 4 GBq for the intrapleural, intraperitoneal and occasionally intrapericardial therapy for malignant effusions and intracavitary therapy for certain carcinomas of the bladder, (b) 50–250 MBq for the intracystic treatment of cranio-pharyngioma and (c) 120–240 MBq for the intra-articular treatment of arthritic conditions of various joints. Yttrium-90 is now regularly used to perform radiation synovectomies.

2.2.4 Phosphorus-32

This radionuclide was used initially as a therapeutic agent for chronic leukaemia but latterly its primary use is for the treatment of polycythaemia rubra vera. It has a physical half-life of 14.3 days and is a pure beta emitter of average energy 0.695 MeV and maximum range of 8 mm in tissue and is administered as sodium orthophosphate either orally or intravenously. Following intravenous injection about 10% of the activity is excreted in the urine during the first day whilst approximately 50% accumulates in blood-forming bone marrow. Treatment regimens vary but typically activities of the order of 4 MBq kg^{-1} of body weight are given initially and this is usually repeated at intervals of several months in order to control the disease. Occasionally the radionuclide is used for treating bone metastases from carcinoma of the prostate or breast.

2.2.5 Strontium-89

Strontium-89 has been used since the early 1970s for the treatment of skeletal pain associated with metastatic disease from prostatic and breast carcinoma. The radionuclide, which is predominantly a beta emitter, has a physical half-life of 50.5 days. The mean energy of the beta particles is approximately 0.5 MeV corresponding to a maximum range of 7 mm in tissue. Typical activities administered are 1.5 to 3 MBq kg^{-1} of patient weight, i.e. between 75 and 300 MBq per patient.

2.2.6 ARSAC requirements

Before administering radioactive materials to a patient it is a legal requirement under The Medicines (Administration of Radioactive Substances) Regulations (1978)[1] (see Chapter 1, section 1.4.1) that the clinician in charge of the management of the patient be authorised to do so by the Administration of Radioactive Substances Advisory Committee (ARSAC). The authorisation certificate issued for the therapeutic administration of radioactive medicinal products details the radionuclide, its chemical form and the treatment for which authorisation is allowed together with the route of administration and the institution(s) where it can be undertaken. It must be emphasised that the clinician has authorisation only for the procedures using radionuclides identified on the certificate; the certificate does not permit the holder to use radionuclides in a manner other than as specified. The administration of therapeutic doses of unsealed radionuclides is strictly monitored by ARSAC and certificates are issued only to doctors above registrar level who have received training in radiation techniques and who have adequate scientific support and facilities. The certificates for routine applications are issued for 5 years in the first instance and then must be renewed if the procedure is to continue. However, it is not necessary for all clinicians carrying out unsealed source radiotherapy to hold an authorisation certificate. Clinicians who routinely work under the direction of an authorised practitioner may administer radionuclides under the authority of that practitioner's certificate. This implies that junior staff can administer radionuclides under the authorisation certificate of the consultant in charge of their patient's treatment provided they have received training in the safe use of radionuclides, as specified in (POPUMET)[2] (see Chapter 1, section 1.7).

2.2.7 Administration of radionuclides

The use of therapeutic quantities of radionuclides requires care to be taken in the dispensing and administration of the radionuclide to ensure that any possible spillage is contained and that exposure to personnel is kept to a minimum. It is therefore highly desirable that, where outpatient treatment is permissible, the patients should receive treatment in a room which is part of, or immediately adjacent to, the dispensing area. When large therapeutic quantities of radionuclide are administered, for example in the treatment of carcinoma of the thyroid, the radionuclide should be administered in the patient's own room, set aside and prepared for this procedure, on the ward.

During administration precautions must be undertaken to minimise the risk of spillage and to reduce the exposure to the body, fingers and hands of the staff concerned. For sources to be dispensed or administered using a syringe, the use of syringe shields must be considered in order to minimise the exposure to the fingers and hands. These shields, which are designed to absorb the majority if not all of the beta particles, as well as attenuate the gamma ray photons, are typically made of high atomic number metals or thick cylinders of transparent plastic. There are, however, further considerations in the use of each type. Whilst the metallic syringe shields are less bulky and therefore easier to use, they are not ideal for pure beta emitters as bremsstrahlung can contribute significantly to the finger and hand dose: the thicker plastic syringe shields which can be 10 mm to 15 mm in diameter are, however, awkward to use. It is appropriate to consider the dispensing techniques being used when attempting to reduce the dose to the hands. In the situation where volumetric accuracy is not essential, an effective reduction in dose can be achieved by using the inverse square law such that a syringe with a capacity several times larger than the volume to be dispensed is used. In preparing and administering therapeutic quantities of radionuclides the dose to the fingers and hands is probably the most likely to approach a dose limit. All operations, therefore, must be completed as speedily as possible. However, in certain techniques involving the administration of radiopharmaceuticals (e.g. I-131 MIBG) the injection time required may be as long as 90 minutes. In this situation a shielded syringe pump should be used. This technique also requires special measures to be taken in the care of the patient such as the monitoring of the patients' blood pressure. To minimise dose to staff this should be done automatically. Similarly if the injection is into a young child it may be necessary to anaesthetise or sedate the child during the administration. In all of these procedures monitoring of staff, including the dose to the fingers, should be performed to ensure that the relevant dose limits are not exceeded.

The availability of therapeutic doses of I-131 in capsule form greatly reduces the risk of contamination in the administration area from coughs and sneezes as well as being a simpler and quicker method of administration. For these reasons the use of I-131 capsules is highly recommended.

In the unavoidable case of the oral administration of a liquid radionuclide, the activity should be diluted into a volume of about 50 ml so that, should the patient cough or sneeze after drinking the radionuclide, droplet activity will be not too concentrated. The radionuclide should be transported to the administration area in an appropriate shielded container (see Chapter 10). Before administration the patient should be situated in a suitable area and precautions taken to minimise the possibility of contamination. To achieve this polythene sheeting can be used to cover the floor beneath the patient and the table on which the radionuclide may reside in a container. The table also should be covered with 'Benchkote' or a paper towel. Paper tissues should be readily available should the patient need to cough. The dispensed radionuclide can be given to the patient through a straw. Additional water is then added to the bottle and the patient requested to drink the solution to ensure that all the prescribed radionuclide has been administered. If the patient has dentures then these should be removed before the administration of the radionuclide. Whilst the above is acceptable, it is much safer to administer a liquid radionuclide, such as I-131, directly from the vial using the needle end of an 'i/v giving set' and an air-bleed needle. The vial can then be rinsed two or three times via a syringe needle and, by containing it in a shielded lead pot, the finger/hand exposure can be reduced.

The administration of radiocolloids for malignant effusions requires special care due to the activities of radionuclide used. Giving sets are often used which rely on hydrostatic pressure to inject the radionuclide into the peritoneal or pleural cavity. In this procedure a quantity of fluid is removed from the cavity and replaced by an equivalent volume of radionuclide. Since the treatment relies on the colloid being dispersed evenly over the cavity surface the patient must be encouraged to move to ensure adequate dispersal. This however can lead to the possibility of a leak of fluid through the site of the injection. Care has therefore to be taken in monitoring the dressings from the site. Contamination of the hands (especially under finger nails) is a particular hazard and *all* staff assisting with the administration should wear disposable gloves.

Throughout all of these procedures good radionuclide working practices must be observed. These may include the use of disposable gloves and aprons, long handled forceps, syringe shields, protective screens for the body and eyes and swift yet cautious working commensurate with the adequate and safe administration of the radionuclide. In addition where gamma emitting radionuclides are involved the number of staff attending the administration should be kept to a minimum.

2.3 Controlled and Supervised Areas for Unsealed Source Therapy

2.3.1 Definition of Controlled and Supervised areas

A controlled area as defined by The Ionising Radiations Regulations (1985) (IRR)[3] Regulation 8 and Schedule 6 for external radiation is one in which the instantaneous doserate exceeds or is likely to exceed 7.5 μSv h^{-1}. However in Schedule 6 there are important exemptions which define conditions under which the employer is not required to create a controlled area. These exemptions, outlined in Appendix I, should be considered for areas where unsealed source therapy is performed. They can be invoked provided the Radiation Protection Adviser (RPA) is satisfied that suitable steps have been taken to ensure that three-tenths of any relevant dose limit is not exceeded and that, where the concept of time-averaged dose rate is used, it is possible to demonstrate the basis on which use of this exemption can be justified. The other criteria for defining a controlled area relating to the use of unsealed radionuclides are in relation to internal radiation (Schedule 6, Part II, para 6). Typical activities for the radionuclides used in therapy below which it is not necessary to define controlled areas in terms of the various sections in Schedule 6 are given in *table 2.1*.

Supervised Areas are defined in the IRR as those areas where a person is likely to be exposed to ionising radiation to an extent that the dose exceeds one third of that requiring a controlled area. It may be necessary under paragraph 7 of Schedule 6 to designate the area as a controlled area if it is required to be a supervised area for both external and internal radiation, or in relation to internal radiation when both the air and surface contamination level exceed one third of the values specified in sub-paragraphs a) and b) of paragraph 6, Schedule 6 (see Appendix I).

2.3.2 Extent of Controlled and Supervised areas

Using IRR (Schedule 6), it is possible to define the extent of the controlled and supervised areas around a patient undergoing radionuclide therapy. For the

Table 2.1 Threshold levels for which consideration of a controlled area is required.

Radionuclide	Activity levels for controlled areas (IRR Schedule 6)[3]			
	External		Internal	
	Outside patient	Inside patient	Air concentration	Surface contamination
	(MBq)	(MBq)	(Bq m^{-3})	(Bq cm^{-2})
Phosphorus-32	5	Not required	2×10^3	2×10^3
Strontium-89	5	Not required	6×10^2	2×10^3
Yttrium-90	5	Not required	3×10^3	2×10^3
Iodine-131	5	400	2×10^2	1×10^2
Gold-198	5	375	9×10^3	6×10^3

Table 2.2 The initial extent of controlled and supervised areas for patients undergoing various radionuclide therapy with no additional shielding

Technique (typical activity)	Radionuclide	Doserate at 1 m from typical activity (μGy h^{-1})	Radius of Controlled area (m)	Radius of Supervised area (m)
MIBG (15 GBq)	I-131	750	10	18
Thyroid cancer (8 GBq)	I-131	400	7	13
Thyrotoxicosis (0.4 GBq)	I-131	20	2	3
Intracavitary effusion (8 GBq)	Au-198	500	8	14

clinical situations identified in sections 2.2.1 to 2.2.5, the initial extent of the controlled areas and supervised areas for typical treatments for gamma ray emitting radionuclides assuming no additional shielding is shown in *table 2.2*. To reduce the extent of these areas, which exist around patients, bed shields or shielded rooms can often be employed.

Where patients containing activities sufficient to warrant controlled areas being designated are moved through public areas of the hospital, appropriate precautions should be considered (see also Chapter 10). For example, it may be necessary temporarily to restrict access to a lift by other users. While it may not be necessary to designate a controlled area around one patient, the situation can arise where a group of patients undergoing radionuclide therapy are nursed together thereby causing an exposure rate exceeding that allowed for an uncontrolled area. It is therefore essential when considering the extent of controlled and supervised areas to include all eventualities and draw up systems of work accordingly.

2.3.3 Delineation of Controlled areas

When the extent of the controlled area for all situations in unsealed source therapy has been defined it is necessary to delineate the area. This is achieved under Regulation 8 (3) by considering the normal physical boundaries of the working area or treatment room, or by describing the area generically under Regulation 8 (5). It may be convenient to delineate the whole treatment room where therapeutic doses of unsealed radionuclides are used as a controlled area, whereas for a 'mobile' controlled area, such as may exist around a source container, it can be delineated by reference to distances from the movable source. It is not necessary physically to demarcate all boundaries of the controlled areas; however, warning signs indicating the existence of a controlled area, which comply with the recommendations of Appendix II of the Guidance Notes[4], must show the extent of that area. It should not be possible to have a controlled area extending into an area where access cannot be controlled. This problem is often experienced where a corridor or ward is adjacent to the room where patients are undergoing unsealed source therapy or radionuclides are being dispensed. In these circumstances further shielding, such as a lead screen or a course of protective bricks, may be required to reduce exposure levels below the limits for a controlled area.

2.3.4 Requirements for treatment areas and source dispensing

Patients undergoing unsealed radionuclide therapy with activities greater than those indicated in column 4 of *table 2.10* (page 27), should ideally be treated in single bed wards. If circumstances do not permit this then treatment should be given in a radiotherapy ward with not less than 2.5 m between the centres of the beds. In any area where unsealed sources are used the floors of the room should be covered with a smooth, continuous and non-absorbent surface such as linoleum or PVC sheet: tiles should not be used. The surface of the floor covering should be removable for decontamination purposes and other surfaces such as walls and ceilings should be finished with a hard gloss paint. Patients receiving high-activity radioactive treatments should be allocated a designated toilet for their exclusive use, ideally with a bathroom and in a specialist suite for the use of such patients only. Bedpans and urine bottles should only be used if clinically essential.

Within the treatment area it is useful to have a separate area for bins for the temporary storage of contaminated material such as linen and waste. These areas and bins must be clearly marked using the radioactive warning sign. Extra care must be taken when handling specimens or waste from a patient treated with unsealed radionuclides. Where there is any possibility that staff could become contaminated in handling the patient or specimens, protective gowns and gloves should be worn. A place should also be provided adjacent to the room for keeping the protective clothing to be worn by staff.

Only in extreme situations should patients undergoing high activity unsealed source radiotherapy be treated in a general ward and the RPA must be consulted prior to the treatment taking place. In this situation it is a requirement to assess the dose to a patient in the adjacent bed who must be considered to be a member of the general public: similar consideration applies to visitors. The extent to which this situation should be allowed to affect the non-radioactive patient is defined in ACOP (2/31): *'The degree of restriction of dose to other patients may be influenced by the consideration of what significance the dose would have in relation to that individual's personal circumstances. For example a proportionally small further accumulation of dose to a radiotherapy patient ..... may not be significant but would almost certainly be so to a young patient who was not to undergo medical exposure'.*

2.4 Local Rules

2.4.1 General content of Local Rules

The local rules for a treatment area must clearly indicate the

 a) Purpose of Local Rules
 b) Responsibilities and personnel involved in management of treatment area.
 c) Details of controlled areas
 d) Systems of work for entering controlled areas
 e) Operational policies for treating patients with unsealed sources
 f) Hazard assessments where appropriate
 g) Contingency plans
 h) Procedure to be followed when discharging a patient.

It is essential that staff working in a radiation environment are made aware of the Local Rules governing work within the area and that managerial chains of responsibility are well defined. It is also important that the Radiation Protection Supervisor should occupy a position of authority within the management chain since his role is to ensure that staff comply with the Local Rules. The employer however is responsible through the local manager for arranging the production and promulgation of local rules. This must be done in conjunction with the RPA.

2.4.2 System of work for entering a Controlled area

Entry to a controlled area is restricted to a classified person or someone working under a system of work. This system of work should define who can enter the area and under what conditions. The purpose of such a written system of work is to ensure that an employee of 18 years or over does not receive in any calendar year a dose of ionising radiation exceeding three-tenths of any relevant dose limit and that in the case of any other person they do not receive a dose of ionising radiation exceeding any relevant dose limit. The employer under Regulation 8 (7) has to be able to demonstrate by personal dose assessment, or other suitable measurements, that the doses are kept below the relevant dose limits. It is expected that only in exceptional circumstances would the dose to a person working under a system of work approach the specified dose restrictions in Regulation 8 (6). An example of a possible system of work for entering a controlled area in a ward is given in *table 2.3.*

2.4.3 Operational policies for treatment areas

The purpose of operational policies is to inform all staff of the procedures which have been agreed relating to the nursing of patients undergoing sealed and unsealed source radiotherapy. These policies can take a general form relating to all aspects of nursing such patients and then more detailed policies relating to specific forms of treatment. An example of a typical general operational policy is given in *table 2.4.*

Table 2.3 System of work for entering controlled areas

a) Nursing personnel shall wear a personal dosemeter at all times when on duty.

b) The Nurses' Handbook must be read and the nurse shall sign the form at completion to say that it has been read and understood.

c) Housekeeping staff must attend a suitable training programme before working in radiation areas. Once completed, these staff can enter the defined controlled areas to carry out normal duties when authorised by the nurse in charge of the ward.

d) Visitors are allowed to visit patients in accordance with the guidelines given in the appropriate protocol for that patient's treatment. These protocols are detailed in the operational procedures and are indicated by the sign and symbols shown.

e) Any member of staff who believes she may be pregnant must notify the Radiation Protection Supervisor.

Table 2.4 General operational policy for patients treated with unsealed sources

a) Unsealed radionuclides may only be used by a radiotherapist authorised by the Administration of Radioactive Substances Advisory Committee (ARSAC) to use that particular radionuclide. Another clinician may act on behalf of the certified clinician with prior permission.

b) All patients being given unsealed sources must be treated in the nominated side wards when the activity levels ('high activity') exceed the following:

400 MBq of I-131	400 MBq of Au-198
1.5 GBq of Y-90	4.5 GBq of P-32

Only in extreme medical emergencies can such patients be treated in the general ward.

c) Staff must not loiter in the controlled areas.

d) Patients are to be monitored wherever possible using closed circuit TV. Only essential nursing procedures should be carried out and these should be done as rapidly as is consistent with good nursing practice.

e) Radiation warning signs are to be hung on the door of each room indicating the radionuclide therapy being carried out, the exposure rate at 1 m and the possible hazard.

f) The working practices associated with these warning signs are detailed in the nursing area, and outline the times allowed in the controlled areas for staff and visitors.

g) Patients receiving treatment with high activities of I-131 are to be 'Barrier Nursed' — given disposable crockery and cutlery and special disposal bags for waste.

h) All linen and waste bags must be monitored before disposal.

i) The patient must be monitored prior to discharge and given an appropriate instruction card.

j) Subsequent to the discharge, the areas used by the patient must be monitored, under the supervision of a physicist, prior to reuse.

Treatment-specific procedures depend primarily on the levels of activities being used. While these depend on the patient and the radionuclide used, it is possible to produce general rules which are related to the activity used and hence to the consequent exposure and contamination risk. A possible set of guidelines for handling patients undergoing unsealed source therapy with 'high activities' is given in *table 2.5*.

Table 2.5 Local nursing procedures for handling patients undergoing treatment with unsealed sources of high activity

---

Radiation risks

    a)   High exposure risk
    b)   High contamination risk

Administered activity of radionuclides

Radionuclide	Therapy application	Residual activities (GBq)	Typical doserate at 1 m from patient (μSv h^{-1} GBq^{-1})
Iodine-131	Thyroid	1–8	50
Gold-198	Intracavitary	1–8	60
Yttrium-90	Intracavitary	<2	0.8

---

1) The member of staff administering the dose of radionuclide must hang a notice at the end of the patient's bed and place a radiation warning notice on the door.
2) The patient must be confined to his/her own room.
3) The patient must use the designated toilet adjacent to the room.
4) All utensils, e.g. bed pan, tooth mug, etc, must be for the exclusive use of the patient, and must not be returned to ward stock until it has been ensured that they are not contaminated.
5) Crockery and cutlery should be disposable and must be collected in the room in polythene bags for disposal by the Medical Physics Department. If disposable utensils are not used, the patient should wash up their own crockery and cutlery. Food waste must be stored separately and will also be disposed of by the Medical Physics Department, **if necessary**.
6) Bed linen, towels, pyjamas, etc must be kept in the room for monitoring by the Medical Physics Department and only included in ward laundry when it has been checked that they not contaminated.
7) All waste, e.g. paper tissues, etc must be collected for disposal by the Medical Physics Department.
8) Staff must wear disposable aprons and gloves when handling the patient and dealing with excreta and any articles which may be contaminated. Disposable gloves must be included in waste as in 7, and gowns dealt with as linen as in 6.

9) **Nursing time limits**
   (a) All nursing procedures should be carried out in the least time compatible with proper nursing care.
   (b) A **maximum** nursing time of 30 minutes per day for each nurse is recommended.
10) Visiting by children and pregnant women is not permitted. Other visiting is allowed but subject to a limit of 1 hour per day for each adult and with the visitor keeping a distance of 1–2 m from the patient.
11) The patient must not be discharged from the ward or transferred to another ward without the assurance by the Medical Physics Department that the level of activity of radionuclide has reached a sufficiently low level.
12) In the event of the patient being sick or incontinent all attempts must be made to ensure minimal contamination of floor and furniture. The Medical Physics Department must be immediately informed. Absorbent disposable paper should be used for mopping up, avoiding spread. Protective gowns, gloves and overshoes must be worn by staff.
13) The Medical Physics Department must be informed of the discharge of the patient and the ward must be monitored by the Medical Physics Department to ensure that it is uncontaminated before being occupied by another patient. All utensils, etc used by the patient must be monitored and, if necessary, decontaminated before being returned to ward stock.
14) In the event of the death of the patient, special precautions may need to be taken. Discussion must take place with the DUTY PHYSICIST before the corpse is released for post-mortem, burial or cremation.

In deriving the times for which various groups of people can stay in the vicinity of the patient and/or sources, estimates have to be made of nursing work patterns and of the dose visitors are likely to receive. In general the length of time allowed for visits during the course of treatment should be such that no visitor will receive more than a total of 0.5 mSv. With unsealed source therapy however, exposure dose consideration may be of secondary importance if there is any possibility of a visitor spreading contamination. Under these circumstances visitors may not be permitted beyond the doorway of the room and if entry is essential, monitoring of the visitor on leaving the room is necessary. In addition it is advisable that visiting should be avoided for the first day of the treatment. In drawing up these rules there must be an overriding concern that in certain circumstances, (e.g. a medical emergency or serious illness where visitors should be with the patient), staff and visitors will be allowed a longer time in the vicinity of the patient. This should be done at the discretion of the nurse in charge of the ward after consultation with the RPA or other responsible person.

2.5 Hazard Assessment and Contingency Plans

2.5.1 Hazard assessment

Under IRR Regulation 25, the employer is required to carry out a hazard assessment to identify the nature and magnitude of any forseeable accident, occurrence or incident which could cause a radiation hazard to employees and other persons. In addition the employer is also required to take steps to limit the consequences of any such event. There is also a requirement under Regulation 26 to make a special hazard assessment and notify the HSE if radionuclides are to be used in quantities in excess of the levels defined in Schedule 2, Column 6. Since these activity levels are in excess of 20 TBq for the radionuclides used in unsealed source therapy there should be no need to notify the HSE. However a hazard assessment must be carried out whenever radionuclides are used, although there is no legal requirement to produce a written assessment.

The hazards to staff from handling radionuclides are those due to internal as well as external irradiation. Work practices must therefore be designed to minimise the hazards. To reduce the external radiation hazards, distance, time and shielding must be optimised. In particular for beta emitting radionuclides, there can be a high surface doserate if the thickness of the container wall is insufficient to attenuate the beta and bremstrahlung radiation. Radioactive material should therefore be handled with long handled forceps; lead glass screens should be used to protect the eyes. To reduce the hazards of internal radiation through either the absorption, ingestion or inhalation of a radionuclide, consideration must be given preventing or reducing the risk of dispersal of radioactive materials to the environment, for example by spillage.

2.5.2 Contingency plans

Regulation 27 (1) requires that where an assessment, made in accordance with Regulation 25 (1), shows that an accident could result in either a dose limit being exceeded or a controlled area being created beyond its originally defined boundaries, a contingency plan must be prepared and kept with the appropriate local rules. Such plans are necessary to cope with a possible spill of radionuclide, of a patient dying who has recently received a therapeutic dose of radionuclide and a fire in the treatment area.

2.5.3 Spillage of an unsealed source

In the clinical situation there are various ways in which the spill of a radionuclide can occur. These include accidental spillage in dispensing or administration and contamination resulting from urinary incontinence or the patient vomiting following the oral administration for therapy. Contingency plans should be drawn up to identify the procedure to be taken in the event of such occurences. The levels at which contamination should be regarded as significant are detailed in the Guidance Notes (Appendix IV) and are defined in section 2.7.4 for the radionuclides used in therapy. A typical contingency plan to cope with the spillage of a radionuclide is given in table 2.6.

In certain circumstances it is necessary to notify the HSE in the event of a major spill under Regulation 31 (1) (b). For radionuclides used in unsealed source therapy, every employer must notify the Executive in any case where a quantity of radionuclide under his control and with an activity greater than 20 GBq has been spilled and given rise to significant contamination. The levels at which contamination should be regarded as significant are detailed in ACOP 1/177, namely

a) the surface contamination exceeds 100 times the quantity in column 4 of Schedule 2 when averaged over 1000 cm^2; OR

b) the instantaneous dose rate measured at 1 m above the contaminated surface is greater than 1 mSv h^{-1}.

For the radionuclides used in therapy these correspond to activities of 10 kBq cm^{-2} for I-131, 600 kBq cm^{-2} for Au-198 and 200 kBq cm^{-2} for all other beta emitters.

Table 2.6   A typical contingency plan for spillage of radioactive material

a)	Inform sister or nurse in charge of ward and Radiation Protection Supervisor.
b)	CONTACT DUTY PHYSICIST, Radiotherapy Physics Unit.
c)	Restrict movement into the room — if it is necessary to enter, wear plastic aprons, gloves and overshoes.
d)	If there is a pool of fluid, use absorbent material, ie paper towels or tissues, and soak up the fluid (do not rub) to prevent spreading.
e)	Carry out decontamination procedures requested by physicist or Radiation Protection Supervisor.
f)	When removing any contaminated clothing, place it in plastic bag for collection by Medical Physics Department.
g)	If the spill is on the skin, the area should be rinsed thoroughly with water taking care not to spread the contamination and dried with paper towels which should be retained for monitoring.
h)	Radiation Protection Supervisor to write a report.

2.5.4   Death of patient undergoing radionuclide therapy

In the event of the death of a patient who has recently received a therapeutic dose of a radionuclide care has to be taken to ensure that personnel receive as low a dose as possible at all stages prior to the burial or cremation. A contingency plan is therefore required to alert staff to what must be done immediately and details given of how further advice can be obtained: an example is shown in *table 2.7*.

Table 2.7   Contingency plan for death of patient undergoing unsealed source therapy

If a patient dies following the therapeutic administration of an unsealed radionuclide, the Radiation Protection Supervisor must be informed prior to the release of the corpse or a post-mortem procedure in order that appropriate information can be given. The DUTY PHYSICIST should also be contacted for advice.

The nature of the advice to be given by the Radiation Protection Supervisor (RPS) or duty physicist can be derived from the Guidance Notes which give levels of activities at which a post-mortem, embalming, burial and cremation can take place without any special precautions. For radionuclides used in therapy the levels are shown in *table 2.8*. These are based on complying with the requirements of IRR Schedule 6. If a post-mortem is necessary before the activities reach the levels given in *table 2.8*, then the RPA must be consulted so that potential hazards can be identified. Similarly the RPA must be consulted before a corpse can be released if the activity levels are greater than those shown in *table 2.8*.

Table 2.8 Activities above which special consideration should be given to the handling of corpses containing therapeutic quantities of radionuclide.

Radionuclide	Post mortem or embalming	Burial	Cremation
Phosphorus-32	100 MBq^a	2000 MBq^c	30 MBq^d
Strontium-89	50 MBq^a	2000 MBq^c	20 MBq^d
Yttrium-90 colloid	200 MBq^a	2000 MBq^c	70 MBq^d
Iodine-131	10 MBq^a	400 MBq^b	400 MBq^b
Gold-198 colloid	400 MBq^b	400 MBq^b	100 MBq^d

The values given relate to the greatest risk to those persons involved in the procedures.

a   Based on contamination hazard (IRR Schedule 6, para 6)
b   Based on dose rate external to the body (IRR Schedule 6, para 2 (b) (ii))
c   Based on bremsstrahlung dose at 0.5 m
d   Based on contamination hazard from ash (one third of values in a).

2.5.5   In the event of fire

It is a requirement under Regulation 27 (2) that there should be consultation between the Radiation Protection Adviser and the appropriate Fire Authority so that fire services have some prior knowledge of the possibility that there may be patients within a given ward area being treated with unsealed sources. In the event of a fire, the potential risks from the fire are very much more serious than the limited radiation hazards and neither the evacuation of patients nor the fighting of the fire should in any way be hampered by inappropriate restrictions. However, nursing staff should be advised to limit (but not avoid) close contact with patients receiving high activity radioiodine therapy. These patients should be found appropriate accommodation as soon as is reasonably practicable. Both the RPS and the RPA should be informed. A typical contingency plan is given in *table 2.9*.

Table 2.9 Contingency plan in the event of a fire, for patients undergoing unsealed source therapy

a)   Follow standard hospital evacuation as if patient(s) were not radioactive.

b)   After evacuation these patients must be kept away from other persons if at all possible.

c)   After the fire, Duty Physicist must ensure that any area temporarily used by radioactive patients is monitored and decontaminated (if necessary) prior to reuse.

In Chapter 8, further consideration is given to the handling of incidents and reporting procedures.

2.6 Discharge of Patient

2.6.1 Activity levels for discharging patients

Patients to whom radionuclide therapy has been given can leave hospital or be sent to another hospital provided consideration is given to the method of travel, time of journey and any other relevant personal circumstances. The necessity arises because these patients are likely to represent a potential contamination risk and exposure hazard to other people. In general, patients should not be discharged unless the residual activities at the time of departure are below the levels specified in column 5 of *table 2.10*. In addition, patients who have been treated with an intraperitoneal or intrapleural administration of radioactive colloid should remain in hospital for 48 hours to check for possible leakage from the instillation site. The recommendations regarding the restrictions on discharge are given below for radionuclides used in unsealed source therapy:

  a) For travel by public transport the residual activity should be below the level given in column 4 of *table 2.10*.

  b) For private transport, including taxis, the residual activity must be less than that specified in column 5.

In all cases where the activity level exceeds that specified in column 4, the RPA should give the vehicle driver clear, simple instructions. These activity levels relate to a single patient; the RPA should be consulted when there is the possibility of several patients travelling together. Since the activity levels typically used in Sr-89 therapy are less than 250 MBq there are no travel restrictions for discharge from hospital.

Table 2.10 Threshold activity levels (MBq) for discharging patients

Radionuclide	Return to radiosensitive work, etc < 10 MBq MeV	No restrictions[a] < 50 MBq MeV	Travel by public transport < 150 MBq MeV	Travel by private transport < 300 MBq MeV
Phosphorus-32	300	1500	4500	9000
Yttrium-90 colloid	100	500	1500	3000
Iodine-131	30	150	400	800
Gold-198 colloid	30	150	400	800

a   except for radiosensitive work or close contact with children or pregnant women.

2.6.2 Procedure for discharge

Before discharge it is the responsibility of the employer under ACOP 2/33, to

a) identify any critical groups of employees or members of the public who, it is foreseen, may come near such persons and whose resulting exposure may be significant.

b) determine any steps that may be required to restrict the exposure to those critical groups.

To exercise this responsibility the employer is likely to expect the clinician, together with the Radiation Protection Supervisor, ward sister or other qualified person to establish the home and working environment of the patient in order that appropriate advice can be given to reduce exposure to other persons. Patients should be advised not to return to work if the residual activity in their body is likely to cause any hazard at work, e.g. during work with young children. While the residual activity exceeds the level in column 3 of *table 2.10*, return to work should be discussed with the RPA. Similarly advice must be given concerning conduct at home. There should be no close contact with other people until the residual activity is less than the level in column 3 of *table 2.10* and patients should not play with, nurse or fondle children until the activity is less than the level in column 2; there is, however, no need to place additional restrictions on visitors. Patients should also be told that they must avoid close public contact as in cinemas, theatres, etc, until the residual activity is less than the level in column 3. A guide to the maximum times required to reach the activity levels before return to work and the removal of all restrictions is given in table 5a in the Guidance Notes[4]. This assumes physical decay only, but for systemically administered radionuclides where biological clearance occurs, guidance on time reductions should be sought from the RPA.

2.6.3 Instruction form to be given to Patient

All patients whose residual activity exceeds the level in column 3 of *table 2.10* at the time of discharge should be given appropriate information about precautions to be taken on leaving hospital. This may take the form of a card (*figure 2.1*) and should give the necessary information on when to return to work and when no restrictions apply. The need to carry out these instructions must be emphasised.

2.7 Unsealed Source Custody and Record Keeping

2.7.1 Role of the unsealed source custodian

When radioactive substances are used in clinical practice it is essential that arrangements are made to provide security against loss or theft of the sources and damage by fire as well as protection against radiation hazards to staff and other persons. While the employer has overall responsibility for the safe storage of radioactive materials, the Authority may appoint a custodian for unsealed sources to be responsible for organising the security of the substances during storage, their safe use and ensuring that all necessary records are kept. On a day-to-day basis it is possible that another person is made directly responsible to the custodian for the receipt, storage and issue of radioactive materials.

2.7.2 Custody and storage of unsealed radioactive sources

One of the major roles of the unsealed source custodian is to ensure that the employer complies with Regulations 19 and 20 of the IRR which relate to accounting for and keeping of radioactive substances. Accounting procedures are

Figure 2.1 Instruction card for patient leaving hospital where there is still significant residual activity[4]

	RADIONUCLIDE INSTRUCTION CARD
Radionuclide: Activity: Administered on: ..../..../19....	Patient Name: Address: Hosp No: Department: Hospital: Address: Consultant:
4	1

Observe the following instructions (1) Avoid journeys on public transport until .... (2) Avoid going to places of entertainment until .... (3) Avoid prolonged personal contact at home until .... (4) Do not return to work until .... (5) .... Signed: Doctor.	This card should be carried at all times until latest date shown on page 2. In case of difficulty, telephone Dr .... At .... Extension ....
2	3

The card should have a distinctive colour, preferably yellow.

essential to know the location of a radioactive substance at any time and to be able to identify as quickly as possible the loss of any significant quantity of that material. Records relating to each source must be kept and each source identified by number, mark, label or other appropriate method. Any container holding a radionuclide should be marked with the radiation symbol. This accounting requirement is however not necessary (ACOP 1/116) if the activity of the radionuclide is lower than the levels given in IRR, Schedule 2 column 2. The lower limits for radionuclides used in unsealed source therapy are given in *table 2.11*. The records to be kept of each substance should include:

a) identification of the substance by name and batch number
b) date of receipt
c) activity at a specified times and date
d) activity used and date and time of use
e) date and manner of disposal

Such a record then forms part of the stock record which is a compilation of all individual records. These records must be kept until at least 2 years after the disposal of the radionuclide.

Table 2.11 The threshold level of activity above which accounting records must be kept

Radionuclide	Column 2, Schedule 2 activity levels (IRR)
P-32, Sr-89, Y-90, Au-198	500 kBq
I-131	50 kBq

On receipt of a consignment of radioactive material the package should be opened by a responsible person and the activity of the radionuclide checked, against the consignment certificate, in a radionuclide calibrator with the known calibration factor for that radionuclide. The material is then labelled in an appropriate manner and a record created which is then entered into the stock record. Each time any of the radionuclide is used, the activity removed should be recorded in the stock record. If the radionuclide is to be administered to a patient it is essential to check the activity in a radionuclide calibrator prior to administration. A record of the activity given must be made in the patient's individual notes. Issuing of such activities must only be done by a responsible person. Once the radionuclide is given to the patient further accounting procedures can be disregarded except for samples obtained from the patient which contain activities in excess of the limits given in *table 2.11*. If these samples are kept for more than 24 hours they must be treated as discrete radioactive substances. Once the consignment has been used finally an entry must be made in the record relating to its disposal as radioactive waste. For accounting purposes in terms of Regulation 19 the records kept for waste disposal control and the clinical administration of radioactive material are sufficient. At regular intervals the stock of unsealed sources should be inspected to ensure that it agrees with the entries of receipts, issues and disposals in the stock record, taking into account radioactive decay. If during such an audit or at any other time, it is suspected that a quantity of radionuclide in excess of the limits in *table 2.11* is lost, then an investigation must be carried out (Regulation 31). If the suspicion is justified, the HSE must be informed and a report of the investigation must be prepared and a copy kept for at least 50 years from the date of the incident.

In order to ensure their safe custody, radioactive substances must be kept in a suitable store which may be in a room or a separate space outside the working area. Once radiopharmaceuticals have been prepared for administration a short-term store such as a cupboard or safe situated in the working area may be used. The main store should preferably be near the working area and provide resistance to fire sufficient to minimise dispersal and loss of shielding. The shielding should reduce the instantaneous dose rate to below 2.5 μSv h^{-1} if non-classified persons can approach the outside of the store. In any case the shielding should be of such a thickness that the radiation dose rate at any accessible position outside the store is less than 7.5 μSv h^{-1}. Within the store the dose rate should not exceed 200 μSv h^{-1} at 5 cm from any source or source container, or 2 mSv h^{-1} where only the hands of a person can enter. In all situations the store should be kept locked and be suitably labelled with the radiation warning sign. It is important that the local Fire Officer is made aware of the location of the store and its likely contents. Fragile containers of unsealed radioactive substances should be stored inside a leakproof outer container. If there is the possibility that radioactive solutions are chemically unstable and volatile, the container should be vented and placed in a ventilated storage area. When radioactive materials are to be stored in a refrigerator or a cold-storage unit, the containers must be checked to ensure that they do not crack at low temperatures. All containers of radiochemicals in store should be closed securely to prevent leakage and the area where containers are stored should be routinely monitored for contamination.

2.7.3 Collection and disposal of radioactive waste

Even though accounting for radioactive substances ceases once the radionuclide is administered to the patient, it is essential that adequate provision is made for the collection and disposal of radioactive waste. Common practice is to collect low activity solid waste for subsequent incineration or disposal by the local authority refuse services. Liquid radioactive waste is disposed of via the sewers. In hospitals, excreta from patients undergoing radionuclide therapy is not normally collected and is disposed of as liquid waste. Where the patient's physical condition does not permit access to a designated toilet, excreta must be collected carefully and disposed of as soon as possible via the designated toilet. When the activity levels administered are greater than those in column 4 of *table 2.10*, the patients should have exclusive use of toilets connected to designated drains. These drains should be connected as directly as possible to the main sewer. The drainage system, which should be easily identified, should take account of the possible build-up of contamination on the surfaces and the use of large traps should be avoided. If repairs are necessary to designated drains they should be done under the supervision of the RPS who should make measurements of the radiation levels as the drain is opened and advise on the necessary precautions to be taken.

Occasionally it is necessary for clinical reasons to collect samples from patients. A defined store area should be provided for the temporary retention of these radioactive specimens. If the doserates from these samples are significant, the store may need to be shielded. Samples from patients such as blood and urine which contain quantities of radioactive substance where the activity is greater than those given in *table 2.11* must be accounted for in the stock record if they are to be kept for more than 24 hours before disposal. If large activities of a radionuclide are unused following a therapy administration they should be disposed of in accordance with the appropriate authorisation certificate from the Department of the Environment.

Solid radioactive waste such as used disposable crockery and cutlery, paper tissues or swabs should be collected in a suitable receptacle prior to disposal. The site for storage should be well marked and the receptacles easily and uniquely identified. Disposal must be in accord with the hospital's authorisation. The disposal of radioactive waste is further discussed in Chapter 9.

2.7.4 Contamination monitoring

In any area where unsealed radionuclides are used it is essential that monitoring is carried out on a regular basis to ensure that contamination levels are as low as reasonably practicable and using equipment calibrated in accordance with Regulation 24. It is important that the surfaces in the treatment rooms (i.e. the walls, floor, locker tops, chairs, sinks, etc), are monitored after each treatment together with the bedding used. Designated toilets must similarly be monitored. In addition, to reduce the risk of spreading contamination, staff working with 'high activity' patients should regularly monitor their hands for signs of contamination and in particular check for contamination under the fingernails. Direct monitoring of surfaces is always preferable but where this is not practical a wipe test can be carried out. In this situation the assumption has to be made that the activity removed and measured represents only 10% of the total contamination. Prior to the discharge of 'high activity' patients it is advisable to monitor personal property and to give appropriate advice (e.g. to wash it separately, or retain it in hospital 'hot store').

Acceptable levels for contamination are not specified but derived limits for surface contamination that should not be exceeded have been defined in the Guidance Notes[4]. The derived limits are such that continued exposure at that level could lead to an annual dose limit for adults being reached. The derived limits for surface contamination for all the radionuclides used in unsealed source therapy are shown in *table 2.12* together with the area over which the contamination can be averaged. All contamination should be reduced to a level as low as reasonably practicable. If the contamination levels exceed those given in *table 2.12* decontamination procedures should be continued until the levels are acceptable, or else the contaminated area may need to be designated a controlled area.

On occasions it is necessary to make a judgement on when a contaminated treatment area can be reused. Even after decontamination procedures it may not be possible to reach the derived contamination limits. One possibility is to close the room until the derived activity levels are reached. This is often only feasible with short-lived radionuclides since the room is often required for another patient. In other circumstances the surface should be covered with impermeably coated paper or strong polythene sheeting to prevent the spread of contamination when the treatment room is reused, although in such circumstances it may be necessary to review the system of work for entry into the controlled area. Further consideration of monitoring and suitable instrumentation is given in Chapter 7.

Table 2.12 The derived limits for surface contamination together with maximum permissible averaging area

Surface	Averaging area cm^2	Levels of contamination not to be exceeded Bq cm^{-2}
Surfaces in Controlled Areas		
a) Floors, walls, ceilings	1000	30
b) Other surfaces	300	30
Surfaces of body	100	3
Supervised & public areas, bedding, clothing	300	3

2.7.5 Decontamination procedures

Before any decontamination procedure, thought must be given to the nature of the problem and the steps to be taken to handle the situation in order that contamination can be contained. This is highlighted above in section 2.5.3 on contingency plans for the spillage of a radionuclide. Once the extent of any contamination has been established then the method of decontamination, which will be dependent upon the surface to be decontaminated, can be chosen to avoid raising dust or spreading contamination.

Decontamination problems can be divided into three main areas: surfaces, personnel, and clothing and linen. For cleaning contaminated surfaces such as walls, floors and paintwork, staff should wear appropriate clothing depending on the nature of the problem. Rubber or plastic gloves, overshoes and plastic aprons may be required. The contaminated area should be washed and scrubbed initially with detergent and water and then if necessary with a decontaminant chemical such as Decon-90. In all washing procedures care must be taken not to extend the contaminated area. It may be necessary to repeat the washing procedures several times to reach the derived activity limits appropriate to the surface. In the case of high levels of contamination with long-lived radionuclides it may be necessary to close the room until the affected surface, eg a floor covering, can be removed and replaced. Contaminated equipment such as forceps should be washed with a heavy-duty detergent. Articles used for cleaning contaminated areas should, where necessary, be regarded as low level radioactive waste and disposed of accordingly.

In cases of personnel contamination the areas of skin affected should be washed with soap and water until the derived limits are achieved. If this fails to reduce the levels below those given in *table 2.12*, detergent or chelating agent specific to the chemical form of the contaminant should be used. Excessive brushing of the skin should be avoided to prevent injury to the skin. If the skin is broken then the injury should be irrigated immediately with tap water taking care not to contaminate the wound. If, however, contamination is extensive, and a shower is required, then care must be taken to ensure that contamination is not spread over a wider area. Extreme care is also required to ensure that contamination does not enter the eye during showering or when hair is being shampooed to remove contamination. If the eyes are contaminated they should be irrigated immediately with large amounts of water followed by normal saline or another isotonic solution.

Articles of clothing and bedding which exceed the levels given in *table 2.12* must not be sent to a public laundry and should be either stored in an impermeable bag until the activity levels are such that normal laundering can take place or laundered in an automatic washing machine kept for this purpose. All clothing or bedding should be monitored before re-use to ensure that decontamination has been successful. If contaminated bedding represents a biological hazard or if it cannot be decontaminated satisfactorily then it should be treated as radioactive waste.

References

1 *The Medicines (Administration of Radioactive Substances) Regulations 1978* (SI 1978 No 1006) (HMSO, London)
2 *The Ionising Radiation (Protection of Persons Undergoing Medical Examination or Treatment) Regulations 1988* (SI 1988 No 778) (HMSO, London)
3 *The Ionising Radiations Regulations 1985* (SI 1985 No 1333) (HMSO, London)
4 *Guidance Notes for the Protection of Persons against Ionising Radiations arising from Medical and Dental Use* 1988 (HMSO, London)

CHAPTER 3

Imaging and other Diagnostic and Research *in vivo* Procedures

E D Williams

3.1 General Measures for Radiation Safety

Technetium-99m is the most commonly used radionuclide for *in vivo* procedures in UK hospitals. In this chapter it is therefore assumed that this is the radionuclide being used most frequently. Where additional radiation safety measures are needed to deal with special hazards associated with other radionuclides, this will be noted.

3.1.1 Building design

The design of a hospital department used for *in vivo* procedures with radionuclides depends on the extent and nature of the clinical services to be provided[1] although it is often constrained by the available space. Some general requirements are given below.

Entrances to all rooms in which radioactivity is handled or used must carry appropriate warning signs bearing the radiation warning symbol (trefoil) and an indication of the nature of the hazard (e.g. 'Unsealed Radioactive Sources').

In rooms in which liquid radioactive sources are to be handled, there is a requirement for smooth impermeable surfaces on benches and floors (e.g. welded vinyl flooring). Walls, which could be splashed with radioactive liquid, should be gloss painted in order to make decontamination easier.

Adequate space should be provided for the work to be performed in order that the radiation exposure to staff from radioactivity in patients shall be as low as reasonably achievable. Close proximity of the clinical rooms to the radionuclide dispensary helps to minimise both the hazards and the work associated with transport of radioactivity. Since patients must inevitably move from place to place, using internal walls for shielding is of limited value for reducing radiation exposure of persons, but may be important for shielding imaging and counting equipment. However, it may still be undesirable to locate a waiting room immediately adjacent to a clinical investigation area unless there is adequate shielding, because the radiation emitted by patients who are in the waiting area may interfere with radiation detectors. Floors need to be strong enough to bear the weight of imaging equipment, which can exceed 1 tonne on 0.1 sq m, and benches strong enough, if required, to take a lead safe or other lead shielding.

Consideration should be given to requirements such as heating, energy conservation and dust exclusion. Forced ventilation can be an advantage if radioactive gases or aerosols are used but is not an essential requirement, since other measures, e.g. local extraction via a mask or mouthpiece, can also be effective in limiting radiation exposure from such sources.

Hand-washing facilities, with elbow or foot operated taps, must be provided in rooms where unsealed radioactive sources are handled. A toilet for use by patients should also be nearby.

3.1.2 Equipment

All equipment used for clinical procedures must be appropriate to the work being done and be in good working order. Equipment used for imaging or other *in vivo* studies, for measuring radioactive preparations before administration to patients and for monitoring radiation levels and contamination, must have a regular performance assessment. The rationales for this in radiation safety terms are that malfunctioning equipment can result in a patient being given the wrong amount of radioactivity; inefficient equipment can result in administration to a patient of larger amounts of radioactivity than is usually considered necessary; and if invalid results of an investigation are produced, the administration of radioactivity may need to be repeated. Details of suitable quality control procedures are given elsewhere[2,3].

Equipment should have at least a check of constancy of performance made and recorded before each period of use. In the case of radionuclide calibrators (ionisation chambers), such checks are done most conveniently with a long-lived sealed radioactive source. However, any calibration must be 'traceable' to a national standard of radioactivity. Guidance on the quality control of radionuclide calibrators has been published jointly by the Institute of Physical Sciences in Medicine and the National Physical Laboratory[4].

For a gamma camera the response to a uniform source is the most commonly accepted test. Records of quality control assessments should be kept in such a way that deterioration in performance can be detected easily. Wherever possible 'action levels' should be set: if assessments give results outside a range considered acceptable, the action to correct the situation should be initiated. If equipment deteriorates in performance, such that it is inappropriate for a particular clinical application, then it should not be used.

Contamination monitors are discussed separately in Chapter 7.

3.1.3 Staff training and experience

The Head of Department is responsible to the Employing Authority for ensuring that staff working with radioactivity have appropriate training for the work which they carry out. Appropriate levels of training are specified by the relevant professional bodies (e.g. Institute of Physical Sciences in Medicine, Royal College of Radiologists, College of Radiographers etc)[5]. Staff who are receiving training must be adequately supervised.

A clean and tidy department is also an aid to radiation safety, since radioactivity is then unlikely to be left out of its shielding, not stored away, or left awaiting disposal.

3.2 People who may be Exposed to Radiation

Shielded containers are the primary means by which radiation exposure of people is restricted. Exposure can also be reduced by avoiding, so far as possible, close proximity between people and unshielded radiation sources (which includes patients). However, clinical use inevitably results in some exposure: the following paragraphs note the people who may be exposed and the limits which should be applied to their exposure.

3.2.1 Departmental staff

This term includes all staff who deal directly with radioactivity or with radioactive patients, and therefore may include medical staff, physicists, pharmacists, technicians, radiographers, nurses, receptionists and porters. The annual limit of dose equivalent for whole body exposure for employees aged 18 years and over is 50 mSv, with other limits for individual organs, tissues or body extremities (e.g. hands) of 500 mSv, and for the lens of the eye of 150 mSv. It is necessary to designate as a 'classified person' any employee who might exceed three-tenths of these limits, but at present most hospital staff working with unsealed radioactive sources in imaging departments are unlikely to exceed this level, and consequently do not need to be classified. The corresponding limits for (trainee) employees under 18, who may not be designated, are 15 mSv, 150 mSv and 45 mSv respectively. In practice most staff seldom receive a radiation dose of more than one tenth of the dose limit for whole body exposure. However, it is still good practice to monitor such individuals in order to verify that these levels are not exceeded, and vigilance is necessary to ensure that radiation doses are as low as reasonably achievable. Further guidance on this subject is given in Chapter 7.

3.2.2 Other hospital staff and the general public

The dose limits for the general public are one tenth of those for employees aged over 18. Since the public will not usually be subject to monitoring individually, it is necessary to ensure by other means that their radiation exposure is kept suitably low. Experience again shows that exposure below the limits is readily achievable in practice: relatives accompanying patients are unlikely to do this more than a few times per year. It is generally considered appropriate to apply the same dose limits to hospital staff whose work is not normally in a department using radiation, as must be applied to the general public. The principle of keeping exposures 'as low as reasonably achievable' also needs attention. Thus care needs to be taken to ensure that, for example, the same nurse does not frequently escort patients to whom radioactivity has been given, particularly if such patients require close attention for adequate nursing care.

3.2.3 Patients

Those staff concerned with carrying out diagnostic or research procedures on patients have a responsibility to ensure that the techniques used are appropriate for their purpose, and that they are carried out in a manner which will deliver a radiation dose to the patient which is no higher than is sufficient to achieve that purpose. Staff should therefore be aware of the radiation doses delivered by different procedures so that alternative techniques may be considered and compared. Effective dose equivalents for some common procedures[6] are given in *table 3.1* with mean values for common radiographic procedures for comparison[7]. Such information should be available for consideration by the doctor directing the examination. Staff should also be aware of measures which can be taken to reduce radiation dose. For instance, a patient who has been given a radiopharmaceutical which is excreted via the urinary tract should be encouraged to drink fluids and empty the bladder frequently, thus reducing the dose to the bladder wall. Iodide or perchlorate may be given to patients receiving diagnostic doses of radiopharmaceuticals labelled with I-125 or I-131 (e.g. I-125 fibrinogen or I-131 MIBG), to block uptake by the thyroid of free radioactive iodide released *in vivo*. Perchlorate may also be used to block thyroidal uptake of Tc-99m pertechnetate. Appendix II of the ARSAC Guidance Notes[6] gives detailed assistance on dosage.

Table 3.1 Effective dose equivalent from some common investigations (a) using radionuclides[6] and (b) radiography[7]

(a)

Radionuclide	Chemical form	Typical administered activity MBq	Effective dose equivalent mSv
H-3	water	4	0.06
K-42	potassium ion	1	0.2
Cr-51	chromic ion	4	0.4
Cr-51	labelled RBC (survival)	2	0.5
Cr-51	EDTA	3	0.007
Fe-59	ferric citrate	0.4	5
Co-57	vitamin B12	0.04	0.2
Co-58	vitamin B12	0.04	0.3
Ga-67	gallium citrate	150	15
Se-75	selenonorcholesterol	8	14
Tc-99m	pertechnetate	500	7
Tc-99m	colloid (liver)	80	1.0
Tc-99m	DMSA	80	1.0
Tc-99m	macroaggregate	100	1.0
Tc-99m	phosphonates	600	5
I-123	iodide	20	3
I-123	ortho-iodohippurate	20	0.3
I-125	albumin	0.2	2*
I-125	fibrinogen	4	0.5
I-131	iodide	0.2	3
Xe-133	gas (5 minutes rebreathing)	200	0.1
Tl-201	thallous ion	80	25

*no thyroid blocking

(b)

Examination	Effective dose equivalent per examination (mSv)
Lumbar spine	2.2
Chest	0.05
Skull	0.15
Abdomen	1.4
Thoracic spine	0.9
Pelvis	1.2
Intravenous urogram	4.4
Barium meal	3.8
Barium enema	7.7
Cholangiography	2.6

Care is necessary when carrying out procedures on women of child-bearing age. It is necessary to determine by appropriate questioning whether the woman is or may be pregnant. If the answer is yes, then the doctor requesting the investigation should be sure that it is justified and appropriate, and that the benefits outweigh the risks to the mother and the foetus. The procedure should be carried out so as to minimise the radiation dose to the foetus, by reducing the administered radioactivity if possible. The amounts of radioactivity administered to children should always be reduced compared to the normal adult dosage in proportion to their body weight or body surface area relative to that of the average adult. Further information concerning precautions in investigating children and pregnant or breast-feeding women is given in Chapter 4.

3.3 Administering Radiopharmaceuticals

3.3.1 General

Radiopharmaceuticals should normally be administered only in rooms or areas specified for this purpose. If this is not possible, for example in dynamic studies, a specified area to which access can be restricted should be used. Staff administering radiopharmaceuticals will be exposed to radiation once the radioactivity is outside its shielding and when it is inside the patient. The dose received at this time can be a significant proportion of the total exposure of staff[8]. Therefore, instructions to the patient and explanation of the procedure should be given before administering the preparation. The time subsequently spent by staff near the patient should be minimised. It is essential to check both the patient's identity and radiopharmaceutical before administration and to confirm that the procedure has been properly requested and justified on the request form. A record must be kept of all administrations of radiopharmaceuticals to patients. The period for which this record needs to be preserved is at least eight years in the case of an NHS hospital[9], but that requirement may now be superseded by the terms of the Consumer Protection Act (1987) which necessitate keeping records of products and their use for a minimum of 13 years. The consequences of this Act have yet to be established in the Health Service and advice from the Employing Authority should be sought. This record should be made at the time of administration: a section of the request form is often convenient for such a record. A note of the amount of radioactivity, the pharmaceutical, route and time of administration should also be incorporated in the report of investigation or treatment which is placed in the patient's case notes.

Staff should wear protective clothing so that any spilt radioactive solution will not contact the skin and an overall (coat) should be worn, buttoned up, when administering radioactivity to a patient. Disposable gloves should also be worn and carefully removed after use to avoid transferring any spilt radioactivity to the skin. The hands should always be washed after administering radioactive materials. It should be noted also that contamination may result from an invisible aerosol produced, for example, when a vial is punctured or a syringe is used. A contamination monitor should be available to detect radioactive material which may have been spilt on floor or clothing or transferred to the hands. All the necessary equipment can be located on a trolley (see *figure 3.1*).

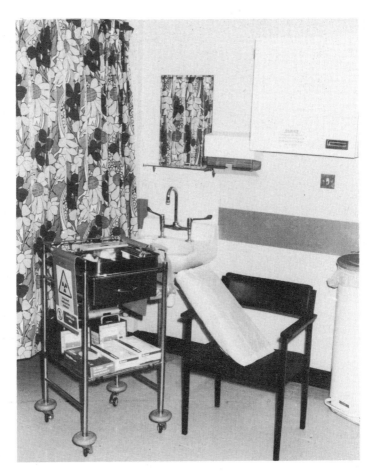

Figure 3.1 A trolley containing equipment for administering radiopharmaceutical injections. This can be used either in the area where injections are usually given, or as required in a gamma camera room. On the lower shelf are boxes of disposable gloves in assorted sizes, and small radiation monitors which can be used to check adequacy of injection or search for spilt radioactivity. A warning sign hangs on one side of the trolley to indicate a temporary Controlled Area. On the chair there is a piece of foam rubber covered with a paper tissue and polythene sheet pad, which is used to support the patient's arm when giving injections, and will absorb any spills. A wash-hand basin is nearby.

3.3.2 Intravenous injections

The majority of radiopharmaceuticals are administered by intravenous injection. Equipment must be prepared and set aside for this purpose and should include a tray, over which any transfer of radioactive solutions can be carried out, a shielded container in which the radiopharmaceutical is transferred from the dispensary to the injection area and an impermeable receptacle for discarded materials (*figure 3.2*). The possibility of spilling radioactivity, e.g. by dislodging a needle

40

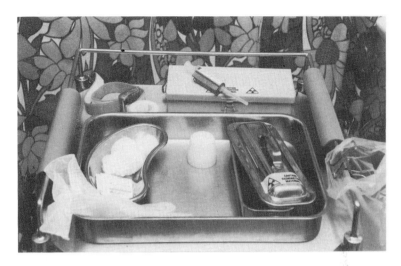

Figure 3.2   A close-up view of the injection trolley. The syringe is kept until required for use in the lead-lined box at the back, loaded into the tungsten syringe shield and suitably labelled. On the tray in front, over which any manipulation of the dose can be carried out, there is a plastic block into which the needle guard can be inserted and replaced on the needle without hazard to the hands. Discarded sharp material is placed in the covered steel tray on the right. Other disposable material including gloves is put in the plastic bag clipped to the trolley. Discarded materials are transferred to appropriate bins as soon as possible after injections are given.

from a syringe, should be considered and it is therefore advisable to carry out the injection (usually into an arm vein) over some absorbent disposable material (e.g. an incontinence pad which has a paper tissue pad on one side and polythene sheet on the back). The patient's limb should be rested firmly, e.g. on a pillow, pad, bed or table and the person administering the injection, and anyone assisting, should wear disposable gloves. A syringe shield made of tungsten (or other suitable shielding material), with a lead glass window or slot in the side, can be fitted over the barrel of the syringe so that the contents are visible. This is a convenient method for reducing (by a factor of up to 8) radiation exposure to the hands of the person giving the injection[10]. Such shields are usually designed for use with Tc-99m, and will be less effective with high energy gamma emitters, including radionuclides with positron-decay. With practice, gloves and a syringe shield can be used for most injections. If there is difficulty in using a syringe shield, or if it is necessary to ensure that the needle used for injection lies within the vein before drawing back any blood, then a butterfly needle (scalp vein cannula) should be used and its correct position ascertained with sterile saline solution before administering the radiopharmaceutical. This is the preferred method of administration both for materials such as macroaggregated albumin, which would clot if mixed with blood drawn back into the syringe before injection, and for radionuclides such as Tl-201, Ga-67 and In-111 which emit low energy electrons and can consequently give a very high local radiation dose if deposited in tissue, as a result of an extravasated injection[11]. Generally precautions should be taken to prevent the extravasation of an injection. One convenient method other than (or in addition to) using a butterfly needle is to ensure that the volume of solution injected is at least 2 ml so that incorrect injection will be noticed quickly and can be stopped.

Syringes and needles are usually disposed of intact to avoid the risks associated with handling sharp pathogenic material. The needle guard can be replaced if this is done by a safe technique, e.g. using a plastic block to hold the guard[12]: this method is recommended if a syringe shield is being used. It enables the syringe to be removed from the shield after use without the risk of contaminating the inside of the shield with blood or radioactivity.

3.3.3 Oral administration

Precautions should be taken to minimise the possibility of a spill when administering radioactive solutions orally. The container should be adequately stabilised on a tray to contain any possible spill, and placed on a bench or table. Where appropriate, a straw or tube should be used to transfer the liquid to the mouth. Capsules should not be handled directly, both because of the possible high surface dose rate and the risk of surface contamination. Subsequently, the principal hazard is if the patient should vomit: the likelihood of this needs to be judged and appropriate advice given. If there is a high likelihood of vomiting, then use of anti-emetic drugs should be considered. In other circumstances the patient should be confined to a suitable area (e.g. in the radioisotope suite) or under supervision such that any radioactive vomit can be contained, until the period of possible hazard from vomiting has passed.

3.3.4 Gases and aerosols

There is a potential hazard to staff from radioactive gases or aerosols that are emitted into the air and subsequently inhaled. The use of suitably designed equipment which does not leak should minimise this hazard. Careful testing and examination of equipment are therefore advised.

Forced ventilation of the room is clearly an advantage in removing radioactivity which has been released. The decay of Kr-81m is sufficiently rapid (half-life 13s) that collection of exhaled radioactivity is not usually considered necessary, but it is clearly advisable for the person administering the radioactivity to keep away from the immediate vicinity of the patient during use of this gas. A more significant exposure may originate from the generator and consideration should be given both to location and shielding. For longer-lived gases such as Xe-133 or Xe-127 exhaled radioactivity should be collected in a bag or box, or vented through a tube out of the building, or absorbed in a charcoal filter.

Equipment for administering aerosols should contain filters to trap radioactive aerosol which passes through the apparatus or which may be exhaled. Equipment which employs a nebulizer to generate an aerosol should be tested before clinical use with an inactive solution and then a very small amount of radioactivity to detect leaks or other malfunction. Usually, dilution of any leakage of radioactive gases or aerosols in the air is such that likely air concentrations of radioactivity are well below the derived air concentration limits: any ingested activity therefore will be well below the annual limit of intake[13]. However, if calculations suggest that exposure from such inhaled radioactivity would form a significant proportion of total exposure of staff, then arrangements should be made to monitor the air concentration and to provide forced ventilation of the area.

3.3.5 Designation of areas

The area in which radiopharmaceuticals are administered might be designated as a controlled area for the purposes of IRR85 on the grounds of the instantaneous dose rate arising from the radiopharmaceutical while giving the injection. Schedule 6 of the Regulations, however, provides alternative limits in terms of the product of activity and gamma energy per disintegration, such that once administered to and inside a patient the limit is 150 MBq MeV. This corresponds to an activity of 1070 MBq of Tc-99m which is greater than any activity listed by ARSAC for routine diagnostic use. An area need not therefore be controlled because of the presence of a patient containing any routinely used diagnostic radiopharmaceutical. Before administration, the corresponding activity-energy product limit is 50MBq MeV. This implies that while a controlled area is not required for many routine investigations, it would be required for those where more than 350 MBq of Tc-99m is administered. Thus it would appear that the room used for administration should be a controlled area, bearing the appropriate warning signs and having controlled access. However, if the relevant dose rate (7.5 μSv h^{-1}) will be exceeded only when the radio-pharmaceutical is removed from its container, then the need for a controlled area will exist only during that time. If this option were chosen, Local Rules should note that a temporary controlled area will exist only during this procedure and that control of access is exercised by the staff involved. The limits of the area will depend on the nature of the source and may be within 1.5 m of the radioactive source of less than 800 MBq Tc-99m (*table 3.2*). The work carried out by the staff must be described by a 'system of work' defined in Local Rules. This is an analogous situation to that pertaining to mobile radiography in hospital wards. The same considerations may be applied to administration of radiopharmaceuticals in other rooms, within the department or elsewhere in the hospital, where for clinical reasons it may be necessary to administer radioactivity to patients.

3.4 The Waiting Room, etc

It is inevitable that patients will wait in the department both for their investigation to commence and possibly for transport afterwards. If such patients contain radioactivity, they are a potential hazard.

3.4.1 Radiation from the patient

Additional exposure from radioactivity in a patient to other patients also having investigations or treatment involving irradiation, will generally add very little to their radiation exposure and can usually be ignored. However, patients are often accompanied by relatives or hospital employees and are a source of hazard to them. Such exposure should be minimised but without causing undue alarm to patients or their relatives. It is preferable if the waiting area is a separate room used only for this purpose, but if this is not possible, then a part of it could be reserved for use by radioactive patients only. At 0.5 m from a patient containing 500 MBq Tc-99m, the instantaneous dose rate will exceed 7.5 μSv h^{-1} (see *table 3.2*) and Controlled Area status must be considered (see Section 3.4.4). The waiting area should therefore be sufficiently spacious that escorting staff or visitors do not need to sit immediately next to radioactive patients, except when this is really necessary for the care of the patient. Staff escorting patients should therefore not perform this duty every working day. Working arrangements should be such that the time patients need to spend in the department is minimised: thus if there is necessarily an interval between administration of radioactivity and subsequent imaging, this time need not be spent in the department. Patients should depart as soon as possible after a procedure is completed. If space within the department is so restricted that the arrangements described above are not practicable, and if the size of workload permits it, then appropriate scheduling of investigations may be another means by which the radiation dose rate in the waiting room can be minimised. Thus, those investigations (such as bone scans) where the largest amounts of radioactivity are given could be spaced out through the week, rather than being concentrated on one day.

Table 3.2 Calculated dose rates from radionuclides used for diagnosis

Radionuclide	Half-life	Usual maximum activity (MBq)	Typical Dose rates (μSv h^{-1}) at 1 m from	
			(a) Point source	(b) Patient
Cr-51	27.7d	4	0.02	0.01
Fe-59	45d	1	0.16	0.10
Ga-67	78.1h	150	4.2	1.6
Se-75	120d	10	0.53	0.20
Tc-99m	6.02h	800	15.6	6.0
In-111	2.8d	80	6.9	2.4
I-123	13h	80	3.3	1.2
I-131	8.06d	40	2.3	0.9
Xe-133	5.3d	200	27	1.1
Tl-201	73.1h	80	1.1	0.3

3.4.2 Contamination hazards

Radioactive urine usually presents the main contamination hazard from patients who have been given radiopharmaceuticals. Probably the most significant such hazard in routine clinical diagnosis arises from patients having bone scans who are required to empty their bladder before imaging commences. A toilet should be set aside for use by such patients and should be suitable for a patient in a wheelchair. While such a toilet will in consequence be designated as a route for disposal of radioactive waste, it may be considered inappropriate to label it as such to avoid undue alarm. However, it might have a notice indicating a restriction on its use to patients having radionuclide examinations. This room should be subjected to regular monitoring for contamination.

Other sources of possible radioactive contamination are due to secretion of sweat and saliva. The concentration of radioactivity in such fluids is usually sufficiently low for Tc-99m pharmaceuticals that they can be ignored. Normal hygienic practice, involving frequent changes of linen, or use of disposable paper couch covers, should minimise any such possible contamination hazard.

3.4.3 Patients leaving the department

The Guidance Notes[6] (Table 5) indicate limits which should be applied to the residual radioactivity in patients leaving hospital. These limits are generally well above the amounts of radioactivity normally used in diagnosis. In practice because of time averaging considerations (IRR Schedule 6) no special precautions or advice are required except in the case of mothers and children, a subject which is treated in detail in Chapter 4. In the case of patients returning to a hospital ward, nursing staff should be aware that the patient has been given radioactivity and consequently that excreta will be radioactive. Normal hygienic precautions, including the use of disposable gloves, are adequate.

3.4.4 Designation of the area

A waiting room may be designated as a controlled area by reason of the instantaneous dose rate, resulting from patients containing radioactivity, exceeding 7.5 μSv h^{-1}. As previously noted, Schedule 6 of IRR85 provides for an exception where the product of activity and gamma energy in the area does not exceed 150 MBq MeV. This limit is not exceeded for any routine diagnostic procedures so it should always be possible to accommodate one patient under this condition. However, where several patients may be present then this limit could be exceeded and the RPA should advise whether time averaging is appropriate (IRR Schedule 6). Designating a waiting room as a controlled area raises several problems. It may be difficult to control access as required by the Regulations, since hospital waiting rooms are often part of an open reception area. Also, warning signs and demarcation of the boundary of such an area may be considered unduly alarming, although an area could be reserved for 'Nuclear Medicine patients' without disclosing the reason for segregation.

It is helpful to take into account the workload of the department in considering the need for designation of a controlled area. In departments having a relatively small number of patients, it may be unnecessary for the activity-energy product of 150 MBq MeV (corresponding to a total of 1070 MBq of Tc-99m in all patients present) to be exceeded in the waiting area, if there are appropriate rules governing the timing of investigations. Providing it can be shown that staff and visitors do not spend prolonged periods near patients containing radioactivity, and thus would not exceed dose limits, the provisions of Schedule 6 paragraph 3 could be interpreted such that a waiting room does not then need to be a controlled area. However, it is clearly an area which should be subject to special supervision and should therefore be a supervised area and described as such in the Local Rules. If the workload of the department is larger and it is not possible to distribute waiting patients to separate areas, nor to reduce their presence in the department sufficiently by rescheduling, then there may be no alternative but to designate the waiting room a controlled area.

3.5 The Imaging Room

3.5.1 The patient

The time spent by staff near a radioactive patient should be minimised, for example by carrying out positioning for imaging as efficiently as possible, and then withdrawing as far as possible consistent with the limits of the room and with the requirement to observe the patient. Immobilizing devices should be used where possible and appropriate: e.g. foam rubber supports, restraining straps or bands where a patient is required to remain still for a long period (e.g. during tomography). An appropriately designed couch and chair should be available so that the optimum positioning can be obtained for each patient without the requirement for continual restraint or support by staff (figure 3.3). To minimise radiation exposure of staff, it may be possible to obtain the assistance of an adult relative. For examinations on small children the necessity for restraint or sedation should always be considered, mainly to obtain satisfactory results, but also because a restless child will greatly extend the time required for examination and consequently increase the dose to staff.

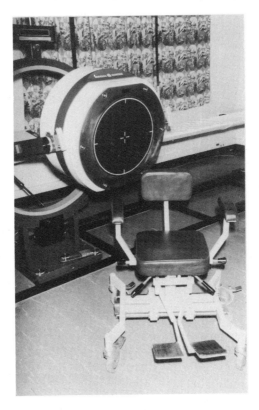

Figure 3.3   An appropriately designed chair is an aid to limiting radiation exposure of staff, since the patient can be positioned securely for a variety of views of the upper body.

3.5.2   Amount of administered radioactivity

Image quality is related to total acquired counts in each image, which in turn is related to the product of total administered radioactivity and imaging time. To obtain good quality images it is generally preferable to keep the imaging time as short as possible, since significant patient movement during each exposure is then less likely. However, there are upper limits recommended by ARSAC[6] for administered radioactivity, and in some cases limitations may be imposed by the maximum counting rate of the detector. Also the radiation dose to staff will increase if the administered radioactivity is increased, because of the exposure

46

during the time spent administering the radioactivity and positioning the patient for imaging.

The aim is to obtain information adequate for the purpose of the test for the minimum 'cost' in terms of radiation dose to patient and staff. The relevant factors tend to oppose one another, so judgement is needed for each investigation as to where the optimum lies. Recommended upper limits of activities to be administered for routine tests are given by ARSAC, but local circumstances (equipment, patient's condition, specific objectives of the investigation) require a local decision on the protocol to be adopted for each test.

In dynamic studies, the required activity to be given may be determined by the statistical accuracy required in the parameters to be measured. In general, an image data recording system (computer) should be used to avoid the necessity for repeated imaging in static studies, or repeat of the whole study due to film or cassette faults in the case of dynamic investigations.

3.5.3 Marker sources

The most convenient method for transferring anatomical landmarks to scintigraphic images is often by the use of radioactive marker sources. Such sources should be constructed so that during handling the radiation dose rate to the hands does not exceed 75 μSv h^{-1}. Thus a source consisting of a flat plastic disc with a small radioactive bead at its centre should be handled by the edges. If the source is 4 MBq of Co-57, the dose rate at 2 cm will be about 75 μSv h^{-1}. A marker source on the end of a rod gives a lower radiation dose to the hands, but can be more awkward to use. Such sources should be kept in a shielded container when not in use, checked regularly to avoid loss, inspected to ensure the integrity of the containment and stored securely outside normal hours of usage. The sources should of course be suitably labelled and must be checked for leakage at least every 2 years.

3.5.4 Radioactive sources used for testing

Every imaging device should be subject to a programme of regular quality control procedures. For a gamma camera the most appropriate regular test is the response to uniform irradiation. Such a test can be carried out in several ways, using (a) a small source at a distance of 2 metres or more from the camera with its collimator removed, (b) using a uniform sealed source containing (usually) Co-57 or (c) a perspex tank containing a solution of Tc-99m or another appropriate radionuclide. The latter two measurements are made with the collimator in place. There need be little hazard to staff in handling the source for a test of type (a), which might typically contain 10 MBq of Tc-99m. However, the sources for (b) or (c) may contain 100–500 MBq and the dose rate at the surface of such a sealed source may be sufficiently high that the IRR would prohibit direct handling. The dose rate at the point where such sources are handled should therefore be examined. While a refillable tank containing radioactivity is clearly not a sealed source, it seems appropriate in this circumstance to apply a similar approach as regards the radiation dose from handling it as if it were a sealed source. The dose rate to the hands from such sources should not exceed 75 μSv h^{-1}. A dose rate below this level may be achieved by limiting the total radioactivity in the source, adding handles to the source or some other means of manipulating it without direct contact, or by marking points of lowest dose rate (usually the edges) where it may be handled. Thus a tank (dimensions 450 mm diameter $\times$ 50 mm thick) containing 200 MBq Tc-99m gives a dose rate below 75 μSv h^{-1} at the edges where it should be handled. Such a test source should always be shielded when not in use and protected from damage. While it would be possible to provide shielding (e.g. a lead sheet) for the side distant from the gamma camera when it is in use, such a measure is unlikely to result in a substantial reduction in dose to staff, since most is received during handling. The source should be clearly marked with radiation warning symbols and with the radionuclide content and its activity. A clearly visible warning sign should be displayed when the source is in use to warn staff of its presence. While the measures described above are necessary, the radiation exposure from quality control procedures needs to be kept in perspective. One study has shown that for staff involved in a nuclear medicine service, the additional radiation dose from these procedures will usually be a small fraction of their total dose[14].

Liquid sources used for uniformity measurements require thorough mixing before use, and it is desirable that this is achieved without significant radiation exposure to staff. A pump or stirrer could be used to circulate fluid in the tank. Radioactive solutions used for testing or calibrating equipment should be handled in such a way as to minimise radiation exposure. Disposable gloves should be worn and absorbent material and impermeable coverings used to contain spills. An impermeable and an absorbent sheet placed between a tank and gamma camera is a suitable precaution to contain any leaks, and avoid contaminating equipment.

3.5.5 Designation of areas

A gamma camera room used for routine diagnostic procedures usually need not be designated a controlled area on account of the radioactivity within a patient, because only one patient would be in the room at a time and the activity-energy product would be below the limit of 150 MBq MeV. Even if a large room contains more than one imaging device, it is unlikely that it will need to be designated a controlled area. A source used for testing the gamma camera need not cause a controlled area to be designated if for example in the case of Tc-99m its activity does not exceed 350 MBq (i.e. less than 50 MBq MeV). If radioactive injections are carried out in the imaging room so that the 50 MBq MeV limit is exceeded, a temporary controlled area can be declared as described in section 3.3.5. The whole imaging room may alternatively be declared a permanent controlled area with appropriate controls on access and work within it. If it is not, and the philosophy outlined above is adopted, then the room should be a supervised area, have radiation warning signs on doors, and be subject to environmental monitoring for contamination of floors and other surfaces. The choice between these two approaches should be made by consultation between the RPA, RPS and head of department, taking all relevant circumstances into account.

3.6 Waste Management

Radioactive waste remaining after administration of radiopharmaceuticals should be transferred quickly to a shielded container with the minimum of handling, to reduce risks from microbiological infection. The multiple hazards from such waste in terms of its radioactivity, presence of pathogens and potential for injury from sharp needles should all be recognised. Waste should be stored in a place away from both the clinical imaging room, the dispensing area and behind suitable radiation shielding. It is advisable to segregate such waste into short and long lived radioactive categories to facilitate subsequent disposal.

Radioactive excreta and waste produced by incontinent patients should be disposed of as directly and rapidly as possible: preferably via an appropriate and designated WC or drain. Access to a bedpan disposal unit which is designated as a disposal route for radioactive waste is also a convenient method. Information about dealing with such situations should be supplied to staff in wards and operating theatres who may be dealing with patients after administration of radionuclides.

Records must be kept of all receipts of radioactive materials, and of all disposals, both of solid and liquid radioactive waste, and of the disposal of gas, which is ventilated out of the building. Liquids will include not only radioactive waste which is poured down a designated sink or drain, but also radioactive excreta from patients. The records are most conveniently kept as an account, so that the location of radioactivity at all times can be traced. The only exception is for radioactive substances with a half-life of less than three hours, for which such accounting is not required. Disposals may conveniently be estimated by applying simple rules and assumptions to the amounts of radioactivity administered to patients. The Department of the Environment has advocated the assumption that 30% of most Tc-99m radiopharmaceuticals or 100% of most other radionuclides is excreted. While such assumptions may be inaccurate, a relatively simple calculation from the number of patients examined or treated, yields a result which estimates the maximum disposal to the correct order of magnitude. This subject is considered in greater detail in Chapter 8.

3.7 Pathological Specimens

Samples for analysis taken from patients may require storage before or after preparation for assay. It is necessary to recognise that such specimens are both radioactive and pathogenic. A refrigerator or freezer, as appropriate for the samples, should be set aside for this purpose and bear the appropriate warning signs. Such specimens should be handled in accordance with the 'Code of Practice for prevention of infection in clinical laboratories and post-mortem rooms', commonly known as the 'Howie Code'[15]. Similar precautions to those applied against intake and spread of radioactive contamination should also limit the pathological hazards. Centrifuges should be of safe design which do not permit access to samples until spinning has stopped, and have enclosed buckets giving protection against broken sample containers.

In the routine diagnostic use of radionuclides, blood samples and urine aliquots from the patient would not constitute a significant external radiation hazard, so shielding is generally unnecessary. The whole of a urine collection obtained shortly after a radioactive administration is likely to contain a substantial fraction of that dose: it should therefore by discarded as soon as possible after removing aliquots for analysis. Although a pathology laboratory may have many specimens at one time, it is most unlikely that more than a few contain radioactivity: a controlled area is not therefore needed for specimen storage. This may not always be true if, for example, research on a series of patients results in the production of a large number of radioactive samples simultaneously. There are however, potential hazards from radioactive contamination or infection, so warning signs may be needed.

A potential problem in record-keeping arises from the requirement (in

ACOP 1/119) to account for radioactive sources which are kept for more than 24 hours and whose radioactivity exceeds the amounts in column 2 of Schedule 2 of IRR. Such an amount would for example be 5 MBq of Tc-99m or 0.5 MBq of Ga-67. Hence a test which requires a 24 hour urine collection on a patient who is simultaneously having a radionuclide imaging investigation would result in production of a specimen which apparently needs to be recorded as a radioactive source, together with a record of its storage and disposal. While such a procedure might be feasible if managed wholly within a nuclear medicine department, it is likely to cause difficulty where a separate (e.g. pathology) department or a hospital ward is involved. Advice might therefore be given to avoid collecting 24-hour specimens during a suitable period (24 hours in the case of Tc-99m) after giving radioactivity for imaging, provided this does not interfere with medical care of the patient. Alternatively, labels for recording the urine collection could be supplied at the time the activity is given to the patient. A further alternative is to consider that Regulation 19 of the IRR can be fulfilled without one of the above procedures by simply recording administration to the patient. This may be the case since the ultimate fate of the excreted radioactivity is the same, whether it goes directly to the sewer, or spends a short time in the ward or pathology laboratory first.

If a patient is scheduled for operation while significant residual radioactivity remains in the body, operating theatre staff should be warned and given advice. The operating theatre may be monitored afterwards for contamination if this is considered necessary by the RPS or RPA, depending on the nature of the operation and the administered radioactivity.

References

1. Langan J K, Wagner H N and Buchanan J W 1979. Design concepts of a nuclear medicine department *J Nucl Med* **20** 1093–4.
2. Hospital Physicists' Association 1983 *Quality Control of Nuclear Medicine Instrumentation* (CRS 38) (HPA, London)
3. World Health Organisation 1982 *Quality Assurance in Nuclear Medicine* (WHO, Geneva)
4. IPSM/NPL Protocol for Quality Control of Radionuclide Calibrators (in press)
5. *Implementation of Ionising Radiation (Protection of persons undergoing medical examination or treatment) Regulations 1988* HC(88)29 (DHSS, London)
6. ARSAC 1988 *Notes for guidance on the administration of radioactive substances to persons for purposes of diagnosis, treatment or research* (DHSS, London)
7. Shrimpton P C, Wall B F, Jones D G, Fisher E S, Hillier M C, Kendall G M and Harrison R M 1986 *A national survey of doses to patients undergoing a selection of routine X-ray examinations in English hospitals* NRPB-R2000, (HMSO, London)
8. Harding, L K, Mostafa A B, Roden L and Williams N 1985 Dose-rates from patients having nuclear medicine investigations. *Nuclear Medicine Communications* **6** 191–4.
9. Department of Health *Health Services management, preservation, retention and destruction of records Responsibilities of Health Authorities under the Public Records Acts* HC(89)20 (DHSS, London)
10 Harding L K, Hesslewood S, Ghose S K and Thomson W H 1985 The value of syringe shields in a Nuclear Medicine Department *Nucl Med Comm* **6** 449–54
11 Shapiro B, Pillay M and Cox P H 1987 Dosimetric consequences of interstitial extravasation following IV administration of a radiopharmaceutical *Eur J Nucl Med* **12** 522–3
12 Bessent R G, Donnet R and Shaw A 1987 Device to permit recapping of syringes without risk of infection *Br Med J* **295** 307–8

13 International Commission on Radiological Protection 1979 *Limits for intakes of radionuclides by workers* Publication 30 (Pergamon Press, Oxford).

14 La Fontaine R, Graham L S, Behrendt D and Greenwell K 1983 Personnel exposure from flood phantoms and point sources during quality assurance procedures *J Nucl Med* **24** 629–32

15 *Code of Practice for the Prevention of Infection in Clinical Laboratories and Post-mortem Rooms* 1978 (HMSO, London)

16 Department of Health 1990 *Guidance for Clinical Health Care Workers: Protection Against Infection with HIV and Hepatitis Viruses* (HMSO, London)

Chapter 4

Parental and Paediatric Radionuclide Protection

P J Mountford

4.1 General Precautions

The radiation protection precautions peculiar to the administration of radio-nuclides to pregnant women, to parents, and directly to children are discussed in this chapter. The Approved Code of Practice (ACOP 2/33) requires that members of the public must be identified who will have a significant exposure from radioactivity administered to another person, and that the exposure of such critical groups must be restricted[1]. Firstly, there are several instances where a foetus or an infant will be irradiated as a result of administering radionuclides to an adult. When a woman is pregnant, the foetus will be irradiated by radioactivity in adjacent maternal organs and by radioactivity which crosses the placental barrier. A young infant cuddled by the adult will be exposed to radiation emitted from retained radioactivity, and a breast-fed infant will receive a radiation dose from radioactivity secreted in the mother's milk. Secondly, the care of young infants and child patients necessitates parents and hospital staff spending periods of time in close contact with them. If these patients receive radioactivity, then parents and staff will also be unavoidably exposed to radiation emitted from retained radioactivity.

Perhaps the greatest chance of mistaken uncontrolled irradiation in any of these circumstances arises from the difficulty of identifying a patient who is only just pregnant or who is nursing a young infant. Completion of the request form by the referring clinician cannot be relied on as the sole method of communicating these facts. Signs can be displayed prominently in waiting areas asking such patients to inform a member of staff, but this approach assumes that every patient will see the notice and will not be prevented from comprehending it because of language or reading difficulties. Questioning patients by a member of staff at the time of examination has been suggested as an added safeguard against inadvertent irradiation of a foetus or infant[2]. However, once the details relevant to any situation have been resolved, careful consideration must be given to the risk to the mother of not carrying out a radionuclide procedure.

It is impossible to compile rigid instructions to deal with the radiation protection problems arising from each of the applications of radionuclides, since the appropriate course of action will depend on the immediate clinical problem and on the local working practices. For instance, some of the radiation protection precautions peculiar to the paediatric administration of radionuclides will vary with the age of the child. Before administering radioactivity, the radiation dose should be minimised by applying the ALARA (as low as reasonably achievable) principle[3] with the following questions[4]:

1. Is there an alternative technique which does not rely on the *in vivo* use of radioactivity?
2. Will a delay in carrying out the procedure reduce or eliminate the radiation hazard without compromising the patient's clinical management?

3. Is there an alternative radiopharmaceutical which yields a lower radiation dose?
4. Can the desired result be obtained with less than the usual administered radioactivity?
5. What is the possibility of a repeat investigation in the near future, and will this affect the magnitude of the administered activity?

In addition to an increased sensitivity to ionising radiation at lower ages, it must be recognised that evidence now points to a greater fatal risk due to malignancy from ionising radiation than previously perceived[5,6]. Furthermore, when formulating the appropriate precautions to follow, it must also be realised that there is no consensus on an acceptable level of dose to a foetus or infant resulting from parental administration of radioactivity. The International Commission on Radiological Protection (ICRP) recommend that the occupational exposure of pregnant women should not exceed 3/10 of the dose-equivalent limits[7]. Under these conditions, the dose to the foetus during the critical period of 8–15 weeks after conception would not be expected to exceed 1 mSv (see section 4.2.2), which is the single annual limit of effective dose equivalent (EDE) recommended by the National Radiological Protection Board (NRPB) for members of the public[8]. ARSAC[9] have recommended that special justification is required for procedures resulting in a foetal dose greater than 0.5 mSv. However, the National Council on Radiation Protection and Measurement in the USA has suggested[10] that doses below 50 mSv to the embryo-foetus may be considered an acceptable risk when compared to the potential medical benefit to the patient and embryo-foetus. This is one of the many situations when the clinician and the RPA should confer.

4.2 Administration of Radionuclides in Pregnancy

4.2.1 Embryonic and foetal radiopharmaceutical dosimetry

Calculations of the absorbed dose to an embryo or foetus are limited by the absence of biokinetic data for the pregnant woman and for the foetus at different stages after conception, and by the limited knowledge of human placental transfer of the radiopharmaceuticals in current use. In the early stages of pregnancy, the foetus and uterus form virtually a single unit and do not displace the maternal organs. Therefore, if there is no foetal concentration of radioactivity, the foetal dose during the early stages can be taken as the dose to the uterus. In all subsequent stages of pregnancy, calculations of the foetal dose are complicated by displacement of the maternal abdominal organs.

Specific absorbed fractions (SAF) as a function of photon energy and values of absorbed dose per unit cumulated activity (S-factors) have been published by Smith and Warner for various radionuclides, with the embryo as the target organ[11]. In their model, the embryo was represented simply as a sphere appropriately positioned in a standard 70 kg hermaphrodite phantom. These fractions were derived to correspond to the time of 10–41 days after conception during the period of organogenesis. Maximum values of the published estimates of the absorbed dose to the embryo based on these specific absorbed fractions are listed in *table 4.1* for various radiopharmaceuticals[11-13]. In practice, the greatest embryro doses of about 10 mGy arise from the use of activities of 800 MBq of Tc-99m pertechnetate or Tc-99m glucoheptonate and 150 MBq of Ga-67 citrate. Where the radioactivity is excreted predominantly in urine (as for several Tc-99m radiopharmaceuticals), the dose to the embryo is significantly higher than the gonad dose[12].

53

Table 4.1 Maximum values of published estimates of absorbed dose to the embryo* for various radiopharmaceuticals[11-13]

Radiopharmaceutical	Maximum embryo absorbed dose (μGy MBq^{-1} administered to the mother)
Tc-99m pertechnetate	10.5
Tc-99m polyphosphate	6.8
Tc-99m phosphate and phosphonate	9.7
Tc-99m DTPA	9.5
Tc-99m sulphur colloid	8.6
Tc-99m glucoheptonate	10.8
Tc-99m lung aggregate	9.5
Tc-99m HSA	4.9
Ga-67 citrate	68.0
In-113m DTPA	9.5
Se-75 selenomethionine	103.0
I-123 iodide	8.6
I-131 iodide	41.0

*10–14 days post conception

A model of the pregnant woman was also developed by Cloutier et al[14] by reducing the dimensions of the standard man phantom by a factor of 0.94 and incorporating a progressively enlarged uterus for each of the nine months of pregnancy, but it did not allow for displacement of the maternal abdominal organs. Its use was restricted to the calculation of foetal doses from maternal bladder radioactivity and to the calculation of SAF for the uterus at 3 months when there is little organ displacement[14,15]. These values of SAF have been taken to be a good estimate of SAF for the foetus at this stage, and they are similar to the SAF of Smith and Warner[11] for the gamma-ray energies of diagnostic and therapeutic radionuclides[15]. Following administration of I-131 to the mother, the dose from activity in the bladder to a one month old foetus (i.e. representative of very early pregnancy when inadvertent foetal irradiation is most likely) was calculated from the model of Cloutier et al[14] to be 0.032 mGy MBq^{-1}, with a dose to any single embryo compartment being no more than twice this value.

The Administration of Radioactive Substances Advisory Committee (ARSAC) lists estimated doses to the uterus for all radiopharmaceuticals with the advice that these doses can be taken as a guide to the foetal dose in early pregnancy[9]. Adaption of the model of Cloutier et al[14] to include repositioning of the abdominal organs was started but not completed[16,17]. Models are now being developed of the 3, 6 and 9 month pregnant female based on the anatomical phantom of the 15 year old child which will allow for displacement of the maternal abdominal organs. Some preliminary SAF for the three month model have been published[17,18].

The doses in *table 4.1* assume negligible activity in the embryo. There are no data describing the uptake of radiopharmaceuticals by the human embryo, but animal studies have shown uptake of radioiodide, Tc-99m EHDP and Tc-99m pertechnetate[19]. If placental transfer is included in the calculations for *table 4.1*, it has been argued that the total dose to the human embryo may lie in the range 0.005–0.035 mGy MBq^{-1} for Tc-99m pertechnetate administered to the mother[12].

Therefore for an activity of 800 MBq of Tc-99m pertechnetate, the total embryo dose could be 4–28 mGy. Placental localisation by radionuclide procedures has been replaced by ultrasound, but foetal doses from such compounds have been listed in *table 4.2*, for use in cases of administration to a pregnant woman for other purposes[20,21]. The maximum foetal dose for a Tc-99m compound occurs with pertechnetate, where 800MBq will give a dose of 4 mGy and 120 mGy to the foetus and foetal thyroid respectively.

Table 4.2 Estimates of absorbed dose to the foetus from radiopharmaceuticals used for placental localisation

Radiopharmaceutical	Absorbed dose to foetus (μGy MBq^{-1} administered to the mother)
I-131 HSA	618* (thyroid: 98)
I-123 HSA	25* (thyroid: 26)
Tc-99m HSA	5.7* (thyroid: 12)
	3.2† (thyroid: 7.6)
In-113m chloride	4.6*

*30 week foetal age[20]
†3.3 kg foetus[21]

The foetal thyroid does not concentrate radioiodide until the end of the first trimester[22,23]. The variation of foetal thyroid doses with foetal age for I-123, I-125 and I-131 iodide taken from Johnson[23] are given in *table 4.3*. The maximum permitted activity of 800 MBq (300 MBq Mev) of I-131 administered to a mother as an out-patient at the start of her second trimester would result in a foetal thyroid dose of 500 Gy.

Table 4.3 Variation of foetal thyroid dose with foetal age from maternally administered I-123, I-125 and I-131 iodide[23]

Age (days)	Foetal thyroid dose (Gy MBq^{-1} administered to the mother)		
	I-123	I-125	I-131
91	0.001	0.06	0.1
100	0.008	0.24	0.6
130	0.011	0.38	1.0
150	0.009	0.38	0.9
200	0.006	0.24	0.6
250	0.004	0.19	0.4

4.2.2 The risks associated with irradiation in pregnancy

In deciding whether to proceed with the administration of a radionuclide to a pregnant woman, the radiation risk must be balanced against the risk to the health of the mother and foetus from not obtaining a diagnosis. If a radionuclide investigation is essential, then the minimum activity must be administered without compromising the diagnostic result (section 4.1). It must be realised that even without placental transfer, all foetal tissues will receive a dose from activity in adjacent maternal organs following administration of a radionuclide. Mental impairment and carcinogenesis have been identified as the major post natal consequences of irradiation in utero[24].

Mental impairment with an unquantifiable risk was the only abnormality recorded in live-born children exposed *in utero* to abdominal irradiation given unsuccessfully as a means of therapeutic abortion during the 1920s[24]. The greatest risk of mental impairment in children exposed *in utero* to atomic bomb radiation at Hiroshima and Nagasaki was found to be in the period 8–15 weeks after conception, with an intermediate risk at 16–25 weeks[25]. No risk of mental retardation has been found in the periods 0–7 weeks and beyond 25 weeks after conception. The risk of mental retardation from irradiation *in utero* was apparently dose-related, and at 8–15 weeks and 16–25 weeks has been given as 40 percent per Gy and 10 percent per Gy respectively[7,24,25]. A recent update has confirmed a threshold of 700 mGy for 16–25 weeks, and at 8–15 weeks, the maximum likely threshold is about 250 mGy although a linear model without a threshold gives a statistically adequate fit[26].

Although the atom bomb survivors irradiated *in utero* showed no excess in childhood cancer, an increase in both cancer mortality and incidence has been found in children exposed *in utero* to diagnostic X-radiation. Pooled data from these radiological studies give an excess rate of one cancer death in 4000–5000 children[24]. The United Nations Scientific Committee on the Effects of Atomic Radiation (UNSCEAR) gives a fatal malignant risk of 2–2.5 percent per Gy of foetal tissue dose based on observations over the first ten years of life[27]. However, a very recent report from the Oxford Survey of Childhood Cancer (OSCC) has estimated a greater excess fatal cancer rate after foetal irradiation of 20 percent per Gy[28]. A review of the available data published in 1987 concluded there was no convincing evidence that the embryo and early foetus were more sensitive to induction of malignant disease than later stages of pregnancy[24]. In contrast, the more recent OSCC study found a cancer risk after first trimester radiography which was almost three times greater than the risk for other prenatal radiography and six times as great as the risk for children not irradiated *in utero*[29], although the validity of this risk estimate has been questioned[30].

These radiation-induced risks should be compared with an estimate of a probability of 1 in 30 for a normal pregnancy resulting in a markedly handicapped child[31], and with an estimate of a probability of 4–6 percent of normal pregnancies resulting in children described as having varying degrees of congenital defects[10]. Despite these relatively high risks of abnormalities from other causes, calculations of foetal doses are subject to large uncertainties, and every administration of radioactivity to a pregnant woman must be justified on an individual basis, regardless of the magnitude of the radiation dose. It should not be assumed that there is no cause for concern if the foetal dose does not exceed an arbitrary limit. ARSAC advises that a dose to the foetus of greater than 0.5 mGy requires particular justification, that this level of dose is comparable to variations in natural background radiation and that it carries a risk of an abnormal birth of 1 in 20,000[9]. Previously it was considered that a pregnancy should be allowed to proceed if the embryo was exposed to less than 100 mGy[2]. There is a clear need for this latter dose limit to be reviewed in the light of the currently perceived increase in the fatal malignant risk of radiation, and to take account of any variations in sensitivity during different stages of pregnancy.

Accumulation of I-131 in the foetus or embryo and its thyroid during the first few weeks of pregnancy is negligible. The number of spontaneous abortions and foetal and neonatal abnormalities following I-131 treatment for hyperthyroidism in the first trimester has been found to be no greater than might normally be expected[32]. However, beyond the twelfth week of pregnancy, administration of I-131 can lead to hypothyroidism in the infant[32,33].

4.2.3 Administration of radionuclides to adults of reproductive capacity

Guidance on the administration of radionuclides to women of reproductive capacity is to be published shortly by the Institute of Physical Sciences in Medicine. In particular, this publication will include recommended delays before a woman should conceive following radionuclide therapy.

ICRP and NRPB recommend that women of reproductive capacity can be investigated with diagnostic X-radiation during any part of their menstrual cycle[34-36]. During the first ten days of the menstrual cycle, conception generally does not occur (the basis of the old 'ten day rule'), and during the remaining time of the four week cycle, the risk to the foetus of maldevelopment is considered small enough not to warrant a special limitation on exposure. It has been concluded that abandonment of the 'ten-day rule' by diagnostic X-ray services could lead to one extra foetal abnormality in 30 years in the United Kingdom, and that by delaying an examination in order to comply with the rule, the potential hazard to maternal and foetal health is likely to outweigh any benefit[37]. The NRPB has advised that for diagnostic X-ray exposure, a woman should be considered pregnant when menstruation is known to be overdue or clearly missed, and that when the uterus lies in or near the useful beam, she should be regarded as pregnant unless her answer is 'No' to the question 'Are you, or might you be, pregnant?'[36].

Compared to direct diagnostic X-ray exposures, embryo doses from diagnostic radionuclide procedures are generally smaller, there are fewer nuclear medicine investigations per annum, and in general, nuclear medicine patients (particularly those undergoing radionuclide therapy) are subject to greater and closer clinical management. Although the risk of mental retardation has been shown to be absent in the first few weeks of pregnancy, there remains the risk of radiation-induced cancer at all stages of pregnancy. Thus while some nuclear medicine services have abandoned the 'ten day rule'[38], others have preferred to retain its cautious approach, and not to change a tried and tested system of patient referral.

It has also been argued that the risk of serious radiation-induced genetic injury in the seven weeks before a mother becomes pregnant is greater than or comparable to the risk in the first two weeks of pregnancy[2]. The testis is also sensitive to radiation during spermatogenesis which can occur several months before fertilisation. Gonad doses for various radiopharmaceuticals are listed in table 4.4[39-49]. Calculations have indicated that irradiation of the ovaries resulting from I-131 treatment of thyroid cancer should not increase the risk of foetal anomalies and does not warrant permanent sterilisation[50]. Patients treated with I-131 in childhood or as adolescents for either hyperthyroidism or thyroid cancer had no increase in complications during subsequent pregnancies and no increase in abnormalities of their own children[51,52].

Table 4.4 Gonad doses for various radiopharmaceuticals

Radiopharmaceutical	Gonad dose (μGy MBq^{-1} administered)		(Reference)
	Testes	Ovaries	
Tc-99m pertechnetate	4.6	4.9	(41)
Tc-99m MAA	0.3	0.8	(41)
Tc-99m glucoheptonate	4.1	4.9	(41)
Tc-99m DTPA	3.8	5.6	(42)
Tc-99m DMSA	1.6	3.0	(43)
Tc-99m MDP	3.2	4.6	(44)
Tc-99m polyphosphate	3.8	5.4	(44)
Tc-99m HSA	4.3	4.6	(41)
Tc-99m colloid	0.5	1.6	(41)
Tc-99m erythrocytes	4.3	4.6	(41)
Tc-99m PIPIDA	3.2	12.2	(45)
I-123 iodide (oral)	3.2	8.4	(46)
I-123 OIH	4.1	7.8	(47)
I-131 iodide (oral)	23.8	37.8	(46)
I-131 MIBG	57	52	(48)
Tl-201 chloride	81		(49)
In-111 leucocytes	59	100	(39)
Ga-67 citrate	146	173	(40)
Se-75 selenomethionine	2970	1350	(41)
Cr-51 erythrocytes	65	70	(41)
P-32 phosphate	810	810	(41)

4.3 Administration of radionuclides to parents

4.3.1 Precautions for radioactive parents handling infants

a) Assessment of an external dose

When a radionuclide has been administered to an adult patient, a child may be exposed to radiation emitted from the retained radioactivity. The maximum exposure is likely to occur to very young infants when tended at home by a parent to whom radioactivity has been administered. The exposure is occasional, and therefore any hazard can be reduced not only by considering the ALARA principle (section 4.1), but also by delaying the start of close contact and by reducing the frequency of contact. If the parent is a lactating mother, the emitted radiation dose can be reduced by another person feeding the infant with milk which the mother has expressed into a bottle (subject to the breast feeding restrictions in section 4.3.2). Close contact between a parent as an in-patient and a young infant will be more restricted and can be more easily controlled.

Two methods can be used to estimate close contact doses to young infants. Firstly, integral doses over a prolonged period can be measured with thermoluminescent dosimeters (TLD) secured to the skin surface of the parent or the infant. Secondly, the doserate at the surface of the patient can be measured with a dosemeter. A large volume ionisation chamber is probably most suitable, because of its high sensitivity and uniform energy response[53]. If radioactivity has just been administered to a patient and a potential close contact dose has to be estimated at short notice, the only immediate course of action may be to measure the surface dose rate and convert to a total dose by multiplying by an effective exposure time. The values of effective exposure time listed in *table 4.5* allow for the decay of the surface dose rate and for the specified intermittent nature of close contact between a parent and an infant[54]. If for a particular patient different sequences of close contact are considered more appropriate, the method outlined by Mountford[54] can be used to calculate effective exposure times.

Table 4.5 Estimation of close contact doses to an infant from a radioactive parent[54]. This table MUST be read in conjunction with section 4.3.1. The total close contact dose to the child is obtained by multiplying the doserate measured at the surface of the mother by the factor f given in the table.

Radiopharmaceutical	f (h)*
Tc-99m (all compounds)	2
I-123 iodide	2 (a)
	3 (b)
I-131 iodide	16 (a)
	18 (b)
I-123 MIBG	2
I-131 MIBG	7
In-111 leucocytes	21
Tl-201 chloride	18
Se-75 selenomethionine	340
Ga-67 citrate	19
In-113m (all compounds)	1
Y-90 colloid	20
P-32 phosphate	80
Sr-89 chloride	370

(a) euthyroid   ⎫ Note: error in original reference[54]
(b) hyperthyroid   ⎰   data corrected
* Assuming close contact, in each 24 hour period after injection, of: 20 min hr⁻¹ at the start of each hour for 8 h, 20 min h⁻¹ at the start of each fourth hour for the next 12 h, and 20 min h⁻¹ at the start of each h for the remaining 4 h.

b) Diagnostic radionuclide procedures

Close contact doses to young infants have been estimated as above from TLD integral doses, and from dose rates measured with an ionisation chamber at 0.1 m from the mid-trunk of patients in a sitting position just before they left the nuclear medicine department[53,54]. The annual EDE limit of 1 mSv will not be exceeded by the maximum ARSAC activities of any of the Tc-99m, Ga-67, In-113m and Tl-201 labelled compounds examined[9], because the maximum close contact doses per unit activity administered were 0.7 μSv MBq^{-1}, 3 μSv MBq^{-1}, 0.6 μSv MBq^{-1} and 0.4 μSv MBq^{-1} respectively. However, an EDE of 1 mSv can be received by an infant after administration of less than the maximum ARSAC activity (40 MBq) of In-111 labelled leucocytes to the parent (maximum close contact dose: 90 μSv MBq^{-1}), and thus the activity administered to the mother should be minimised. The activity of Tc-99m and I-123 secreted in sweat and saliva after a diagnostic procedure does not warrant any precautions[55,56]. Therefore once the parent has returned home, no restrictions in close contact between a parent and a young infant should be necessary following the administration of diagnostic activities.

However, in some cases, this conclusion is based on measurements made on patients as they left a department, and in all cases refers just to an infant tended at home by one radioactive adult. Doses to infants brought by parents into the waiting area of a department will be larger than the above values due to the greater radioactivity in the parent immediately after injection, and due to their exposure to radiation emitted from other radioactive patients. The contribution of the latter component to their total dose is more difficult to quantify because of the variable nature of this source of exposure (e.g. times, distances, number of patients, activities and radionuclides). Therefore parents undergoing diagnostic radionuclide procedures should be discouraged from bringing young infants into a waiting area.

Restrictions are unnecessary for older children who spend longer periods of time at greater distances from their parents[53]. However, where I-131 has been given for whole body imaging of a parent (e.g. iodide for thyroid metastases or MIBG for certain tumours), the same precautions at home should be followed as for I-131 given for out-patient treatment (see below).

c) Therapeutic radionuclide procedures

Using the maximum doserate recorded in the ionisation chamber study[53] and the effective exposure time given in *table 4.5*[54], a young infant would exceed 1 mSv for activities of I-131 greater than 110 MBq administered to a hyperthyroid parent as an outpatient. More pessimistic assumptions for the doserate could substantially reduce this activity, and the Guidance Notes[57] recommend that restrictions or close contact with young children should continue until the residual activity in the patient falls below 30 MBq. Radioactivity will also be secreted in the parent's sweat and saliva[55]. Thus close contact must still be avoided, and cutlery and crockery must not be shared until this latter limit of 30 MBq is reached. Instructions issued to patients for resuming normal conduct can assume that this limit will be reached with an effective half-life for I-131 in the body of 3 days.

Measurements of weekly doses and of thyroid uptake in older children of parents administered I-131 as out-patients have shown that it is unnecessary to restrict time and distance, other than to avoid prolonged close contact until the retained activity falls below 30 MBq[58,59]. Similar precautions should be followed after administration of I-131 MIBG. For other therapeutic radionuclides given to out-patients, an estimate of a close contact dose can be made from a dose rate measurement multiplied by the effective exposure time given in *table 4.5*, ensuring that for a pure beta particle emitter, the dosemeter will respond to the low energies of the associated bremsstrahlung radiation.

Young infants should not be allowed to visit in-patients given activities of I-131 iodide or I-131 MIBG which necessitate a stay in hospital, and the restrictions on time and distance for visiting by older children can be derived by sequential measurements at the patient's bedside or by recourse to published retention data. Before being discharged from hospital, these patients should be issued with instructions to prevent close contact with infants, as for I-131 out-patient treatment.

4.3.2 Precautions for breast-feeding mothers

If a radionuclide is administered to a lactating mother, then radioactivity may be secreted in her milk and her breast-fed infant will receive a radiation dose from the radioactivity ingested (*figure 4.1*)[60-64,81]. Metabolic models and limits of intake for ingested radioactivity recommended by ICRP apply to occupationally exposed workers. However, because of the absence of an accepted method to calculate the ingested dose to a breast-fed infant, approximate estimates of such doses can be obtained from the ICRP adult values of EDE per unit activity ingested after a simple correction for the weight of the infant (as given in *table 4.6* for a 4 kg infant)[65]. These doses should be considered to be approximate estimates because ICRP factors do not account for the age dependence of the fractional absorption from the gut, the anatomical distribution, and the metabolism of the ingested radioactivity.

Table 4.6 The effective dose equivalent (EDE) per unit activity ingested for a 4 kg infant derived from ICRP adult data by body weight ratio[65]

Radionuclide	EDE per unit activity ingested (μSv MBq^{-1})
Tc-99m	0.28
I-123	2.3
I-125	175
I-131	245
Se-75	45
Ga-67	3.4
In-111	5.7
Cr-51	0.6
P-32	36
Tl-201	1.4

The radioactivity secreted in milk can be minimised by considering the ALARA points listed in section 4.1. The ingested dose can be further reduced either by the mother interrupting feeding until the secreted activity has reached an acceptable level or by ceasing breast-feeding. The exact form of these latter instructions will depend on the magnitude and effective half-life in milk of the secreted activity. Both parameters vary according to the radiopharmaceutical administered to the mother[60,61]. If feeding is to be interrupted, then the mother can be advised to express milk before administration of radioactivity, store the milk in a refrigerator, and feed her infant with it during the period of interruption. A simple method has been proposed of quantifying secretion data and deriving an appropriate period of interruption calculated to reduce the infant's EDE to 1 mSv[61].

An excessive delay in the resumption of breast feeding should be avoided in order not to jeopardise the supply of milk. This is a particularly important consideration in the immediate post partum period, when the mother may be experiencing difficulty in establishing her milk supply. The kinetics of the secretion of radioactivity in colostrum can differ from that of mature milk (*figure 4.1*)[62,63]. It must be established whether the mother is producing mature milk or colostrum before issuing instructions. Precise recommendations for interrupting breast-feeding cannot be issued for many radiopharmaceuticals because of the dosimetric uncertainties and the small amount of available data describing the magnitude and chemical form of secreted activity. Therefore for a mother producing mature milk, radiopharmaceuticals have been allocated in *table 4.7* into one of the following types of recommendation:

Table 4.7 Recommendations for interrupting breast-feeding following maternal administration of radiopharmaceuticals for which measurements have been published[61,64]

A. *Interruption not essential*
Tc-99m DTPA
Tc-99m DMSA
Tc-99m glucoheptonate
Tc-99m MDP
Tc-99m HDP
Tc-99m HMDP
In-111 leucocytes
Cr-51 EDTA

B. *Interruption for a defined period*

Tc-99m MAA (9 h)*

C. *Interruption with measurement*

Tc-99m pertechnetate
Tc-99m erythrocytes
Tc-99m EDTA
Tc-99m plasmin
I-123 iodide
I-123 OIH
I-125 OIH
I-131 OIH
Tl-201 chloride

D. *Cease breast-feeding*

I-125 fibrinogen
I-125 HSA
I-131 iodide
Se-75 selenomethionine
Ga-67 citrate

* For 80 MBq administered activity; based on new data.

A.   An interruption to feeding is not essential, but to help reassure the mother advise her to express and discard the first feed after administration of radioactivity.

B.   Interrupt breast-feeding for the period given in *table 4.7*, during which time milk should be expressed and discarded at normal feeding times.

C.   Advise the mother that although feeding can be resumed within a few days, she should express milk at her normal feeding times, and the appropriate period of interruption to reduce the EDE to 1 mSv can then be calculated from measurements of the concentrations of radioactivity in each sample of milk.

D.   Cease breast-feeding unless the mother insists on trying to maintain her milk supply; in which case, do not issue any advice on the length of interruption (which will be at least a week and in some cases a lot longer), and follow the same procedure as in type C to calculate the interruption period.

It is assumed for types A and B that the radionuclide is administered entirely in the chemical form specified, and the presence of other forms (particularly 'free' iodide or pertechnetate which the mammary gland is known to concentrate) must be excluded before the issue of advice to the mother. It is also assumed for types A and B that the administered activity does not exceed the ARSAC maximum values[9]. If any radiopharmaceutical is administered while the mother is producing colostrum, then unless the radiopharmaceutical is covered by recommendation D, the radioactivity in expressed samples should be measured, and the mother must not be allowed to resume feeding until the EDE to the infant deduced from these measurements reduces to 1 mSv (recommendation C).

Regardless of the composition of a mother's milk, Tc-99m pertechnetate should be avoided for brain scans in preference to Tc-99m DTPA or Tc-99m glucoheptonate, with Tc-99m DTPA as the first choice for brain and renal studies. I-123 should be considered instead of I-125 or I-131, and In-111 leucocytes should be used instead of Ga-67 citrate. Of the radiopharmaceuticals in common use, there are no data to describe the secretion in milk of Tc-99m colloid, Tc-99m HIDA, radioiodinated MIBG, and radiolabelled antibodies.

4.4   Administration of radionuclides to children

4.4.1   Administered activity

The radioactivity administered in a paediatric study must be the minimum compatible with obtaining a diagnostic result. Young infants cannot be expected to keep absolutely still for very long and it may be necessary to administer some form of sedation. If sedation is contraindicated on medical grounds or may not be effective, or the child is known to be uncooperative, then to avoid administration of radioactivity for a repeat investigation, the administered activity should be increased to allow the test to be completed within a shorter time.

For the purposes of paediatric radiopharmaceutical dosimetry, a series of organ weights has been adopted for different ages. The ratios of the weight of most organs to total body weight remain more or less constant with age (*table 4.8*)[13,66,67]. Therefore assuming that the fractional uptake by body organs of children is similar to that of adults, the appropriate administered activity to give the same radiation dose for a diagnostic study can be derived by simply correcting the usual adult administered activity by the ratio of the child's body weight to that of an adult. Exceptions to the latter rule are the brain, intestine, yellow marrow and

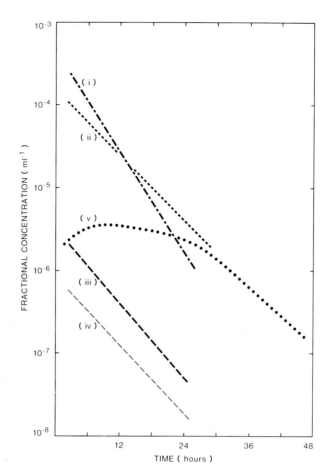

Figure 4.1 Variation of the concentration of radioactivity secreted in mature milk with time after administration (expressed as a fraction of the administered activity), of (i) Tc-99m pertechnetate, (ii) Tc-99m DTPA (aerosol)/Tc-99m MAA (as a fraction of the administered MAA activity only), (iii) Tc-99m glucoheptonate, (iv) Tc-99m DTPA, and of (v) Tc-99m MAA where the secretion was nearly all colostrum during the first 20 h[62,63].

gonads with the brain reaching 70 percent of its adult weight by the age of 1 year (*table 4.9*). Therefore body weight ratio may give too small an administered activity for paediatric brain studies with radiopharmaceuticals which penetrate the blood-brain barrier (such as Tc-99m HMPAO). Blood volume per unit body weight remains almost constant with age[68], and thus body weight ratio will be appropriate for calculating the activities of brain scanning agents which do not cross this barrier.

As the age and weight of an infant decrease, the reduction in the appropriate level of administered activity in a diagnostic study will be accompanied by a

Table 4.8 Ratio of organ to whole body weight independent of age[13,66,67]

Organ	Ratio (Mean $\pm$ SD) ($\times 10^{-3}$)
Bladder Wall	0.68 $\pm$ 0.05
Kidneys	5.1 $\pm$ 1.0
Liver	27 $\pm$ 3
Lungs	12 $\pm$ 1
Pancreas	0.86 $\pm$ 0.12
Skeleton	140 $\pm$ 10
Spleen	2.5 $\pm$ 0.1
Thyroid	0.25 $\pm$ 0.03
Stomach	2.4 $\pm$ 0.3
	(decreases to 1.5 for newborn)
Red Marrow	19 $\pm$ 2
	(decreases to 14 at 1 yr, 10 for newborn)

Table 4.9 Ratio of organ to whole body weight dependent on age[13,66,67]

Organ	Age:	Ratio ($\times 10^{-3}$)					
		Newborn	1 yr	5 yr	10 yr	15 yr	Adult
	Whole body weight:	4 kg	10.4 kg	20 kg	32 kg	57 kg	70 kg
Brain		93	97	59	42	24	21
Intestines		8	14	15	–	22	25
Yellow Marrow		0	0	3	18	26	21
Ovaries		0.075	0.067	0.10	0.10	0.088	0.11
Testes		0.20	0.14	0.08	0.06	0.28	0.53

decrease in the area of the image of the organ of interest. Therefore an alternative approach for imaging studies is to aim for a constant information density per unit surface area of the organ, and to assume that the organ surface area maintains a constant fraction of the body surface area with age. The usual adult administered activity is corrected by the ratio of the child's body surface area to that of an adult, where the body surface area is taken to be proportional to the two-thirds power of body weight. A greater activity will be administered by the surface area method compared to the body weight method, particularly for young infants (*table 4.10*). However, the magnitude of these activities must be sufficient to provide diagnostic images, and the minimum administered activity should be identified for each paediatric procedure[69].

4.4.2 Paediatric radiopharmaceutical dosimetry

The absorbed dose to a target organ irradiated by activity in a source organ is given by the product of the cumulated activity and the mean dose per cumulated

Table 4.10 Comparison of paediatric administered activities
derived from body weight and body surface area

Weight (kg)	Fraction of adult activity	
	By weight	By surface area
2	0.03	0.09
4	0.06	0.15
10	0.14	0.27
20	0.29	0.43
30	0.43	0.57
40	0.57	0.69
50	0.71	0.80
60	0.86	0.90
70	1.00	1.00

activity (S-factor). In the absence of paediatric data, cumulated activities for
paediatric dosimetry are derived from adult and animal studies[13,39,66,68]. S-factors
based on the organ weight data given in *tables 4.8* and *4.9* have been published for
Cr-51, Ga-67, Tc-99m, In-111, I-123, I-131 and Tl-201 in different paediatric age
groups[13,66].

When a child is referred for a radionuclide investigation, then, apart from the
child's age, the only information immediately available is usually the whole body
weight and the adult doses per unit administered activity. The latter can readily be
found, for instance, in the radiopharmaceutical package insert leaflet. Radiopharmaceuticals labelled with Tc-99m and I-123 are probably the most commonly
used compounds in paediatric nuclear medicine because of their associated low
doses per unit activity. In order to derive a quick estimate of a paediatric dose for
these compounds, ratios of total body, critical organ and gonad doses (per unit
activity) to those for the adult are summarised in *table 4.11* for different ages and
weights[13,39,66,68,70,71]. Despite its much greater total body dose per unit activity
(0.17 mGy MBq^{-1} for an adult), ratios for In-111 leucocytes are also listed,
because its increasing use has warranted a comprehensive dosimetric evaluation[39].
However, Tc-99m-labelled leucocytes (using HMPAO) are now becoming
established as an alternative scanning agent and yield a lower radiation dose to
the patient. Although the radiopharmaceutical doses published recently in
ICRP 53[72] are based on different biokinetic and paediatric anatomical data and
are not included in *table 4.11*, they yield ratios similar in value to those given in
the table.

At any particular age, the total body ratios differ by not more than $\pm$ 10 percent
for a range of Tc-99m compounds. Except for young infants, this relatively small
variation also applies to Tc-99m critical organ doses. Because of their similar
physical properties, the ratios for I-123 iodide total body and gonad doses are
similar to the ratios for Tc-99m compounds, and therefore it is probable that these
ratios can be applied to other I-123 radiopharmaceuticals. Compared to I-123 and
Tc-99m compounds, lower activities of In-111 leucocytes are given to adults, and
the latter is an example of where the minimum administered activity can exceed the
weight-corrected activity[39]. The ratios for In-111 leucocytes were generated from

Table 4.11 Summary of whole body, critical organ and gonad absorbed doses for radiopharmaceuticals in common paediatric use[13,39,66,68,70,71]

Radiopharmaceutical	Organ*	Ratio of paediatric absorbed dose per unit activity administered to that of the adult†				
	Age: Total weight:	Newborn: 4 kg	1 yr 10.4 kg	5 yr 20 kg	10 yr 32 kg	15 yr 57 kg
Tc-99m Compounds	WB	10.9 ± 1.2	4.0 ± 0.4	2.7 ± 0.3	1.8 ± 0.1	1.2 ± 0.1
	CO	11.4 ± 2.9	4.0 ± 0.6	2.6 ± 0.3	1.7 ± 0.2	1.2 ± 0.1
	O	12.2	4.2	2.5	1.8	1.2
	T	8.5	6.6	6.1	5.5	1.2
I-123 Iodide	WB	11.7	4.3	2.7	1.7	1.5
	CO (thyroid)	14.5	7.4	3.5	2.0	1.5
	O	12.2	4.2	2.5	1.8	1.2
	T	8.5	6.6	6.1	5.5	1.2
I-123 OIH	CO (kidney)	9.9	3.3	2.6	1.9	1.4
In-111 Leucocytes	WB	11.4	5.0	2.8	1.9	1.2
	CO (spleen)	14.5	5.5	3.2	2.1	1.4
	O	8.9	4.5	2.9	2.0	1.4
	T	59.1	25.5	13.6	8.6	5.5

* WB = whole body; CO = critical organ; O = ovaries; T = testes
† Adult weight = 70 kg

biodistribution data in normal adults and from anatomical data in paediatric phantoms. Doses (mGy MBq^{-1}) estimated from paediatric patients (assuming physical decay only) showed a wide range of organ uptake which could not be correlated to patient age (3 months to 18 years old) or size: 31 ± 23 (spleen), 3.8 ± 2.1 (liver), 2.1 ± 1.0 (marrow), 0.7 ± 0.3 (total body)[73]. I-131 iodide thyroid doses per unit administered activity are about two orders of magnitude greater than I-123 iodide thyroid doses for all ages from newborn to adult[68,74,75]. There has been a recent reassessment of the thyroid radioiodide dose in the newborn to account for its greater fractional uptake (70–80 per cent) found in the immediate post partum period[75].

4.4.3   Precautions for adults handling radioactive infants

In the absence of data describing dose rates on the surface of children administered radionuclides, precautions for adults handling radioactive infants have to be deduced from published measurements of radioactive adults.

a)   Hospital staff

Nuclear medicine staff are continuously exposed to ionising radiation, and it has been shown that the dose received by imaging staff is primarily due to the time spent close to patients[76]. Children and young infants may need comforting or restraining in front of imaging equipment. Allowing parents or ward staff to handle the child for the short time necessary for such procedures will reduce the dose to imaging staff and should be less traumatic for the child.

From a series of adult patients given typical Tc-99m, Ga-67, In-113m and Tl-201 radiopharmaceutical activities, a maximum time average dose rate (over 8 h) was recorded of 0.16μSv h^{-1} MBq^{-1} at a distance of 0.1 m[53]. Compared to an adult, the greater dose rate per unit activity expected from a child should be counteracted by the lower activity administered. Therefore, the daily dose limit of 60μSv for a Controlled Area[77] should not be exceeded for the estimated time of 20 min that a nurse spends in close contact with a self care patient in an acute ward[78]. Larger doses will be received by a nurse in a day if the time in close contact is extended, as may be necessary with young infants or on an intensive therapy unit.

Larger doses may also be received if there is more than one patient on the children's ward to whom radioactivity has been administered. Nuclear medicine services may allocate a particular session to paediatric studies. Therefore during these times there may be several radioactive patients on a children's ward, including outpatients recovering from sedation. For Tc-99m compounds, the time average dose rates are in proportion to the administered activity[53]. Therefore dose limits need only be considered where higher activities of Tc-99m are usually given (e.g. bone, brain and dynamic cardiac studies). Anticipating simultaneous high activity referrals, issuing instructions to nurses concerning time and distance, and spreading high activity injections over a protracted period of time will limit the daily dose to staff and should avoid the imposition of a Controlled Area (IRR Schedule 6) on a children's ward[77]. However, a Controlled Area will have to be imposed in isolation rooms where children receive I-131 iodide or I-131 MIBG for cancer treatment. Protective clothing must be worn when handling such children, and nursing time and distance from a child must be restricted.

b) Parents

The same data and precautions for infants nursed by radioactive parents as derived in section 4.3.1 can be applied in reverse. Therefore for diagnostic radionuclide procedures, the close contact dose received by a parent cuddling a radioactive infant will be less than the recommended 1 mSv annual limit for a member of the public. Restrictions at greater distances following radioactive administration to older children are not necessary, and it is not essential to restrict close contact between a pregnant woman and a radioactive infant following a diagnostic procedure[53,54].

Parents, caring for children treated as in-patients with high activities of I-131 MIBG for malignant adrenergic tumours such as neuroblastoma, can, with a few simple precautions, limit their own doses to around 1 mSv per treatment. Some centres have recommended the administration to the parents of potassium iodide for thyroid blockade[79] in addition to the use of protective clothing. However, the principal risk is from external radiation exposure and normal hygiene should preclude any significant ingestion of radioactivity by the parents. Under normal conditions, therefore, thyroid blockade of the parents, with its own attendant risks, should not be necessary, and would in any case require prescription by a clinician. Similar considerations apply to children treated with I-131 for thyroid carcinomas. A thyroid block will not be necessary for parents looking after children treated with I-131 for hyperthyroidism because of the much lower administered activities, but a disposable apron and gloves should be worn when handling these children. Instructions for resuming normal behaviour after I-131 treatment and the assessment of the external radiation dose from other therapeutic radionuclide procedures are the same as in section 4.3.1.

4.4.4   Contamination hazards

Young infants present a contamination hazard from radioactive excreta trapped in nappies or bed linen. The greatest excretion of radioactivity in urine from Tc-99m radiopharmaceuticals will probably result from administration of Tc-99m DTPA. For an administered activity of 200 MBq to a 1-year-old infant (based on a two-thirds power of weight correction for a 10 kg infant and a maximum activity to an adult of 800 MBq), around half could be excreted into urine in the first two hours after injection. This level of activity does not require a Controlled Area (IRR, Schedule 2)[77], and therefore parents and staff should handle the nappy with normal hygiene precautions such as wearing a disposable apron and gloves. Towelling nappies and bed linen can then be laundered, since the retained activity will not exceed the authorised limits for a hospital's foul water drainage system. For long lived radionuclides, separate washing may be necessary to avoid contamination of other items of laundry. Disposable nappies may have to be bagged and stored (in a Controlled Area if necessary) to allow the retained activity to decay to the hospital's authorised incineration and refuse disposal limits. Where therapeutic activities have been administered, contaminated nappies and linen should be sealed in a bag, using the same precautions as before. If the doserate at the surface of the bag exceeds the limit for a Controlled Area (7.5 μSv h^{-1}) (IRR, Schedule 6)[77], then it should be stored in a part of the hospital already designated as a Controlled Area. For infants investigated as out patients, if towelling nappies are used parents should be advised to follow the same handling and laundry procedures as above. Generally, however, children receiving diagnostic administrations, or who have been discharged home following therapy, will not give rise to very hazardous nappies at home and disposable nappies (requiring less handling) may be preferable. More detailed advice on Waste Disposal is given in Chapter 9.

Urine or blood spilt on the floor or other surfaces should be removed by methods described in Chapter 8. If the doserate on the surface still exceeds the Controlled Area limits, then either the contaminated item should be removed (e.g. a toilet seat), bagged and stored in a Controlled Area, or the contaminated site should be covered with a plastic sheet and a Controlled Area declared around it.

4.5 Data collection

This chapter has considered the occasions where a child, a young infant, or a foetus will be directly or indirectly exposed to radiation emitted from unsealed radionuclides. Although appropriate precautions and recommendations have been drawn up to limit unnecessary exposure, they have been based on data which is either sparse or adapted from adult studies. ICRP have not recommended age dependent radiation risk factors even though the revised atomic bomb survivor studies have found a greater perceived risk for children irradiated under the age of 10 years[80].

The lack of paediatric biokinetic and anatomical data for calculating internal doses has been cited for many years[67], without any apparent improvement with time[66,70], despite the steadily increasing demand for paediatric radionuclide studies. Not only is there a need to rectify this lack of data and methodology, but measurements of close contact dose rates are scarce for radioactive adults and absent for radioactive infants. The small amount of published data describing the secretion of radioactivity in breast milk is surprising particularly in the post partum period (ie when colostrum is being produced), since even a small nuclear medicine service based on just one gamma camera is likely to investigate several lactating patients each year. Expression of milk samples during a period of interruption will help a mother to maintain her milk supply. The collection and assay of radioactivity in milk samples expressed during this period will provide vital data and represents little extra work. It is hoped that this chapter will stimulate the acquisition of more data in all of the above areas, in order to consolidate the appropriate safety precautions.

References

1 Approved Code of Practice 1985 *The protection of persons against ionising radiation arising from any work activity* (HMSO, London)
2 Russell J G B 1986 The rise and fall of the ten-day rule *Br J Radiol* **59** 3–6
3 International Commission on Radiological Protection 1984 *A compilation of the major concepts and quantities in use by ICRP* Publication 42 (Pergamon Press, Oxford)
4 Coakley A J and Mountford P J 1985 Nuclear medicine and the nursing mother *Br Med J* **291** 159–160
5 International Commission on Radiological Protection 1977 *Recommendations of the ICRP* Publication 26 (Pergamon Press, Oxford)
6 Preston D L and Pierce D A 1987 *The effect of changes in dosimetry on cancer mortality risk estimates in the atomic bomb survivors* Technical Report RERF TR 9–87 (Radiation Effects Research Foundation, Hiroshima)
7 International Commission on Radiological Protection 1986 *Developmental effects of irradiation on the brain of the embryo and fetus* Publication 49 (Pergamon Press, Oxford)
8 National Radiological Protection Board 1986 *Dose limits for members of the public* NRPB-GS4 (HMSO, London)

9　Administration of Radioactive Substances Advisory Committee 1988 *Notes for guidance on the administration of radioactive substances to persons for purposes of diagnosis, treatment and research* (DHSS, London)

10　National Council on Radiation Protection and Measurements 1977 *Medical radiation exposure of pregnant and potentially pregnant women* Report No 54 (NCRP, Washington DC)

11　Smith E M and Warner G G 1976 Estimates of radiation dose to the embryo from nuclear medicine procedures *J Nucl Med* **17** 836–839

12　Husak V and Wiedermann M 1980 Radiation absorbed dose estimates to the embryo from some nuclear medicine procedures *Eur J Nucl Med* **5** 205–207

13　Kereiakes J G and Rosenstein M 1980 *Handbook of radiation doses in nuclear medicine and diagnostic X-ray* (CRC Press, Boca Raton FL)

14　Cloutier R J, Smith S A, Watson E E, Snyder W S, and Warner G G 1973 Dose to the fetus from radionuclides in the bladder *Health Phys* **25** 147–161

15　Cloutier R J, Watson E and Snyder W S 1976 Dose to the fetus during the first three months from gamma sources in maternal organs, in *Radiopharmaceutical Dosimetry Symposium* (ed R J Cloutier, J L Coffey, W S Snyder and E E Watson) HEW Publication (FDA) 76-8044 pp 370–375 (US Department of Health, Education and Welfare, Rockville MD)

16　Cloutier R J, Snyder W S and Watson E E 1977 Pregnant woman model for absorbed dose calculations, in *Proceedings of the IVth Congress of the International Radiation Protection Association* pp 479–482 (IRPA, Paris)

17　Watson E E and Stabin M G 1987 A mathematical model of the nine-month pregnant woman for calculating specific absorbed dose fractions, in *Age-Related Factors in Radionuclide Metabolism and Dosimetry* (ed G B Gerber, H Metivier and H Smith) pp 381–388 (Martinus Nijhoff, Dordrecht)

18　Davis J L, Stabin M G, Cristy M and Ryman J C 1987 Dosimetric data for the fetus derived from an anatomical model of its mother at the end of the first trimester, in *Age-Related Factors in Radionuclide Metabolism and Dosimetry* (ed G B Gerber, H Metivier and H Smith) pp 389–394 (Martinus Nijhoff, Dordrecht)

19　Mahon D F, Subramanian G and McAfee J G 1973 Experimental comparison of radioactive agents for studies of the placenta *J Nucl Med* **14** 651–659

20　Sastry G K, Reddy A R and Nagaratnam A 1976 Dosimetry in radioisotope placentography. *Indian J Med Res* **64** 1527–1535

21　Herbert R J T, Hibbard B M and Sheppard M A 1969 Metabolic behaviour and radiation dosimetry of ^{99m}Tc albumin in pregnancy *J Nucl Med* **10** 224–232

22　Book S A and Goldman M 1975 Thyroidal radioiodine exposure of the fetus *Health Phys* **29** 874–877

23　Johnson J R 1982 Fetal thyroid dose from intakes of radioiodine by the mother *Health Phys* **43** 573–582

24　Mole R H 1987 Irradiation of the embryo and fetus *Br J Radiol* **60** 17–31

25　Otake M and Schull W J 1984 In utero exposure to A-bomb radiation and mental retardation: a reassessment *Br J Radiol* **57** 409–414

26　Otake M, Yoshimura H and Schull W J 1988 *Severe mental retardation among the prenatally exposed survivors of the atomic bombing of Hiroshima and Nagasaki: a comparison of the T65DR and DS86 dosimetry systems* Technical Report RERF TR 16–87 (Radiation Effects Research Foundation, Hiroshima)

27　United Nations Scientific Committee 1977　*The Effects of Atomic Radiation* (*UNSCEAR*) (United Nations, New York)

28　Knox E G, Stewart A M, Kneale G W and Gilman E A 1987 Prenatal irradiation and childhood cancer *J Soc Radiol Prot* **7** 177–189

29　Gilman E A, Kneale G W, Knox E G and Stewart A M 1988. Pregnancy X-rays and childhood cancers: effects of exposure age and radiation dose *J Radiol Prot* **8** 3–8

30　Mole R H 1989 Carcinogenesis following medical uses of ionizing radiation, in *Low Dose Radiation: Biological Bases of Risk Assessment* (ed K F Baverstock and J W Stather) pp 100–113 (Taylor and Francis, London)

31 Mole R H 1979 Radiation effects on pre-natal development and their radiological significance *Br J Radiol* **52** 89–101

32 Stoffer S S and Hamburger J I 1976 Inadvertent ^{131}I therapy for hyperthyroidism in the first trimester of pregnancy *J Nucl Med* **17** 146–149

33 Russell K P, Rose H and Starr P 1957 The effects of radioactive iodine on maternal and fetal thyroid function during pregnancy *Surg Gyn Obs* **104** 560–564

34 International Commission on Radiological Protection 1982 *Protection of the patient in diagnostic radiology* Publication 34 (Pergamon Press, Oxford)

35 International Commission on Radiological Protection 1983 *Principles for limiting exposure of the public to natural sources of radiation* Publication 39 (Pergamon Press, Oxford)

36 National Radiological Protection Board 1985 *Exposure to ionising radiation of pregnant women: Advice on the diagnostic exposure of women who are, or who may be, pregnant* ASP8 (HMSO, London)

37 Russell J G B 1984 How dangerous are diagnostic X-rays? *Clin Radiol* **35** 347–351

38 Jewkes R F 1985 Death of the ten day rule *Nucl Med Commun* **6** 613–614 and *Nucl Med Commun* **7** 245–247

39 Marcus C, Stabin M G and Watson E E 1986 Paediatric radiation dose from ^{111}In leukocytes *J Nucl Med* **27** 1220–1221

40 MIRD Dose Estimate Report No 2 1973 Summary of current dose estimates to humans from [66]Ga, ^{67}Ga, ^{68}Ga, and [72]Ga citrate *J Nucl Med* **14** 755–756

41 McEwan A C 1975 Patient radiation doses from radiopharmaceuticals *Aus Radiol* **19** 72–76

42 Thomas S R, Atkins H L, McAfee J G, Blaufox M D, Fernandez M, Kirchner P T and Reba R C 1984 Radiation absorbed dose from [99]Tc[m] diethylenetriaminepentaacetic acid MIRD Dose Estimate Report No 12 *J Nucl Med* **25** 503–505

43 Handmaker J, Young B and Lowenstein J M 1975 Clinical experience with [99]Tc[m] DMSA (dimercaptosuccinic acid), a new renal imaging agent *J Nucl Med* **16** 28–32

44 Subramanian G, McAfee J G, Blair R J, Kallfelz F A and Thomas F D 1975 Technetium-99m methylene diphosphonate — a superior agent for skeletal imaging: comparison with other technetium complexes *J Nucl Med* **16** 744–755

45 Williams L E, Ponto R A, Forstrom L A, Loken M K and Hoogland D R 1979 Human dosimetry of [99]Tc[m] PIPIDA (abstract) *J Nucl Med* **20** 607

46 MIRD Dose Estimate Report No 5 1975 Summary of current radiation dose estimates to humans from ^{123}I, [124]I, ^{125}I, [126]I, [130]I, ^{131}I and [132]I as sodium iodide *J Nucl Med* **16** 857–860

47 Elliott A T, Britton K E, Brown N J G, Pearce P C, Smith F R and Barnasconi E W 1976 Dosimetry of current radiopharmaceuticals used in renal investigation, in *Radiopharmaceutical Dosimetry Symposium* (ed R J Cloutier, J L Coffey, W S Snyder and E E Watson) HEW Publication (FDA) 76-8044 pp 293–304 (US Department of Health, Education and Welfare, Rockville MD)

48 Jacobson L, Mattsson S, Johansson L, Lindberg S and Fjalling M 1986 Biokinetics and dosimetry of ^{131}I-metaiodobenzylguanidine (mIBG), in *Fourth International Radiopharmaceutical Dosimetry Symposium* (ed A T Schlafke-Stelson and E E Watson) CONF-851113 pp 389–398 (Office of Science and Technological Information, Oak Ridge TN)

49 Feller P A and Sodd V J 1975 Dosimetry of four heart-imaging radionuclides: [43]K, [81]Rb, [129]Cs, and [201]Tl *J Nucl Med* **16** 1070–1075

50 Sobels F H 1969. Estimation of the genetic risk resulting from the treatment of women with ^{131}I iodine *Strahlentherapie* **138** 172–177

51 Safa A M, Schumacher O P and Rodriguez-Antunez A 1975 Long-term follow-up results in children and adolescents treated with radioactive iodine (I-131) for hyperthyroidism *New Eng J Med* **292** 167–171

52 Sarkar S D, Beierwaltes W H, Gill S P and Cowley B J 1976. Subsequent fertility and birth histories of children and adolescents treated with ^{131}I for thyroid cancer *J Nucl Med* **17** 460–464

53 Harding L K, Mostafa A B, Roden L and Williams N 1985 Dose rates from patients having nuclear medicine investigations *Nucl Med Commun* **6** 191–194

54 Mountford P J 1987 Estimation of close contact doses to young infants from surface dose rates on radioactive adults *Nucl Med Commun* **8** 857–863

55 Honour A J, Myant N B and Rowlands E N 1952. Secretion of radioiodine in digestive juices and milk in man *Clin Sci* **11** 447–462

56 Beasley T M, Palmer H E and Nelp W B 1966 Distribution and excretion of technetium in humans *Health Phys* **12** 1425–1435

57 National Radiological Protection Board 1988 *Guidance Notes for the protection of persons against ionising radiations arising from medical and dental use* (HMSO, London)

58 Buchan R C T and Brindle J M 1971 Radioiodine therapy to out-patients — the radiation hazard *Br J Radiol* **44** 973–975

59 Buchan R C T and Brindle J M 1970 Radioiodine therapy to out-patients — the contamination hazard *Br J Radiol* **43** 479–482

60 Ahlgren L, Ivarsson S, Johansson L, Mattsson S and Nosslin B 1985 Excretion of radionuclides in human breast milk after administration of radiopharmaceuticals *J Nucl Med* **26** 1085–1090

61 Mountford P J and Coakley A J 1987 A review of the secretion of radioactivity in human breast milk: data, quantitative analysis and recommendations *Nucl Med Commun* **10** 15–27

62 Heaton B 1978 The build up of technetium in breast milk following the administration of $^{99}Tc^m$ O_4-labelled macroaggregated albumin *Br J Radiol* **52** 149–150

63 Mountford P J and Coakley A J 1987 Breast milk radioactivity following injection of $^{99}Tc^m$ pertechnetate and $^{99}Tc^m$ glucoheptonate *Nucl Med Commun* **8** 839–845

64 Murphy P H, Beasley C W, Moore W H and Stabin M G 1989 Thallium-201 in human milk: observations and radiological consequences *Health Phys* **56** 539–541

65 International Commission on Radiological Protection 1980 *Limits for intakes of radionuclides by workers* Publication 30 (Pergamon Press, Oxford)

66 National Council on Radiation Protection and Measurements 1983 *Protection in nuclear medicine and ultrasound diagnostic procedures in children* Report No 73 (NCRP, Bethesda MD)

67 Poston J W 1976 The effects of body and organ size on absorbed dose: there is no standard patient, in *Radiopharmaceutical Dosimetry Symposium* (ed R J Cloutier, J L Coffey, W S Snyder and E E Watson) HEW Publication (FDA) 76-8044 pp 92–109 (US Department of Health, Education and Welfare, Rockville MD)

68 Webster E W, Alpert N M and Brownell G L 1974 Radiation doses in pediatric nuclear medicine and diagnostic X-ray procedures, in *Pediatric Nuclear Medicine* (ed A E James, H N Wagner and Cooke R E) pp 34–58 (W B Saunders, Philadelphia PA)

69 Alderson P O, Gilday D L and Wagner H N 1978 *Atlas of pediatric nuclear medicine* (C V Mosby, St Louis MO)

70 Kereiakes J G, Feller P A, Ascoli F A, Thomas S R, Gelfand M L and Saenger E 1976 Pediatric radiopharmaceutical dosimetry, in *Radiopharmaceutical Dosimetry Symposium* (ed R J Cloutier, J L Coffey, W S Snyder and E E Watson) HEW Publication (FDA) 76-8044 pp 77–91 (US Department of Health, Education and Welfare, Rockville MD)

71 Roedler H D, Kaul A and Hine G J 1978 *Internal radiation dose in diagnostic nuclear medicine* (Verlag Hoffman, Berlin)

72 International Commission on Radiological Protection 1987 *Radiation dose to patients from radiopharmaceuticals* Publication 53 (Pergamon Press, Oxford)

73 Gainey M A, Siegel J A, Smergel E M and Jara B J 1988 ^{111}Indium-labelled white blood cells: dosimetry in children *J Nucl Med* **29** 689–694

74 Kereiakes J G, Wellman H N, Simmons G and Saenger E L 1972 Radiopharmaceutical dosimetry in pediatrics *Semin Nucl Med* **2** 316–327

75 Hedrick W R and Milavickas L R 1987 Reevaluation of the newborn thyroid dose from radioiodines *J Nucl Med* **28** 1208–1209

76   Harbottle E A, Parker R P and Davis R 1976 Radiation doses to staff in a department of nuclear medicine *Br J Radiol* **49** 612–617

77   *The Ionising Radiations Regulations 1985* SI No 1333 (HMSO, London)

78   Short M D, Todd J H, Mulvey P J and Ramsey N W 1984 *Radiation protection procedures in the use of $^{99}Tc^m$* Topic Group Report 39 (The Hospital Physicists' Association, London)

79   Marcuse H R, van der Steen J, Maessen H J M, Hoefnagel C A and Voute P A 1986 Radiation exposure to parents nursing their child during treatment with I-131-Meta-Iodobenzyl Guanidine for neuroblastoma, in *Fourth International Radiopharmaceutical Dosimetry Symposium* (ed A T Schlafke-Stelson and E E Watson) CONF-851113 pp 181–185 (Office of Science and Technological Information, Oak Ridge TN)

80   Radford E P 1987 Recent evidence of radiation-induced cancer in the Japanese atomic bomb survivors, in *Radiation and Health* (ed R Russell Jones and R Southwood) pp 87–96 (John Wiley & Sons, Chichester)

81   Rose M R, Prescott M C and Herman K J 1990 Excretion of iodine-123-hippuran, technetium-99m-red blood cells, and technetium-99m-macroaggregated albumin into breast milk *J Nucl Med* **31** 978–984

CHAPTER 5

The Use of Unsealed Radioactive Materials in Laboratories

E M Pitcher

5.1 Introduction

Pathology departments and medical laboratories use a wide range of unsealed radionuclides for both *in vivo* and *in vitro* work. This chapter deals with the radiation safety of the radionuclides and techniques used for *in vitro* and some *in vivo* work.

The laboratories which use radionuclides may be divided into two main types:

a) those which use only very low activities, typically of the order of kilobecquerels. In these laboratories often the radionuclide is in kit form for radioimmunoassays (RIA) or blood culture vials containing 74 kBq of C-14 for use with the Bactec blood culture system;

b) those which use larger activites, often of very high radioactive concentrations, for a variety of purposes such as the iodination of a wide range of proteins for RIA using I-125[1], tritium for labelling or P-32 in molecular biology research.

Although the basic principles of radiation safety which are discussed in this chapter are equally valid for both categories of laboratory, users of small quantities may find that their normal working procedures need only slight modification.

When unsealed radionuclides are used the radiation absorbed dose to a member of staff may be due to radioactive substances outside or inside the body. Any ionising radiation from outside the body will be referred to as external radiation and that from inside the body as internal radiation. Although radioactive contamination is external to the body the main hazard is usually from ingestion and the risks will be dealt with under the heading of internal radiation.

Laboratory staff are potentially at risk from both types of radiation, but the risk of exposure from internal radiation will usually be greater than that from external radiation. The measures required to reduce the risk from internal radiation will be very similar to those for the handling of blood products and biohazardous materials. Laboratory staff will usually be familiar with the 'Howie' Code of Practice for the prevention of infection in clinical laboratories and post-mortem rooms which deals with this subject[2].

The use of ionising radiations is governed by the Ionising Radiations Regulations 1985 (IRR)[3], the associated Approved Code of Practice[4], Guidance Notes[5] and other regulations (see Chapter 1). These are based on the principles given by ICRP Publication 26[6] which recommends a system of dose limitation, the main features of which are as follows:

a) no practice shall be adopted unless its introduction produces a positive net benefit;

b) all exposures shall be as low as reasonably achievable, economic and social factors being taken into account, the ALARA principle; and

c) the radiation dose to individuals shall not exceed the limits recommended.

It is emphasised that although it is the responsibility of the employer to restrict, as far as reasonably practicable, the extent to which employees and other persons are exposed to ionising radiation, employees must take reasonable care not to expose themselves or any other person to ionising radiation unnecessarily as a result of their work.

5.2 Radiation Protection Principles

5.2.1 External radiation

The three well-recognised principles of reducing staff doses from external radiation are that all radioactive sources should be shielded if practicable, handled at the greatest practicable distance and manipulated as quickly as practicable. These methods of radiation protection may be achieved in the following circumstances.

a) Shielding

If practicable, radioactive sources should be shielded so that the dose rate outside the shield or container is reduced to less than 7.5 μSv h^{-1}. The shielding required will depend on the radionuclide and the type and energy of its emissions. The physical data for some of the more common radionuclides used for both *in vitro* and *in vivo* work are given in Appendix II.

Iodine-125 is the most commonly used gamma emitter due to its use in commercially available RIA kits, but others may also be used. Patient samples containing Tc-99m, In-111 or I-131 may also be received. Iodine-125 and Cr-51 emit X-rays after decay by electron capture which are of low energy and therefore easily shielded. However, Cr-51 also emits 320 keV gamma rays which have to be taken into account. In the absence of adequate shielding the X-rays are the main contributors to the doserate from the radionuclide. The doserate at various distances for a number of gamma emitters and the tenth-value-layers in lead are given in Appendices III and IV respectively. If activities greater than kilobecquerel quantities are used regularly, a protective screen between the source and the user should be used. The screen should either be narrow enough so that the source can be manipulated with the arms around the screen or armholes should be provided. The former is often more practical and should be transparent, i.e. made from lead glass or vinyl of an appropriate lead equivalent. If a screen is used in a fume cupboard or laminar flow cabinet care must be taken that the airflow is not interrupted.

Some laboratories are involved with the labelling of monoclonal antibodies for the diagnosis and therapy of various cancers. I-131, which emits both gamma and beta radiations, is the most commonly used radionuclide for three reasons. Firstly the monoclonal antibodies can be labelled with iodine relatively easily, secondly the gamma radiation allows imaging to be performed and thirdly the beta radiation, if large enough activities are used, can impart a therapeutic radiation dose. The high activities used and the high energy gamma radiation mean that the shielding described above may not be adequate. The use of I-131 for therapy is discussed in Chapter 2.

The most commonly used beta emitting radionuclides are tritium, C-14, P-32, and S-35. The range of a beta particle depends on both its energy and the attenuating medium. The maximum ranges in water of beta particles of varying energies are given in Appendix IV. In practice the beta particles of tritium, C-14 and S-35 will be absorbed either by the medium in which they are contained or by the walls of the container. Indeed this is why the activity of these radionuclides is usually measured by liquid scintillation counting. Beta particles emitted from P-32 have a maximum energy of 1.7 MeV and require more shielding. The beta particles have enough energy to produce bremsstrahlung, low energy X-rays produced when a beta particles loses energy in a collision with an atom. Shielding may be provided by lead which absorbs both the beta particles and the bremsstrahlung. Alternatively a low atomic number material, such as perspex, may be used to minimise the production of bremsstrahlung. In practice 1 cm thick perspex is often used to make screens, vial holders and other apparatus[7]. In some techniques S-35 can be used in place of P-32 and this should be done wherever possible to reduce the shielding required.

b) Distance

The doserate from beta and gamma emitters will decrease with the distance from the source. The doserate from a point source of an X-ray or gamma emitter obeys the inverse square law: that is the doserate is inversely proportional to the square of the distance from the source. Most vials or other containers of radionuclides are small enough to be considered as point sources. The dose rate from a low energy beta emitter will fall off more rapidly due to attenuation in the medium. Vials or syringes containing radioactive sources other than low energy beta emitters or activities less than a few tens of kilobecquerels (as in most RIA work) should never be handled directly as the doserate to the basal epidermis of the fingers will be high. Other sources should be shielded or tongs should be used for handling. Doserates for several gamma emitters at 1 metre from a 1 MBq source are given in Appendix III.

c) Time

Procedures for the use of radionuclides should be designed so that handling times are reduced to a minimum. This can be aided by having a clear protocol and giving sufficient training prior to the procedure being undertaken. In some cases carrying out procedures quickly is the only effective means of reducing staff dose as shielding or distance are impractical.

5.2.2 Internal radiation

The main principle in the reduction of staff doses from internal radiation is that of containment of the unsealed radionuclides. This minimises the risk of ingestion, inhalation or absorption through the skin. The dose arising from the intake of a radionuclide into the body depends on the metabolic pathway of the particular chemical involved, its effective half-life in individual organs and the body, the geometry of the organs and the type and energy of the radiation emitted.

The effective half-life takes into account both the biological rate of clearance of the chemical and the physical decay of the radionuclide. Commonly used beta emitters generally have relatively long physical half-lives and therefore unless their biological half-lives are short the effective half-lives will be long and may result in a significant dose. Beta emitters, due to the short range of the particles in tissue, give relatively large radiation doses to the tissues in which they concentrate. Gamma emitters will also irradiate other organs of the body.

The intake of radioactive materials into the body should be avoided if at all possible and must be kept as low as reasonably practicable, such that the annual dose equivalent limits given in IRR are not exceeded. The activity of a radionuclide which, if taken into the body, would irradiate a person to the annual dose limit is called the Annual Limit on Intake (ALI)[8]. The chemical form, the biological pathways and the effective half life of the radioactive material and the type and energy of the emitted radiation are used to calculate the ALI. A further limit is the Derived Air Concentration, DAC, which equals the ALI for inhalation divided by the volume of air inhaled in a working year (2400 cubic metres of air in 2000 hours). The ALI and DAC for some radioactive materials are given in Appendix III. More detailed information on the biological pathways of P-32, tritium and I-125 and other radiation protection details may be found in the literature[7,9,10].

a)   Restriction of personal contamination

In most cases gloves and laboratory coats are all the protection required in medical laboratories. It should be assumed that the outside of any vial or vessel containing radioactive material may be contaminated and therefore gloves should be worn at all times. An exception may be made for handling radioactive materials packaged for transport. Some radioactive materials, such as tritiated water and sodium iodide are capable of penetrating intact skin so extra care must be taken. In the following circumstances two pairs of gloves are often worn:

   (i)   during iodinations or any other procedure involving high concentrations of sodium iodide as this has been shown to penetrate some types of rubber gloves;
  (ii)   when handling beta emitters as the gloves actually act as a radiation shield;
 (iii)   during any other complex open procedure where gloves frequently may be changed to prevent the spread of contamination. The outer glove only is changed and the use of an inner glove minimises the risk of skin contamination.

Any work during which there is risk of splashing, such as when a needle comes off a syringe, should be done behind a splash guard which may also be a radiation shield. When the use of a splash guard is not practicable, safety goggles or glasses may be considered necessary depending on the radionuclide and activities used.

To avoid the risk of infection and internal radiation, mouth pipetting is forbidden in any circumstance. Where volumetric accuracy is not important, disposable syringes may be adequate, but disposable tip automatic pipettes will generally be the preferred method of dispensing liquid sources. Such pipettes reduce the radiation dose to the hands and fingers as a consequence of the inverse square law and greatly reduce the hazards of ingestion. Totally automated systems for pipetting and harvesting of samples are also in widespread use. These instruments effectively eliminate radiation hazards from sample processing but will need care when being cleaned or serviced to avoid spread of contamination.

b)   Containment

Even the simplest procedures involving minimal amounts of radioactive material should be carried out over drip trays made of impervious and easily cleaned materials such as plastic or stainless steel. The interiors of these are often covered with a plastic backed absorbent material such as Benchkote. If there is any risk of the material spraying (e.g. if a syringe is used) a transparent shield should be used as described in the previous section.

If aerosols are likely to be produced or if volatile materials such as sodium iodide or tritiated water are being used, the procedure should be carried out in a contained workstation. This should comply with BS5726[11] and also BS5295[12] if the procedure is aseptic (see Chapter 6) since any protective screen must not interfere with the airflow of the cabinet. Where asepsis is not required, a conventional fume cupboard will be adequate. This should satisfy the requirements of BS7258[13].

In general all unnecessary equipment should be kept away from the area where radioactive materials are being used and the area should be kept in an orderly fashion.

5.3 Design of laboratories

Whenever new or changed facilities or procedures are planned, the RPA must be consulted at an early stage in the design. The design requirements for laboratories where radionuclides are used are discussed in detail in ICRP Publication 25[14] and also in the Guidance Notes (Chapter 10). The facilities required depend on the category of hazard of the radionuclides and the procedures used. ICRP divide laboratories into three categories, 'low', 'medium' and 'high', according to the risk from internal radiation. The activity limits which may be handled daily in these categories of laboratory for the commonly used radionuclides are given in *table 5.1*. The activity limits given must be multiplied by an operational factor, (*table 5.2*), which takes into account the risks of contamination for various procedures. The basic facilities required in relation to the categories of hazard are given in *table 5.3*.

Table 5.1 Activities which may be handled daily for the three categories of laboratories
Based on data from ICRP 25[14]

Radionuclide	Category of laboratory		
	Low hazard	Medium hazard	High hazard
		Activity (MBq)	
I-125, I-131	<0.37	0.37–370	>370
S-35, P-32	<3.7	3.7–3700	>3700
H-3	<370	370–3.7 × 10^5	>3.7 × 10^5

Table 5.2 Operational factors for laboratory use of radioactive materials
Based on data from ICRP 25[14]

Procedure	Factor
Simple storage	100.0
Simple wet operations	10.0
Normal chemical operation	1
Complex wet operations	0.1
Simple dry operations	0.1
Dry and dusty operations	0.01

Table 5.3 Facilities required for radiation protection in relation to category of hazard Based on data from ICRP 25[14]

Category of hazard	Facilities						
	Structural shielding	Floor	Surfaces	Fume hood	Room ventilation	Plumbing	First aid
Low	nil	cleanable	cleanable	no	normal	standard	washing facilities
Medium	nil	continuous	cleanable	yes	good	standard	washing and decontamination facilities
High	possibly	continuous one sheet welded to walls	cleanable	yes special	may require forced ventilation	may require special plumbing	washing and decontamination facilities

Laboratories using only commercial RIA kits or the Bactec blood culture system will be classed as having only a low category of hazard. The facilities provided by a good modern laboratory will be adequate. The work may often be carried out in a specified area of a general medical laboratory.

Many other techniques such as the use of P-32 in cell hybridisation will be carried out in a medium category laboratory. As above, a good modern laboratory should meet the necessary requirements, i.e. that the bench surfaces should be coved against the walls and lipped at the edges and the floors should be in one continuous sheet of an impervious and easily cleanable material. A contained workstation is not always required.

Iodinations, which may be classed as complex operations, often use activities greater than 37 MBq and need to be carried out in high category laboratories. There should be a separate room incorporating a contained work station or fume cupboard. The extraction system to the outside must be well maintained and regularly checked. Structural shielding should not be necessary as the steel casing of the workstation and the room walls should provide adequate shielding for I-125. Protective shielding for staff must be supplied as discussed in a previous section. Extra shielding will be required if therapy levels of I-131 are handled. The radiation dose to staff or members of the public in rooms adjoining the laboratory (upstairs and downstairs included) as well as to the operator must be considered.

5.4 Administrative Procedures

The employer is responsible for ensuring that the requirements of the Ionising Radiations Regulations 1985[3], the Approved Code of Practice[4] and Guidance Notes[5] are fulfilled. In most cases, except for laboratories where very small quantities of radioactive materials are used, the employer must appoint a suitably qualified and experienced person to act as a radiation protection adviser (RPA). Local rules must be written for every laboratory where ionising radiation is used to ensure that the work is carried out in accordance with the requirements of the Regulations. A radiation protection supervisor (RPS) must be appointed to ensure that the local rules are observed. The complexity of the local rules will depend on the techniques used in a particular laboratory and in particular on whether or not any areas are designated as 'controlled' or 'supervised'.

5.4.1 Controlled and supervised areas

An area requires to be designated as supervised if a member of staff working in that area is likely to receive more than 1/10 of any annual dose equivalent limit, or controlled if they are likely to receive more than 3/10 of any annual dose equivalent limit. Persons may only enter a controlled area if they are designated as classified (ie they are likely to receive a dose of ionising radiation which exceeds 3/10 of any relevant dose equivalent limit) or they are operating under a system of work. A system of work should be part of the local rules and should be a detailed written procedure which ensures that anyone entering a controlled area receives less than 3/10 of any annual dose equivalent limit. There are no restrictions on access for supervised areas. A laboratory may need to be designated as controlled on account of either external or internal radiation. The detailed requirements for the designation of a controlled or supervised area are given in Appendix I. A guide to the need for controlled or supervised areas for some common laboratory techniques is given in the following paragraphs.

a) External radiation

In general any area where the instantaneous dose-rate (averaged over one minute) is unlikely to exceed 7.5 μSv h^{-1} need not be controlled. If this doserate is exceeded, which will happen if the doserates at the surfaces of vials, pipettes and syringes are high as discussed earlier, Schedule 6 of the IRR must be referred to and advice sought from the RPA.

For gamma emitters there may be no requirement to designate an area as controlled if the activity-energy product is less than 50 MBq MeV. The activities of some commonly used radionuclides corresponding to this limit are given in Appendix V. It may need to be supervised if the activity-energy product is more than one third of a controlled area limit. Most laboratories use less than these activities and few would need to have controlled areas on this basis although some larger users would require supervised areas. Laboratories where therapy levels of I-131 are used have to be controlled.

A controlled area need not be designated (on account of external radiation) for beta emitters provided:

(i) for a maximum beta energy of 0.3 MeV or more, the activity does not exceed 5 MBq.

(ii) for a maximum beta energy of less than 0.3 MeV, the activity does not exceed 50 MBq.

Laboratories using beta emitters commonly use greater activities than those given. However, in many instances the doserate limits will not be exceeded since the beta particles emitted will be absorbed in the walls of the container and therefore the instantaneous doserate will not exceed 7.5 μSv hr^{-1}.

Areas should be designated as supervised if 1/3 of any of the limits given above are exceeded. It should be noted that some radionuclides (notably I-131) emit both gamma and beta radiation and therefore the most stringent limit identified in the above section will apply.

b) Internal radiation

Any area where the only or potential source of contamination has an activity less than the total activity limit given in Appendix V need not be controlled, although if the activity is greater than one third of the value the area may require to be supervised. One example where the limits may be exceeded is protein iodination (e.g. 40–120 MBq of I-125 may be used and air concentrations as high as 7.8×10^3 Bq m^{-3} have been measured in a fume cupboard during the removal of aliquots from a stock solution[15]). High levels of surface contamination are also possible. This may be 'fixed' or 'removable'; it should be noted that the IRR limits on surface contamination (see Appendix V) refer to unfixed contamination only. Such procedures should be carried out in a fume cupboard or workstation which should be designated a controlled area.

5.4.2 Local rules

Local rules should be as descriptive as possible of the procedures for handling unsealed radioactive materials. They would be drawn up by the RPS in conjunction with the RPA and the head of department. If controlled or supervised areas have been designated they must be specified in the local rules, together with, for the former, appropriate systems of work.

Items which should be given in each set of local rules include:

a) The radiation protection organisation, including the names of the RPS, RPA and employing authority
b) Specification of controlled and supervised areas. This may take the form of plan or a written description. The former is often clearer particularly if only part of a room is designated
c) Systems of work for controlled areas
d) Details of storage of radionuclides. If possible the exact storage location of each radioactive material should be specified along with the maximum activity stored at any one time
e) Details of where and how the radionuclides are handled. Radionuclides should only be handled in specified areas. Some laboratories doing standard assays may be able to define working methods precisely
f) Routine monitoring procedures
g) Records to be kept
h) Action to be taken in event of spill or other mishap
i) Date the local rules were drawn up.

5.5 Personal Monitoring

Staff working in controlled areas must be directly monitored unless their doses can be assessed by other means, e.g. environmental monitoring. If they are classified, monitoring must be done by an Approved Laboratory which fulfills the requirements of the Health and Safety Executive. Staff who do not work in controlled areas may still be monitored to assess personal doses and the safety of the working procedures. It is important that the method used is the most appropriate for the radionuclides and activity levels used. More detailed advice is given in Chapter 7.

5.5.1 External radiation

a) Personal monitoring

Whole body monitors provide an assessment of body dose, produced by higher energy ionising radiations and may also indicate skin dose, produced mainly by beta particles. Thermoluminescent dosimeters (TLDs) or film badges are used for whole body monitoring but are unsuitable for the monitoring of staff using only low energy beta emitters or low activities of I-125. The use of TLDs for extremity monitoring is discussed in Chapter 7.

Both types of monitor have a threshold of detection; 0.1 mSv for the TLDs and 0.2 mSv for film badges. Many staff using I-125 for radioimmunoassay will only be handling activities of the order of 200–400 kBq. Even if this activity were handled unshielded for their total working week at an average distance of 25 cm, the dose equivalent received during a monitoring period of 3 months would be, at most, 0.1 mSv. There is therefore no requirement for external radiation monitoring as the main hazard from these radionuclides is from internal radiation and the monitoring of their presence inside the body is more relevant (see Section 5.5.2). Finger monitoring may occasionally be appropriate, using TLD extremity monitors, but should not generally be necessary if proper handling techniques are used.

b) Contamination monitoring

After handling an unsealed radionuclide, even when it is contained in a vial, the hands and protective clothing should be checked for contamination at the end of the procedure. A contamination monitor appropriate to the radionuclide and the activity handled should be used. Most Geiger-Muller tubes are *insensitive* to I-125; tritium is best detected by wipe testing of contaminated surfaces or by urine monitoring of staff. The contamination monitor should be kept where it is easily available and the background radiation level is low. See Chapter 7 for the selection of an appropriate contamination monitor.

5.5.2 *Internal radiation*

It has been stressed that some of the radionuclides used in laboratories are not best detected by external monitoring due to their physical characteristics or to the small activities handled. Ingestion of gamma emitters may be detected with a whole body monitor, where one is available. Alternatively, both beta and gamma emitters may be monitored in samples of blood or, more commonly, urine taken at regular (e.g. weekly) intervals. Because iodine is concentrated heavily in the thyroid gland, exposure to radioiodine (I-125 or I-131) is conveniently monitored by measurement of activity in the thyroid, either with a simple laboratory contamination monitor or, if available, with a dedicated thyroid uptake counter. Further details are given in Chapter 7.

5.5.3 *Environmental monitoring*

Environmental monitoring is performed both for immediate action, e.g. if contamination is found and for demonstrating, in the long term, that control procedures are efficacious.

a) External radiation

The radiation dose levels in a laboratory are usually very low and the dose to individual staff may be below the detection limit of the monitor. It is therefore sometimes useful to monitor a position rather than a person. Whole body monitoring badges or survey TLDs can be placed at workstations in positions as close as possible to that of the staff. This environmental monitoring then gives an estimate of the maximum whole body dose equivalent a member of staff present over the complete monitoring period might have received. If the estimated dose is less than any 'action threshold' then no individual member of staff will have exceeded this limit.

b) Internal radiation

Most laboratories have contamination monitors for monitoring work surfaces, equipment and personnel. The Ionising Radiations Regulations 1985[3] give no guidance on the sensitivity required of these monitors and rely on the ALARA principle, i.e. contamination levels should be reduced as far as reasonably achievable. However derived levels for surface contamination are given in the Guidance Notes[5] and those for some of the commonly used radionuclides are listed in *table 5.4*.

Every laboratory should have the use of contamination monitors which can measure down to these levels and which have been calibrated for appropriate

84

Table 5.4 Derived limits for surface contamination[3]

Surface	Derived Limit (Bq cm^{-2})		
	Radionuclide category		
	Class III	Class IV	Class V
Interior surfaces and contents of fume cupboards and contained workstations	minimum that is reasonably practicable		
Other surfaces in controlled areas and equipment therein	30	300	3000
All other surfaces (including personal clothing and surfaces of the body)	3	30	300

Notes

Class III radionuclides include P-32, Co-58, Fe-59, In-111, I-131
Class IV radionuclides include C-14, S-35, Co-57, Tc-99m, I-125, Ga-67, Se-35
Class V radionuclides include H-3, Cr-51, Fe-55.

representative radionuclides. This will often mean the purchase of more than one monitor although there are monitors which can detect both the low energy beta and gamma emitters. Tritium can only be directly monitored using specialised instruments on good surfaces. The monitoring of C-14 and S-35 is also difficult since if the activity is contained in only a thin film of liquid most of the beta particles will not escape from the surface. All surfaces should therefore be wiped dry before any direct monitoring is carried out. Alternatively, wipe tests can be used, assuming, in the absence of better information, that 10% of the removable contamination has been transferred to the wipe.

The frequency of contamination monitoring will depend on the level of use of the radionuclides. If a technique is undertaken infrequently, such as iodinations which may be done a few times a month, then monitoring should be carried out after every procedure. Similarly, if other (non-radioactive) procedures are carried out in the same work area, which should be avoided if possible, contamination may be spread and the area should be checked after every use of radionuclides. If a technique is performed routinely and low activities are used then monitoring of work surfaces and floors should be done weekly.

5.5.4 Record keeping

The dose records of classified members of staff must be kept by the approved dosimetry service for a period of 50 years. Records for other staff will normally be kept by the RPS on behalf of the employer for at least two years. They should be kept in such a way that changes which might reflect a change in workload or a problem with a particular technique can be easily identified.

Records of contamination surveys of staff and work surfaces are usually kept within a department by the RPS and should be retained for two years. The record should give the date and the results of the survey which may simply be a tick to show that the results are lower than specified limits. A system which only records results when they are over specified limits is not satisfactory.

5.6 Waste Disposal

Radioactive waste from pathology departments or laboratories must be disposed of either under the Radioactive Substances (Hospitals) Waste Exemption Order (1990) or under a Certificate of Authorisation for the Disposal and Accumulation of Radioactive Waste issued by Her Majesty's Inspectorate of Pollution (HMIP), a section of the Department of the Environment (DoE) (see Chapter 9). These controls usually apply to the whole hospital site: although the activities used by many laboratories in hospitals would be within the limits if they were the only users of unsealed radionuclides, the total amount of radioactive waste may be much greater. The certificate of authorisation is drawn up by the Pollution Inspector taking into account the use of radionuclides and the available routes of disposal.

5.6.1 Methods of disposal

In general the methods agreed on should be those which are most practicable for the laboratory concerned and which require the least handling of the radioactive material so that the risk of contamination is reduced. Reference should be made to Chapter 9 for more detailed guidance on waste disposal.

a)   Liquid waste into the drainage system

Most of the radioactive waste generated will be in the form of aqueous liquid. This may be disposed of down an ordinary sink provided that it is 'designated' as being suitable and labelled as such. This means that the drainage system should not include an open drain and that, if anything more than kilobecquerel quantities are used, the sink should not have a trap. The surround of the sink should be such as to allow easy cleaning and decontamination. In particular, it should be noted that iodine is readily adsorbed onto plastics and surfaces, and drainage pipes will probably be contaminated. After the waste has been poured down the sink it should be flushed down with copious water. It is prudent to have a piece of rubber tubing attached to the tap to prevent splashing. If possible a marked designated sink should be sited in every room where liquid waste is generated to avoid moving large volumes of radioactive liquid around the department or hospital.

b)   Solid waste or non-radioactive waste to a tip or incinerator

Solid waste may be disposed of with non-radioactive waste, provided that the total activity is less than 370 kBq, the activity of any article is less than 37 kBq and the volume of refuse is at least 0.1 m³. Even though the waste leaves the site as non-radioactive waste a record of the activities and the routes of disposal must be kept. The residues in vials from RIA techniques, and many other techniques, may therefore be disposed of into a marked waste bin in each laboratory and then, after monitoring has confirmed that activities are within the above limits, may join the normal routes of disposal for the hospital.

c) Solid waste to an incinerator or to a tip used for the disposal of low level waste

Solid waste of greater activity may be burnt or disposed of to an authorised tip. Higher activity waste like the unused stock vials or the thin layer chromatography plates from some iodination procedures may be disposed of in this way. Incineration is often more convenient and may be necessary if human or animal tissue is involved. A member of the laboratory staff should take the radioactive material to the incinerator to ensure that it is burnt immediately rather than stockpiled for several days.

The vials from the Bactec blood culture system which each contain 74 kBq of C-14 and blood may be burnt if the incinerator is able to cope with glass. If the incinerator is not suitable for glass the blood culture vials must be autoclaved and the contents disposed of as liquid waste. A bottle crusher is useful if large quantities of vials are used.

d) Liquid scintillant waste to an incinerator

Liquid scintillant waste may cause a waste disposal problem not because it contains radioactive material but because the solvents used are often flammable and toxic and may not be poured down the sink. The most convenient method of disposal is to collect the counting vials and contents and to incinerate them. Large volumes of several litres, may be accumulated from vials emptied into a large container. This may be incinerated (if allowed by the hospital) or disposed of to a specialist contractor. This procedure should obviously be undertaken with the authorisation of the Inspector of Pollution. However neither of these may be possible and waste disposal must be considered and resolved before any liquid scintillant procedures are introduced. Fortunately water-miscible biodegradable scintillants are now available which may be discharged as aqueous waste to the drains with the permission of the local Water Authority and their use should ease the problem.

e) Gaseous waste from a fume cupboard to the outside

Some techniques, such as iodinations or those involving tritium or C-14, may give rise to radioactive gases. These are always carried out in a fume cupboard or laminar flow cabinet which must be vented to the outside in such a way as to prevent the recirculation of the gases into any building. If the activities used are large, filters may be used in the exhaust line but these can often themselves cause disposal problems. There should be no need for filters with the activities used in most pathology departments.

f) Solid or liquid waste to a waste disposal service

In some cases a large amount of waste is accumulated which cannot be disposed of by any of the above methods. There are specialist firms which will dispose of this waste provided the laboratory has the authorisation to use this pathway. The filters from the Bactec blood culture system, which may contain 40-80 MBq of C-14, may need to be disposed of in this way.

All disposal routes should be arranged in consultation with the RPA and, if necessary, the Inspector of Pollution, and any problems or queries should be referred to the RPA in the first instance.

5.6.2 Record keeping

The disposal of radioactive waste involves considerable work and record keeping since the activity and mode of disposal must be identified clearly. It is essential that, when more than one area within the hospital or laboratories produces radioactive waste, the records must be collated and kept centrally as the authorisation from the DoE usually refers to the whole site. This may be done by the RPA as it also assists in monitoring the use of radioactive material; alternatively one of the RPSs may perform this task.

Record keeping may be simplified for the longer lived radionuclides by assuming that there is no radioactive decay and therefore the total amount used is the amount disposed. Each technique employed must be assessed to estimate the proportions of the original activity generated as liquid, solid, gaseous or liquid scintillant waste. The total activity disposed of by each route may then be easily estimated from the original activity used. These estimates are usually acceptable to the Pollution Inspector, who will wish to inspect the records on his regular visits. Larger users of radioactive materials may use a computer database for their stock records and then the radioactive decay may be easily taken into account.

References

1 Johnstone A and Thorpe R 1987 *Immunochemistry in Practice* Second Edition (Blackwell Scientific Publications, London)
2 *Code of practice for the prevention of infection in clinical laboratories and post-mortem rooms* 1978 (HMSO, London)
3 *Ionising Radiations Regulations 1985* (SI 1985 No 1333) (HMSO, London)
4 Health and Safety Commission 1985 *Approved Code of Practice: The protection of persons against ionising radiation arising from any work activity* (HMSO, London)
5 National Radiological Protection Board 1988 *Guidance notes for the protection of persons against ionising radiations arising from medical and dental use* (HMSO, London)
6 International Commission on Radiological Protection 1977 *Recommendations of the International Commission on Radiological Protection* Publication 26 (Pergamon Press, Oxford)
7 Ballance P E, Day L R and Morgan J 1987 Phosphorus-32: Practical Radiation Protection *Occupational Hygiene Monograph* No 16 (Science Reviews Ltd, London)
8 International Commission on Radiological Protection 1981 *Limits of intakes of radionuclides by workers* Publication 30 (Pergamon Press, Oxford)
9 Martin E B M 1982 Health Physics Aspects of the Use of Tritium *Occupation Hygiene Monograph* No 6 (Science Reviews Ltd, London)
10 Prime D 1985 Health Physics Aspects of Radioiodines *Occupational Hygiene Monograph* No 13 (Science Reviews Ltd, London)
11 British Standards Institute 1979 *Specification for micro- biological safety cabinets* BS 5726 (BSI, Milton Keynes)
12 British Standards Institute 1976 *Environmental cleanliness in enclosed spaces* BS 5295 (BSI, Milton Keynes)
13 British Standards Institute 1990 *Laboratory fume cupboards* BS 7258 (BSI, Milton Keynes)
14 International Commission on Radiological Protection 1977 *The Handling, Storage, Use and Disposal of Unsealed Radionuclides in Hospitals and Medical Research Establishments* Publication 25 (Pergamon Press, Oxford)
15 Eadie A S, Horton P W and Hilditch T E 1980 Monitoring of airborne contamination during the handling of technetium-99m and radioiodine *Phys Med Biol*, **25** 1079–1087

CHAPTER 6

Dispensing and Manufacture

M Frier and S Hesslewood

6.1 Introduction

The majority of radiopharmaceuticals in current use are administered intravenously and hence, in addition to the requirements for radiation safety, there is a particular need to consider pharmaceutical implications during their preparation. In this context, both radiation protection and good pharmaceutical practice are equally important.

Storage of radioactive material in a radiopharmacy is an important consideration. Areas in which technetium generators are stored or where radiopharmaceuticals are prepared are likely to be controlled areas as defined by The Ionising Radiations Regulations 1985 (IRR)[1] and illustrated in Appendix I. Stores for radioactive preparations or radioactive waste may also be controlled areas. Designation of controlled areas may also be required in relation to internal radiation if the air concentration or surface contamination level of a radionuclide exceeds the level specified in IRR Schedule 6. The appropriate surface contamination levels for radionuclides most commonly encountered in radiopharmacies are shown in Appendix V. In practice air concentrations are seldom relevant since procedures are carried out in a workstation which will in any case be designated as a controlled area.

Where a controlled area has been defined, its boundaries must be clearly described in the Local Rules and appropriate warning signs containing the trefoil symbol and the words 'Controlled Area' provided. Entry into a controlled area is restricted and any person entering must either be a classified employee or enter under a written system of work.

Staff are designated as classified if they are likely to receive in excess of 3/10 of any relevant dose limit defined in IRR Schedule 1[1]. For staff preparing and dispensing radiopharmaceuticals, the most relevant dose limit has been found in practice to be that of 500 mSv per year to the fingers. Thus 3/10 of this dose limit is 150 mSv per year, which is approximately 3 mSv per week. In practice, few workers should exceed this limit. The majority will therefore not need to be classified and will enter a controlled area under a written system of work. The system of work, which must be incorporated into the Local Rules, defines who may enter the controlled area and the way in which they are to work. In addition to staff preparing radiopharmaceuticals, it is important that the system of work covers any cleaning or maintenance staff who may enter the area. It must be written in such a way that if it is followed, the radiation dose to staff is minimised and it is unlikely that any person will exceed 3/10 of any dose limit. The system of work should also specify what protective clothing should be worn in the controlled area (Section 6.2.5).

The IRR also define a supervised area as one in which the radiation levels are likely to exceed 1/3 of those laid down for controlled areas. In practice in a radiopharmacy it may be convenient to extend the controlled area to the boundaries of a room and thus avoid the need for a separate supervised area. In circumstances where a supervised area is designated, it must be described in the Local Rules although there are no special requirements for demarcation or restricting entry.

Hazards arising from the dispensing and manufacture of radiopharmaceuticals in hospitals may be considered in terms of those to the staff preparing the materials (operator hazards) and those to patients receiving the completed preparations (patient hazards). Potential hazards associated with the manufacture and dispensing of radiopharmaceuticals are shown in *table 6.1*. In addition, other hospital staff and members of the public may be exposed to radiation during the transport and movement of materials within and between hospitals. All hazards may be minimised by careful attention to design features of the premises and equipment used during the manufacturing process, the adoption of good working practices and adherence to the philosophy of quality assurance.

Table 6.1 Hazards associated with preparation of radiopharmaceuticals

Operator hazards	Patient hazards
External radiation	Excessive radiation dose
Radioactive contamination	Toxicity/pyrogenicity
Ingestion	Microbiological contamination
Accidental injection	Particulate contamination
Inhalation	

6.2 Design

Radiopharmaceuticals are medicinal products as defined by the Medicines Act (1968)[2] and must therefore be manufactured and dispensed under conditions appropriate to their intended use. The laboratory facilities and equipment required are described in detail in several publications[3,4] and it is intended to consider the design of such facilities from the viewpoint of radiation safety. Clearly the design of premises and equipment forms an integral part of the quality assurance process (Section 6.5). Accidents can happen even in well planned premises and an important aspect of design is accident prevention and minimisation of risks resulting from accidents.

6.2.1 Laboratory design

Many design considerations aimed at producing pharmaceutically-acceptable conditions incorporate desirable features for radionuclide safety. The major conflict is the good pharmaceutical practice of maintaining *positive* air pressure within manufacturing areas to prevent the ingress of dust and airborne microorganisms through doors and structural gaps; however, those specialised radionuclide laboratories in which high activities are handled commonly adopt a system where the air pressure within the laboratory is *lower* than that of the surrounding areas to give containment in the event of escape of airborne radioactivity. Most radiopharmaceuticals are processed in the hospital in solution in sealed vials and therefore the risk of airborne contamination in the form of aerosol droplets, or volatile materials, is small unless the contents of the vial are under positive pressure. The risk is further reducedby handling materials within a contained work station (Section 6.1.3). For these reasons, hospital radiopharmacies are normally maintained at a positive rather than negative pressure.

Radiopharmacy laboratories should be sufficiently compact to allow easy access to all facilities and ease of cleaning. However sufficient room should be allowed so that operators are not required to work too close to radiation sources (Section 6.2.1). Suitable dimensions are described in an appendix to Health Building Note 29[5] where the minimum room dimension is proposed as 2 m. If the laboratory includes a single contained work station, a room width of at least 2.2 m is needed increasing to 3.2 m if a second work station is incorporated.

Wall, floor and ceiling surfaces should be smooth, impervious and durable to resist the repeated action of cleaning agents and to make it easier to remove any radioactive contamination. Covings should be used where walls meet floors and ceilings. Plastic laminate or stainless steel bench tops are recommended and projecting ledges are to be avoided if possible. The boxing-in of equipment, the sealing of pipes and cables inside trunking and the flush mounting of electrical sockets and light fittings all serve to reduce sites for the possible accumulation of radioactive or microbial contamination, dirt and debris. Some means of two-way communication with the radiopharmacy laboratory (e.g. an intercom) should be established and the system should be easy to clean.

IRR Regulation 22 requires the provision of washing and changing facilities for access to controlled areas. The changing area should be provided with sufficient storage space for protective clothing, and have hand-washing facilities. A step-over barrier in the changing area serves to emphasise the special nature of the area and that precautions are to be taken before entering.

Exit from the manufacturing area must be achieved in such a way that spread of radioactive contamination is minimised. A particular risk is the transfer of radioactive materials from gloves to door handles. This risk is reduced by incorporating elbow or arm operated door handles into the design. Sinks within the dispensing and manufacturing areas should be of stainless steel with a foot or elbow operated tap and have a water seal between the rim of the sink and any wall. Drainage should be such that accumulation of radioactive waste, e.g. in large bottle traps, is avoided. Outflow should pass directly to a main sewer to permit rapid dilution of any radioactive solutions. However, sinks also provide a source of potential microbiological contamination and it will generally be necessary and acceptable to locate such sinks away from clean areas.

6.2.2 Storage areas

Facilities should incorporate features which allow the safe and secure receipt, unpacking and storage of radioactive materials. The facilities should ideally be close to the manufacturing and dispensing area such that transfer of materials over excessive distances is avoided. Access should be limited to those staff who work in the area as an important aid to security. Storage areas should be lockable or incorporate lockable storage containers in the form of lead-lined safes or refrigerators and freezers. Provision of ventilation or air extraction may be necessary when unpacking and storing radioactive gases or materials which give rise to gaseous by-products (e.g. Xe-131m arising from the decay of I-131[6] and it may be necessary to incorporate a fume cupboard (Section 6.1.4).

6.2.3 Contained work stations

The objectives of good contained work station design may be summarised as the provision of a partially or totally enclosed region of filtered air within which it is possible to manipulate radioactive materials safely and aseptically. Work stations have been variously referred to as laminar flow cabinets, balanced-air down-draught workstations and unidirectional airflow cabinets but guidance issued from the Department of Health and Social Security[4] adopts the use of the term 'contained work station'. There are several different types commercially available which have certain common features but which differ in other respects. An important design feature of a contained work station is the protection of the operator from airborne radioactive contamination. This is achieved by extraction of the air through grilles or holes in the worksurface and at the front sill.

In some designs, the airflow is totally recirculated within the work station with no demand for additional room air. This type is not recommended for radio-pharmaceutical preparation work. Some contained work stations exhaust the total airflow to the outside environment, while others incorporate partial recirculation (< 80 per cent) and partial exhaust (> 20 per cent). The exhausted or recirculated air may pass through filters designed to trap either particulate matter or gaseous or volatile contamination. Partial exhaust work stations provide a suitable environment for the performance of most radiopharmaceutical manipulations involving non-volatile and non-gaseous material. An additional safety feature in the design of some partial-exhaust work stations is the ability to select a total 'dump' (i.e. the whole of the airflow is exhausted) in the event of a major spillage of potentially hazardous material within the working space. Total exhaust work stations should be used when gaseous materials, or volatile substances such as iodine are being manipulated.

Contained work stations having a totally enclosed working space with access through glove ports are becoming increasingly available. Such contained work stations afford a high degree of operator protection and some have facilities for radionuclide generator storage and elution. They may also incorporate ionisation chamber radionuclide calibrators. Materials and equipment are introduced via double-entry hatches.

When designing departments which incorporate contained work stations, sufficient capacity must be built into any air-conditioning plant to make up for the proportion of airflow exhausted and thus maintain the positive pressure within the manufacturing room. The site for external venting of the exhaust must be carefully chosen to avoid any entrained radioactive contamination re-entering the building.

The interior finish of all contained work stations should be smooth and impervious for ease of decontamination. The bases of contained work stations are perforated by grilles or holes for the passage of air, and should incorporate drip trays to catch any accidental spillage of radioactive solutions. The base must be capable of supporting considerable weight if radionuclide generators are being manipulated or if local shielding is incorporated. It should be noted that the introduction of radiation shielding into the working space may well reduce the operator protection factor of the work station for airborne radioactivity and this requires measurement with the shielding in place (Section 6.5.4).

6.2.4 Fume cupboards

Fume cupboards provide a safe working environment for the handling of gaseous or volatile radioactive materials when asepsis is not a consideration. Fume cupboards should be designed such that an airflow across the aperture of at least 0.5 m s^{-1} is maintained at apertures sufficiently wide to allow access for working. Exhaust vents should be sited such that entrained radioactive materials cannot re-enter the building. This will be dependent upon many factors including the height of the building, the position of windows and the proximity of other buildings[7,8]. As with contained work stations, decontamination is made easier by the provision of a smooth impervious interior finish. Local shielding within the working space may be necessary and the base should be sufficiently strong to support this. Shielding should be designed to create minimum disturbance of the airflow.

6.3 Working Practices

The biggest single factor enhancing safety is the skill of the staff performing the procedures. It is therefore a valuable investment of time when training staff to simulate techniques using non-radioactive materials. In this way expertise can be gained without introducing risks.

There are three fundamental parameters that affect external radiation doses to workers:

a) the distance between the worker and radioactive sources. The radiation dose decreases proportionately with the square of the distance — the 'inverse square law';

b) the time spent manipulating the radioactive source;

c) the amount of shielding used to reduce the dose rate from the radioactive source;

It must be remembered, however, that the optimum procedure may involve a compromise between the above parameters. For example, if the amount of shielding used means that handling of the radioactive material becomes inconvenient and takes longer, there may not be a significant reduction in the radiation dose absorbed by the fingers. In addition, the radiation dose of staff may be increased by radioactive contamination of either the working environment or personnel leading to intake of radioactive material. These effects can be minimised by containment, the use of appropriate protective clothing and good working practices.

It is also essential that all hand to mouth operations (e.g. mouth pipetting, eating or drinking) are forbidden during manipulations with radioactive materials.

6.3.1 Distance: radioactive source and the worker

The dose rate from a radioactive point source decreases with the square of the distance from the source; thus doubling the distance will reduce the dose rate four fold. Working practices should therefore be designed to ensure that the maximum distance, compatible with ease of manipulation, is maintained between personnel and radioactive sources. Laboratory layout should be considered so that technetium generators are stored and eluted as far as practicable from areas used for manufacturing and dispensing of radiopharmaceuticals. Since the elution of generators proceeds automatically once the evacuated vial has been placed in position, it is good practice to move away until the process has been completed.

Vials containing radioactive materials should be removed from shielding with tongs or forceps rather than gloved fingers. Any device must permit rapid and safe manipulation. It must not cause an increased handling time nor increase the risk of radioactive materials being dropped or damaged during manipulation. Care should be taken when handling unshielded syringes: normally a syringe should be handled by the end remote from the needle. The dose rate over a 0.5 ml volume of Tc-99m in a 2 ml syringe has been calculated to be forty times that at the end of the syringe barrel[9]. The use of syringes with a capacity greater than the volume to be transferred (e.g. 5 ml for an injection volume of 2 ml) is advocated in order to increase the distance between fingers and the radioactive solution.

6.3.2   Time: handling radioactivity

Radiation exposure of personnel can be reduced by minimising the time spent performing manipulations. This requires that all procedures are carefully evaluated to avoid unnecessary exposure and re-emphasises the need for new members of staff to practise techniques with non-radioactive materials in order to gain competence. Particular skill is required for the safe, rapid and accurate removal of the final volume of liquid radiopharmaceutical from a shielded vial when visibility is impaired. Spending undue time extracting the last drop of a radioactive solution will significantly increase the operator's finger dose without a corresponding increase in extracted activity.

6.3.3   Shielding

Shielding appropriate for the type of radiation encountered should be used whenever practicable to reduce dose rates in the preparation and dispensing of radiopharmaceuticals. Shielding may be constructed from a variety of materials including lead and tungsten for gamma emitting radionuclides; aluminium or perspex for beta emitters. It is advantageous to use perspex shields when manipulating beta emitting radionuclides, since this minimises the production of bremsstrahlung radiation. If lead is used it should be painted or otherwise covered to provide a cleanable surface and to protect operators from accidental ingestion of lead.

Shielding of equipment is important and reduces radiation exposure in the following areas:

a)   Generators

In current practice, the highest surface dose rates likely to be encountered are from technetium generators, which contain Mo-99. The principal gamma radiation emanating from this radionuclide has an energy of 740 keV and hence several centimetres of lead must be used to reduce the dose rates encountered around generators to acceptable levels which should be checked. For generators containing the smallest amount of shielding supplied by manufacturers the surface dose rate can be several mSv h^{-1} and additional shielding will often be required. With increasing activities of Mo-99, the amount of lead required poses problems in the design of generators and for this reason depleted uranium shielding may be used, which in view of its higher density and atomic number, provides more efficient shielding than that given by the same thickness of lead. Depleted uranium is, however, expensive and classified as a fissile material and hence it is necessary to keep an up to date record of its whereabouts. This means that suppliers require the prompt return of such generators, which may represent an advantage to the radiopharmacy since it will not be necessary to provide space for storage of expired generators.

A technetium generator may be in use for a fortnight and in some departments more than one may be in use simultaneously. The weight of a generator can cause practical problems since members of staff may have difficulty in carrying the generator from its transport packaging into the radiopharmacy. It is good practice to store and elute generators behind further lead shielding. It is important to ensure bench surfaces are strong enough to stand the weight.

b) Contained work stations

Operator protection can be enhanced by the incorporation of local shielding into the structure of the work station in such a way that air flow patterns are not affected. Acrylic lead or lead glass visors offer advantages over perspex and are readily available. Lead shielding in the form of lead sheeting can also be fitted beneath the work surface and to the exterior. Extra shielding in the form of lead bricks or screens may be fitted *inside* the work station and manipulations performed behind them. This will inevitably affect the air flow and care must be taken to ensure that operator protection is not compromised. For this reason, the minimum amount of equipment and materials should be introduced into the work station. Drip trays should, however, always be used in order to contain any spillage that may occur during manipulations.

c) Vials

During preparation and dispensing of radiopharmaceuticals, vials should be kept within appropriate shielding. Since vials are usually inverted during dispensing, the design of shielding should be such that the vial is still retained without the need of being held with the fingers.

For Tc-99m labelled radiopharmaceuticals, (gamma energy 140 keV) a lead shield of 2–3 mm thickness is sufficient to reduce dose rates by several orders of magnitude, whilst retaining ease of handling. Other radiopharmaceuticals emitting higher energy gamma rays, e.g. those based on I-131 (gamma energy 364 keV), need thicker shields to achieve significant reduction in dose rate. The thickness of lead required to reduce the transmission of gamma rays of various energies to 10 per cent of its value (the tenth value thickness) is shown in Appendix IV.

d) Syringes

Many manipulations are performed with syringes and during preparation of Tc-99m radiopharmaceuticals it is common for several gigabecquerels to be transferred between vials using a syringe. Surface doserates of 260 μSv s^{-1} can be encountered over a 0.5 ml volume of 370 MBq of Tc-99m in a 2 ml syringe[9]. Therefore, inappropriate handling of syringes can mean that the annual limit of 500 mSv for fingers is reached rapidly. Syringe shields may be used to attenuate radiation from the syringe. Shields are usually made of lead or tungsten and incorporate a lead glass window to permit visualisation of graduations on the syringe. Lead has the disadvantage that it is soft and easily deformed and tungsten is therefore often preferred. Lead glass does not have as much attenuation as either lead or tungsten of a similar thickness. However, the window should be sufficiently wide to ensure good visibility of the solution within the syringe. Lead glass is also brittle and care must be taken to prevent mechanical damage.

The attenuation factor for Tc-99m gamma radiation in commercially available tungsten syringe shields of various designs has been found to range between 27 and

178[10]. For manufacturing and dispensing of Tc-99m radiopharmaceuticals, it has been found that syringe shields tend to reduce the operator's finger dose from the *complete* procedure by a factor of about two. Syringe shields do, however, produce an eight fold reduction in the finger dose of personnel injecting radiopharmaceuticals, assuming the syringe was fitted in the shield by another person.

Syringe shields are generally heavy, bulky and expensive. For these reasons, they are often unpopular but cost-benefit analysis of radiation protection can be used to show that purchase of syringe shields is justifiable[11]. Although the dose reduction is smaller than may have been anticipated, it is still worthwhile and may even be sufficient to avoid the need to designate personnel as classified employees.

6.3.4   Containment

When manipulating radioactive materials during dispensing and manufacturing, the spread of radioactive contamination can be minimised by working with closed systems within a contained work station or fume cupboard. Some means should also be provided for containing the spread of accidentally-spilled material. Manipulations should be performed over metal or plastic trays of adequate depth. The trays should be scratch resistant and non-absorbent to allow ease of decontamination and also be unaffected by regular washing or autoclaving.

6.3.5   Protective clothing

Personnel may become contaminated as a result of direct spillage of radioactive solutions. Protective clothing which covers vulnerable areas of the body should be worn and the minimum amount of unprotected skin left exposed. The wearing of gloves is particularly important since hands could be contaminated and increase the risk of the spread and ingestion of radioactivity. Head covering is also important, since not only does it help to maintain cleanliness of the environment, but touching the hair with consequent transfer of contamination is also prevented.

After dispensing radioactive materials, gloves should be carefully removed by turning inside out, avoiding contact between the skin and the outside surface of the gloves. They should be discarded into the radioactive waste bin. Other protective clothing should be removed carefully and monitored for contamination. Suitable temporary storage facilities for any clothing found to be contaminated must be provided, ideally within the changing facilities of a controlled or supervised area as defined in the Approved Code of Practice (ACOP 1/136)[12]. The hands should be monitored for contamination after washing and appropriate action taken in the event of contamination.

6.4   Contamination Hazards

All work with unsealed sources of radioactivity poses the risk of contamination of personnel either directly or indirectly since spillage may result in contamination of surfaces and an increase in the air concentration of radioactivity. Both of these in turn may lead to ingestion and inhalation of activity by personnel. Where it is possible for 3/10 of a dose limit to be exceeded as a result of such contamination it is necessary to designate a Controlled Area in relation to internal radiation (See Section 6.1). There is also a requirement that suitable monitoring procedures for personal contamination are available (Chapter 7).

6.4.1 Airborne contamination

Of the radionuclides commonly used in radiopharmacies, the most stringent limits on air concentration are those for radioisotopes of iodine. This is a consequence of the ease with which iodides can be oxidised to free iodine which is volatile and, if ingested, is concentrated in the thyroid gland. Particular care is therefore required when handling these radioisotopes and all work must be performed in suitable enclosures which have adequate ventilation. Because of the high activities used the greatest risk arises from I-131 sodium iodide and for this reason solutions for the treatment of thyrotoxicosis or the ablation of thyroid carcinoma contain sodium thiosulphate as an antioxidant to minimise volatilisation. Solutions of I-131 or I-125 sodium iodide used for protein iodination do not contain sodium thiosulphate, since oxidation of the iodide ion is necessary during the iodination reaction. Capsules containing I-131 sodium iodide should be unpacked in a fume cupboard since in addition to the risk of volatilisation, 1.3 per cent of disintegrations of I-131 proceed via Xe-131m (half-life 11.8 days, gamma emission 164 keV) which is detectable on the packing materials used[6]. Some commercially available capsules contain an activated charcoal disc within the lid of the lead pot to absorb volatile materials. The limits for air concentration of Xe-131m and other xenon radionuclides are much higher than those for iodine which indicates that, should these inert gases be inhaled, their biological residence is much shorter. The hazard to staff is considerably reduced by the use of radioiodine in capsule rather than liquid form because of decreased handling time and avoidance of spillage and aerosols. The use of capsules, especially for therapeutic administrations is strongly encouraged.

Air concentrations of radioactivity may also be increased by the escape from the work station of droplets of volatile or non-volatile materials formed during manipulations. This is particularly relevant during the preparation of technetium-99m radiopharmaceuticals since kit vials have rubber stoppers through which Tc-99m sodium pertechnetate solutions, often at high radioactive concentration, are injected. The majority of such vials contain nitrogen in order to maintain the reducing agent (normally stannous ion), in the correct chemical form. Reconstitution instructions frequently stress the need to avoid the use of breather needles so that the nitrogen atmosphere is maintained above the finished product. Care must therefore be taken when equalising the pressure in the vial to avoid the possibility of aerosol droplet formation when withdrawing the needle.

6.4.2 Surface contamination

In addition to the hazard of any settling aerosol particles, surface contamination will also be increased by spillage of radioactive solutions, e.g. loss of droplets from a needle prior to injection into a kit vial. Containment of any spillage is important eg by the use of drip trays (Section 6.2.4) and appropriate decontamination procedures should be instituted as soon as is practicable. If contamination is not removed, or spillage remains undetected, there is the risk that other surfaces such as door handles, or equipment such as containers, forceps or swabs may inadvertently be contaminated and hence the contamination may be spread. In addition to the hazard posed to staff, there is the remote possibility that cross-contamination between radiopharmaceuticals may occur which could interfere with interpretation of investigations.

6.4.3 Accidental injection of radioactivity

Many preparation techniques involve transfers of radioactive materials between containers via needles and syringes and care must be taken by staff to avoid accidental injection. The greatest risk arises when removing a needle from, or replacing it in, its guard; resheathing devices are commercially available. Care must also be taken when discarding needles and syringes so that unsheathed needles do not protrude from disposal boxes presenting an injury hazard. Although the amounts of radioactivity transferred in this way may be small, they may enter the body by a route not normally used, e.g. intramuscular or subcutaneous. The biological fate of the injected material, and hence the radiation dose absorbed by the body, may be different to that following intravenous administration. Accidental injury of patients where the radionuclide is not injected intravenously is also important. This is exemplified by an incident when 74 MBq of thallous (Tl-201) chloride was inadvertently injected subcutaneously. Two years later, the patient returned to the hospital with ulceration at the site of injection, probably due to radiation damage. Skin grafting was performed. The maximum dose at the injection site was estimated to be 200 Gy[13]. It is advisable to record any incident in which extravasation is thought to have occurred, and it may be useful to record routinely the actual site of injection. The effects of accidental inoculation can be minimised by working with solutions of the lowest practicable radioactive concentration, since only small volumes are likely to enter the body.

6.5 Decontamination Procedures

Procedures are required for decontamination of personnel, working surfaces and equipment used during manufacture or dispensing operations. Greater emphasis must, however, be placed on prevention of contamination than on decontamination procedures since not only is the immediate risk reduced but additional exposure during cleaning-up operations is avoided.

6.5.1 Decontamination: personnel

Any contamination detected on personnel should be removed as soon as practicable. Hands should be washed with soap or mild detergent and water, and monitored. The washing procedure may be repeated if contamination persists but vigorous scrubbing that may break the skin must be avoided. Activity on unbroken skin will usually wash off quite easily if dealt with immediately but activity at any break in the skin or around fingernails can be extremely difficult to remove. A soft nailbrush must therefore be provided as part of the decontamination facilities. In the case of cuts, irrigation with tap water should be performed, being careful not to wash further contamination into the wound. When parts of the body other than the hands are contaminated, local washing should be performed in the first instance. Showers can also be taken provided this does not result in contamination being transferred to other parts of the body. For example radioactivity could be washed into the eyes from contaminated hair; this is particularly undesirable as there is a separate, more stringent dose limit for the lens of the eye. It is unlikely that showers will be necessary to deal with contamination arising from hospital manufacturing and dispensing procedures. Incidents must be reported to the Radiation Protection Supervisor who will advise on action to be taken or arrange further treatment or medical advice if available decontamination procedures are inadequate. Further advice is given in Chapter 8.

6.5.2 Decontamination: surfaces and equipment

It is important that contaminated surfaces or equipment are identified as soon as possible so that the necessary remedial action can be taken. For surfaces, it is also important clearly to demarcate the extent of the contamination.

The majority of work in a radiopharmacy involves Tc-99m. As this radionuclide has a six hour half-life, after initial cleaning it may be convenient to cover stubbornly contaminated surfaces with suitable shielding for a period of 24 hours to allow activity to decay prior to further decontamination procedures. Similarly, contaminated equipment, e.g. tongs or shielding vials, may be kept for a time in a suitable store prior to decontamination.

In the first instance, decontamination should be performed by washing with detergent and water. Monitoring for residual activity should then be performed and the procedure repeated if necessary. Monitoring of worksurfaces adjacent to technetium generators with a scintillation detector is not usually possible because of the high background countrate. In such circumstances, it may be necessary either to remove the generator or to perform wipe testing of the contaminated surface. The Approved Code of Practice (ACOP 1/147)[12] suggests that it should be assumed that 10% of the activity is removed by wiping unless otherwise demonstrated. This statement should be treated with caution since it is a broad generalisation and may represent a gross underestimation of activity removed[14]. Where it can safely be performed, it may be worthwhile determining experimentally the amount of each type of radiopharmaceutical in use that can be removed by wiping surfaces and equipment.

Where contamination persists, it may be necessary to resort to stronger cleaning agents. Commercial decontaminants containing surface active agents are available in the form of towelettes or aerosol foams which lift the contamination from the surface. These must be used with caution to avoid damage to the surface being cleaned. If small, inexpensive items of equipment become contaminated with long lived radionuclides, it may be economically preferable to discard them as radioactive waste rather than to undertake lengthy decontamination procedures.

6.6 Quality Assurance

The principles of quality assurance are defined with the object of ensuring that products will be of the quality required for their intended use. Quality assurance procedures should be designed to ensure that patients receive the correct activity of the correct radionuclide in the correct chemical and physical form and that the material is presented in an appropriate manner, e.g. if it is an injection that it is sterile and pyrogen-free. Because of the short half-life of many radio-pharmaceuticals, it is not always possible to test these parameters before administration to patients. Quality assurance at each stage of manufacture is achieved by strict adherence to written procedures and by the use of appropriate materials and equipment which have been shown to be satisfactory for the intended purposes.

Accurate and complete record-keeping (see Section 6.7) at all stages of the manufacturing process is an essential part of quality assurance. In this way it is possible to trace the source, composition and activity of all radiopharmaceuticals administered to patients. Careful monitoring of the working environment, e.g. measurement of the protection factors of contained work stations and of operator technique help to assure final product quality and to control the exposure to radiation of the operators themselves.

Patient safety is greatly enhanced by strict adherence to the principles of quality assurance bearing in mind the following possible consequences of administration of sub-standard preparations:

a) the patient may suffer an adverse reaction;
b) the radiopharmaceutical may localise in an unintended organ and deliver an unnecessary radiation dose to a sensitive organ or result in misinterpretation of the test;
c) the preparation may contain too much activity or the wrong radionuclide resulting in increased radiation dose;
d) the investigation may be unsatisfactory and may need repeating with a resulting increase in radiation dose to the patient.

The parameters listed in *table 6.2* must be controlled during the preparation of injectable radiopharmaceuticals. Measurement methods are described in detail in another publication[3]. Use of the wrong radionuclide or variations in radionuclide concentration, radionuclide purity and radiochemical purity of the finished product have a direct bearing on the radiation dose to the patient during radionuclide investigations. Other factors such as failure to comply with standards for particle size or pH may contribute indirectly to an increase in radiation dose by causing an altered biodistribution of the injected radiopharmaceutical. Only those factors contributing directly to the radiation burden will be discussed further.

Table 6.2 Quality considerations of hospital-produced radio-pharmaceuticals

---

Radionuclide concentration
Radionuclide identity and purity
Radiochemical purity
Chemical purity
Specific activity
Sterility
Apyrogenicity
Absence of foreign particulate matter
Particle size (where appropriate)
pH (where appropriate)

6.6.1 Radionuclide concentration

Measurements of radioactive content are generally performed using well-type ionisation chambers. These may be of the atmospheric type in which the ionising gas is air, or they may contain pressurised gas (e.g. 2 MPa of argon). Both types of instrument have limitations in performance. Atmospheric chambers are susceptible to changes in atmospheric pressure or humidity. Pressurised chambers are more stable but (because of the thickened chamber walls necessary to withstand the internal pressure) may have reduced sensitivity to low energy radiation (e.g. from I-125). Instruments should be installed and operated in an environment in which the temperature, pressure and humidity are kept constant. It is also important to perform checks on the performance of radionuclide calibrators before first use and whenever the instrument is modified or repaired. These tests require repetition at regular intervals during use. There are four important checks to be made:

a) constancy check repeated at least daily with a sealed reference source of a long lived radionuclide such as Cs-137 or Ra-226;

b) assessment of assay accuracy repeated annually with traceable standardised solutions of appropriate radionuclides. Measurements should generally be within ±5% of certified values;

c) assessment of variation with sample geometry;

d) assessment of linearity of response repeated annually by following the decay of a large (15–20 GBq) source of Tc-99m over a period of 48 hours. Observed readings should be within ±5% of those expected from the known decay rate of Tc-99m.

Detailed guidance is given in the IPSM/NPL protocol for quality control of radionuclide calibrators[15].

6.6.2 Radionuclide identity and purity

Control of radionuclide purity and identity is important in ensuring that the biodistribution following patient administration is that of the stated radionuclide and not complicated by that of any impurity, and in minimising radiation doses to patients. Impurities or foreign radionuclides may arise as the result of a number of factors. During the manufacture of I-123 the occurrence of alternative nuclear reactions may result in the production of high levels of I-125. Radioactive daughter products (e.g. Sc-47 from Ca-47) may be present. Radioactive parent products which may be eluted from generator systems also present potential problems. If the impurity has the longer half-life, radionuclide purity steadily decreases during the shelf life of the product and may limit its usefulness (e.g. Tl-202 in Tl-201). The following methods may be used in the determination of radionuclide purity:

a) Gamma spectroscopy;

b) Attenuation methods e.g. the determination of Mo-99 breakthrough in Tc-99m generator eluates by the use of an attenuating lead insert in the ionisation chamber of a radionuclide calibrator;

c) Determination of nuclides following the decay of others e.g. the estimation of Sn-113 in In-113m generator eluates;

d) Determination by calculation from decay constants.

6.6.3 Radiochemical purity

Control over radiochemical purity is important to ensure the expected biodistribution of the radiopharmaceutical. This in turn will reduce errors in diagnostic interpretation and limit the radiation dose. Determination of radiochemical purity requires the separation and quantification of the various radiochemical species present in the product. The following techniques may be applied:

a) chromatography;

b) gel filtration;

c) ion exchange;

d) electrophoresis;

e) filtration;

6.6.4 Monitoring: working environment

Environmental monitoring required for safety reasons is concerned with demonstrating the absence of radioactive contamination of working surfaces, equipment and the air. Techniques are described in detail in Chapter 7. A further important aspect of monitoring is to demonstrate the containment of possible airborne radioactive contamination by the contained work stations used during manufacturing procedures.

6.6.5 Monitoring: operator technique

It is good practice to monitor the ability of an operator to manipulate radioactive sources safely during dispensing and manufacturing operations. Air samplers incorporating filters placed at appropriate positions provide useful information in demonstrating how much airborne contamination is generated during dispensing and manufacture. Monitoring of surface contamination, and personal dose monitoring also give valuable information concerning an operator's ability to work carefully and safely.

6.7 Movement of Radiopharmaceuticals

When considering safety aspects of movement of radioactive materials on or between sites, the Radiation Protection Adviser (RPA) should be consulted. The basic philosophy must be directed towards minimising radiation exposure of all persons concerned, e.g. drivers, warehouse staff and members of the public. Transport of any kind also involves the risk of accident and thought must be given initially to minimising the occurrence of spillage and secondly to that of containment and reduction of the spread of contamination should spillage occur. Transport and movement of radioactive material is highly regulated and it is essential to read Chapter 10 for details.

6.8 Record Keeping

It is an integral part of any safe system of work that adequate records are maintained. There is a requirement in the IRR (regulation 19) that records of quantities of radioactive materials are made and kept for at least two years from the date of disposal. It is important that the form in which these records are kept is discussed with the RPA and it is likely that the exact manner of keeping will vary from one user department to another. Whatever system is adopted it should be possible to retrieve from the records:

a) a means of identification of the source;
b) the date of receipt;
c) the activity of the source at a specified date;
d) the location of storage;
e) the date and manner of disposal.

In every case records should ensure that all radioactive sources are traceable and that losses of significant quantities can quickly be identified. It is inevitable, however, that some sources will have undergone significant radioactive decay before disposal and this must be allowed for in the accounting procedure. It is good practice to perform an annual inventory of radioactive sources to validate the accounting procedure.

Disposal of radioactivity can be as liquid, solid or occasionally gaseous waste. Permitted quantities for each route of disposal will be specified for each site in the Authorisation Certificate issued under the Radioactive Substances Act (1960)[16] by the Department of the Environment. Records of disposal must be kept by each user department such that total disposal from the site can be collated and recorded in a form suitable for inspection by the Department of the Environment. The total figure for disposal must include radioactivity excreted by patients (e.g. in urine). Good coordination is therefore required between Radiation Protection Supervisors and the Radiation Protection Adviser in ensuring both the accuracy of individual departmental records and in maintaining total levels of disposed radioactivity within the limits specified for the site in the Authorisation Certificate (see Chapter 9).

Records of all monitoring procedures, including environmental (Section 6.5.4) and personnel (Section 7) must be maintained and reviewed. These are to ensure that:

a) all areas remain correctly designated, e.g. as supervised or controlled;
b) personnel requiring designation as classified workers are correctly identified;
c) any trends can be identified and appropriate remedial action initiated as soon as possible.

Changes in working practice can affect radiation protection and it is often from careful record keeping that the efficacy of both radiation protection and radio-pharmaceutical preparation can be confirmed.

References

1   *The Ionising Radiations Regulations 1985* SI No 1333 (HMSO, London)
2   *The Medicines Act 1968* (HMSO, London)
3   Frier M Hardy J G Hesslewood S R and Lawrence R 1988 *Hospital Radiopharmacy: Principles and Practice* (IPSM, York)
4   Department of Health & Social Security 1982 *Guidance notes for hospitals on the premises and environment for the preparation of radiopharmaceuticals* (DHSS, London)
5   Department of Health & Social Security 1985 *Health Building Note No 29* (DHSS, London)
6   Verbruggen A M and De Roo M 1983 Contamination of the packing material of sodium iodide (^{131}I) therapy capsules with an unexpected radionuclide *Eur J Nuc Med* **8** 406–407
7   Hughes D 1986 Laboratory fumehoods and fume-dispersal systems, in *'Ventilation '85'* (ed M D Goodfellow) (Elsevier Science Publishers BV, Amersterdam)
8   British Standards Institute 1990 *Laboratory fume cupboards* BS 7258 (BSI, Milton Keynes)
9   Henson P W 1973 Radiation dose to the skin in contact with unshielded syringes containing radioactive substances *Brit J Radiol* **46** 972–977
10 Harding L K Hesslewood S Ghose S K and Thomson W H 1985 The value of syringe shields in a nuclear medicine department *Nucl Med Commun* **6** 449–454
11 Thomson W H and Roberts P J 1986 Cost-benefit analysis in radiation protection *Nucl Med Commun* **7** 855–856
12 Health and Safety Commission 1985 *Approved Code of Practice. The protection of persons against ionising radiation arising from any work activity* (HMSO, London)
13 European Joint Committee on Radiopharmaceuticals 1985 Memento: injection of radiopharmaceuticals *Nucl Med Commun* **6** 669
14 Scott L E and Gibson C J 1991 Wipe tests to assess Tc-99m surface contamination: effects of surface type, swab type and chemical form *Nucl Med Commun* **12** 127–133
15 IPSM/NPL Protocol for Quality Control of Radionuclide Calibrators (in press)
16 *Radioactive Substances Act 1960* (HMSO, London)

CHAPTER 7

Monitoring

K E Goldstone

7.1 Introduction

Radiation monitoring of both personnel and the environment is an essential part of radiation protection. It is used to demonstrate that safe working conditions have been achieved and that they continue to be maintained. Guidance on how to carry out measurements, interpret the results and keep records should be specified when setting up a schedule for departmental monitoring. The philosophy behind personal and environmental monitoring is covered comprehensively in ICRP 35[1].

7.2 Regulatory Requirements

The Ionising Radiations Regulations 1985 (IRR)[2] give specific legal requirements pertaining to monitoring and these are expanded upon in some detail by the Approved Code of Practice (ACOP)[3]. Advice of a more practical nature specifically for medical and dental uses of ionising radiation is contained in the Guidance Notes[4].

Employers who undertake work with ionising radiation must ensure that employees and other persons are not exposed to ionising radiation to an extent that any dose limit is exceeded (IRR Reg 7). In many circumstances this will necessitate personnel dose monitoring (ACOP 1/33) for both extremity and body doses and, if appropriate, doses arising from internally deposited radioactivity (ACOP 1/36). Furthermore employers are required to keep doses to levels which are as low as reasonably practicable (IRR Reg 6). Ensuring that this is achieved necessitates personnel (ACOP 1/9) and environmental monitoring for both external radiation (ACOP 1/13) and contamination (ACOP 1/17).

Further controls are exercised by the concepts of controlled and supervised areas as defined in IRR Reg 8 (See Appendix I). Employers are responsible for demonstrating by personal dose assessment, or other suitable measurements, that doses to non-classified persons entering controlled areas are restricted to a maximum of three tenths of any relevant dose limit for employees aged over 18 years and any relevant dose limit for anyone else. If personal dose measurements are not made, records of time spent in a controlled area may be used as a basis of ensuring compliance, but this is only feasible if dose rate and contamination levels are fairly constant or known to be below a certain level. In this situation environmental monitoring will be required (ACOP 1/53).

Employees are classified according to the radiation dose they are likely to receive (IRR Reg 9). Basically an employer must designate as classified any of his employees who is likely to exceed three tenths of any relevant dose limit. The mandatory requirement for classified employees to be individually monitored is set out in IRR Reg 13. Much of this regulation is concerned with arrangements made between the employer and the Approved Dosimetry Service and will therefore not be elaborated upon in this chapter. Guidance as to the level at which doses are deemed to be significant is given in ACOP 1/88. If dose assessments show that a particular component of dose or committed dose is less than one tenth of any appropriate dose limit, then that component need not be assessed provided that the total of all unassessed components is unlikely to exceed one-tenth of any appropriate dose limit. It should be noted that this guidance is given only in relation to persons statutorily required to be monitored; however it may be applied to any monitored employees.

The rationale for monitoring the environment is to ascertain that methods used to restrict the exposure of persons to ionising radiation in controlled and supervised areas are effective. Monitoring solely by assessing doses to individuals is specifically excluded (IRR Reg 24). Monitoring outside controlled and supervised areas is also required to ensure that the boundaries of all areas remain correct (ACOP 1/143). Monitoring equipment must be examined and tested at least once every 14 months by a Qualified Person appointed by the employer for the purpose (IRR Reg 10 (7), IRR Reg 24 (3)). Detailed guidance has been given by the HSE[5]. Records of both the monitoring itself and the equipment tests have to be kept (IRR Reg 24 (4)).

The Regulations therefore require systematic, accurate monitoring of both the environment and personnel. However the ultimate aim of monitoring is to provide the information, either directly or indirectly, from which doses to employees can be assessed. This enables the employer to ensure that doses received by employees are being kept as low as reasonably practicable.

7.3   Reference Levels

Before introducing a monitoring programme, predetermined levels should be set so that in the event of their being exceeded a certain course of action must be taken. These are known as reference levels. Three reference levels (recording, investigation and intervention) are proposed by ICRP 26[6] and amplified in ICRP 35[1]. These levels apply to dose equivalent, intake, contamination and environmental dose rate.

7.3.1   Recording level

This is a formally defined level at which results are thought to be of sufficient interest to record. Although recording levels (for routine individual monitoring) are recommended by the ICRP to be set at one tenth of the pro rata dose limit, e.g. 1.3 mSv per month whole body dose for an unclassified employee, they may be set lower if required. Unless a realistic level is set a large amount of data will be accumulated which is difficult to interpret because it will be of doubtful accuracy. Furthermore if the recording level is set too low it may cause unnecessary alarm if exceeded. It is common practice for the recording level for external monitoring to be set at the detection limit of the monitoring device (e.g. 0.1 mSv for a thermoluminescent dosemeter) and for the purposes of annual dose equivalent this is assessed as zero. A recording level for contamination should be at most that given in the Guidance Notes (*table 7.1*) and in practice it may conveniently be set to two or three times the background reading of the measuring instrument. Recording levels should be set after discussion with the Radiation Protection Adviser (RPA) bearing in mind the requirement in the Regulations to keep radiation doses as low as reasonably practicable.

Table 7.1 Derived limits for surface contamination (excluding alpha emitters)

Surface	Levels of contamination that should not be exceeded ($Bq\ cm^{-2}$)		
Surfaces of the interiors and contents of glove boxes and fume cupboards	The minimum reasonably achievable		
	Class III	Class IV	Class V
Surfaces in controlled areas including any equipment therein (other than those in above category)	30	300	3000
Surfaces of the body	3	30	300
Supervised and public areas, personal clothing, hospital bedding	3	30	300

Surfaces of body: average over at most 100 cm²
Floors, walls, ceilings: average over at most 1000 cm²
Other areas: average over at most 300 cm²
Classification of radionuclides commonly used in hospitals:
Class III: Na-22, Na-24, P-32, K-42, K-43, Ca-45, Fe-59, Co-58, Kr-81m, Y-90, In-111, I-131, Xe-133, Xe-127
Class IV: C-14, S-35, Co-57, Ga-67, Se-75, Br-77, Tc-99m, I-125, Tl-201
Class V : H-3, Cr-51, Fe-55

7.3.2 Investigation level

This is set at a level at which the measured result is sufficiently high to justify further investigation. It is usually set in relation to a single measurement. For routine individual monitoring this level is recommended, by the International Commission on Radiological Protection (ICRP), to be three tenths of the pro rata dose limit. For environmental and contamination monitoring a lower investigation level can be set on the basis of the expected level during normal conditions. In many situations a similar policy can be adopted in respect of personnel monitoring. Again the advice of the RPA should be sought in setting realistic investigation levels which satisfy legislative requirements.

7.3.3 Intervention level

This is defined as a pre-established quantity such that if it is exceeded some intervention must be made. For example, if an individual received an overexposure (i.e. a dose in excess of a relevant dose limit) the employer has to take action to limit that employee's subsequent dose (IRR Reg 30). In practice intervention levels should have little relevance in the hospital use of unsealed radionuclides since, in general, activities handled are not sufficiently high. Where greater activities are handled procedures are, or should be, good enough to make the exceeding of an intervention level most unlikely.

7.4   Record Keeping

Record keeping is an important part of a monitoring programme. Some records are legally required; for example for classified persons the employer must arrange with the approved dosimetry service to keep and maintain records for at least 50 years. Where different services are used, e.g. for internal and external monitoring, one of them should be appointed to keep a coordinated record. The employer should receive dose summaries at appropriate intervals (IRR Reg 13).

There is no such legal requirement for records of monitored persons who are not classified — even if an approved dosimetry service is carrying out the monitoring. Nevertheless it is advisable for the departmental Radiation Protection Supervisor (RPS) to keep the dose record for each member of staff whom he/she supervises. This record is helpful in showing that any system of work in force is successful in restricting doses to three tenths of a relevant dose limit and also that doses are as low as reasonably practicable. The dose record should include details of involvement in radiation incidents even if specific dose estimates were not made. The records should be examined at least annually, by the RPA, to ascertain that the summed total dose (from internal and external contributions) remains acceptably low. Arrangements should be made for the employer to receive information of dose monitoring results on his employees at least annually. The information could either come through the RPS or the approved dosimetry service but should include the results of each type of individual monitoring.

Records kept of environmental monitoring for contamination should be sufficient to confirm that controlled and supervised areas are correctly designated and that radiation levels are being kept as low as reasonably practicable. In addition to recording the date, place, result, etc a note should be made of any unusual circumstances pertaining at the time which could have influenced the result. Records of environmental monitoring and records of tests of the associated equipment should be kept for at least two years.

7.5   Monitoring the Environment

7.5.1   Equipment

The basic measurements which can be made are dose rate (μSv h^{-1}), integrated dose (μSv) and contamination level (Bq cm^{-2}).

a)   Dose rate

Dose rate measuring equipment is relatively expensive and is basically of four types. Firstly, there are monitors based on ionisation chambers. These have the merit of a relatively flat energy response over a wide energy range, e.g. $\pm$ 10% for photons of 30 keV to 1.5 MeV. If a monitor with a very thin window is used then, by removing the protective window cover, the low energy range may be extended to about 10 keV photons. It may also be used similarly to measure beta dose rates (above 100 keV) with an accuracy of about 50%. A monitor of this type is shown in *figure 7.1*.

Secondly, monitors are available which incorporate energy compensated Geiger-Mueller (GM) detectors (*figure 7.2*). Even though such devices are energy compensated, they are unsuitable for measuring either photons below about 40 keV (*figure 7.3*) or beta radiation. However these monitors can be made more sensitive than ionisation chamber detectors, and are easily capable of measuring down to 2.5 μSv h^{-1} (the instantaneous dose rate at which a supervised area has to be designated) with about ± 20 per cent accuracy.

Thirdly, there are monitors using proportional counters (*figure 7.4*). They are sensitive devices and cover a large measuring range (e.g. 0.03 μSv h^{-1} to 30 mSv h^{-1}).

Fourthly, there are instruments based on scintillation detectors (*figure 7.5*). These may have a very high sensitivity but should be used with care for dose rate measurements because of their variation in response with photon energy. In some models, the presence of high energy beta radiations may be detected.

The practical choice, for environmental dose rate monitoring, is therefore between an ionisation chamber based system, which is suitable over a wide photon energy range and for beta radiation but is relatively insensitive, and other devices which are frequently unsuitable for low energy photons and betas, but have a greater sensitivity (*table 7.2*). Any monitors which are purchased must conform to the examination and testing procedures (IRR Reg 24, ACOP 1/152 — 1/158 and 1/161). The instrument must have a calibration traceable to a national standard either by being calibrated against a radiation source of traceable output or against an already calibrated dosemeter.

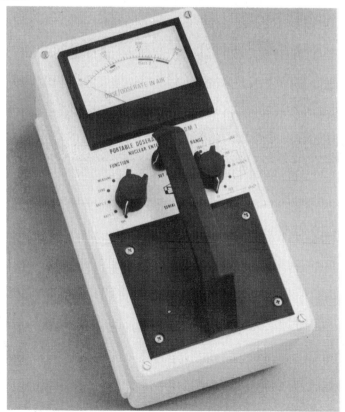

Figure 7.1 Ionisation chamber dose/doserate meter (*courtesy* NE Technology, Reading).

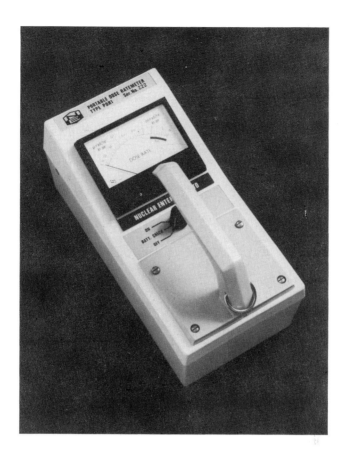

Figure 7.2 Compensated GM tube doserate meter (*courtesy* NE Technology, Reading).

Table 7.2 Dose/doserate measuring equipment

Equipment	Energy Response	Sensitivity	Use
Ionisation chamber	Flat over wide range	poor	Photons Energetic betas
Energy compensated GM tube	Flattish over limited range	good	Energetic gammas (above ~ 40 keV)
Proportional counter	Flattish over limited range	good	Energetic gammas (above ~ 30 keV)
Scintillation detector	Energy dependent	very good	Gammas High energy betas (> 500 keV)

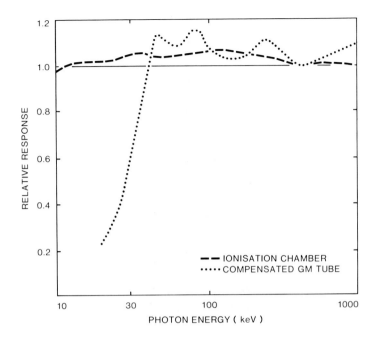

Figure 7.3 Typical energy response curves for ionisation chamber and GM tube type doserate meters.

b) Contamination

Contamination may be monitored by wipe testing which is described briefly at the end of this section. However, where possible, it is preferable to monitor surface contamination directly. Instruments incorporating GM detectors, scintillation detectors or proportional counters can be used. Generally for detection of beta emitters a GM counter is the instrument of choice. For higher energy beta emitters (e.g. >0.7 MeV max) a side window GM counter is adequate (*figure 7.6*). For the detection of lower energy betas the window thickness is critical and suitably thin end window counters must be used. Exceptionally thin window detectors (1.5–2.5 mg cm^{-2}) may be used to detect C-14 (E_{max} 156 keV) (*figure 7.7*). No window is thin enough to allow detection of the beta radiation from tritium which is of very low energy (E_{max} 18 keV).

For detection of gamma-emitting radionuclides scintillation detectors are more sensitive and hence suitable (*figure 7.8*). The low energy response is determined predominantly by the attenuation properties of the front face of the detector; thin window detectors enable photons with energies as low as 5 keV (e.g. Fe-55) to be detected. A scintillation detector suitable for measuring low energy photons is also able to detect the bremsstrahlung radiation from P-32 (E_{max} 1.71 MeV)[7]. This may be particularly useful for laboratories where the principal radionuclides used are I-125 and P-32.

Figure 7.4 Proportional counter doserate meter (*courtesy* Berthold Instruments (UK) Ltd, Hemel Hempstead).

Contamination may also be detected by proportional counters though often these instruments are significantly more expensive than the other types described. Instruments are available which can be preset with predetermined calibration factors for a range of radionuclides (*figure 7.9*). Tritium may be detected by windowless proportional counters thus overcoming the problem of the absorption of the radiation in the front window. However such monitors are very expensive and unsuitable unless the surface on which the contamination is situated is very smooth and impermeable.

When purchasing a monitor, sufficient details should be obtained from the supplier to enable the monitor to be used with confidence for the required range of radionuclides. Contamination monitors require calibration and there are now available from manufacturers large area sources of relatively long-lived materials (e.g. I-129 is used to simulate I-125 since it emits similar characteristic K shell X-rays at 30 keV to 35 keV) which may be used for the purpose. The quoted accuracy of the activity of these sources is of the order of ± 10 per cent which enables a monitor to be calibrated with an accuracy of ± 10 per cent to 20 per cent.

Figure 7.5 Scintillation detector doserate meter (*courtesy* Greenwood Electronics Ltd, Glasgow).

Figure 7.6 Side window GM tube contamination monitor (*courtesy* Mini-Instruments Ltd, Burnham-on-Crouch).

112

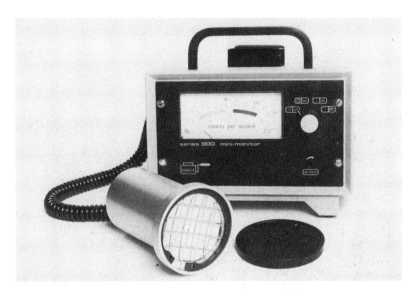

Figure 7.7 Thin end window GM tube contamination monitor (*courtesy* Mini-Instruments Ltd, Burnham-on-Crouch).

Figure 7.8 Scintillation detector contamination monitor (*courtesy* Mini-Instruments Ltd, Burnham-on-Crouch).

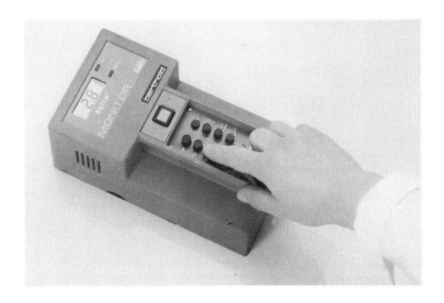

Figure 7.9 Proportional counter contamination monitor (*courtesy* Berthold Instruments (UK) Ltd, Hemel Hempstead).

In departments where a wide range of radionuclides is used, more than one type of monitor will need to be purchased. In some cases it is possible to purchase one measuring instrument with several different plug-in detectors. In all cases when measuring contamination it is most important to avoid contaminating the detector. It is therefore wise to put the detector in a thin plastic bag or protect it with cling film. This results in a slight reduction of sensitivity particularly for C-14 but this may be allowed for in the calibration. Contamination monitoring equipment is summarised in *table 7.3*.

Where contamination is difficult to detect directly either because of the radionuclide, e.g. tritium, Cr-51, or because of the presence of high back-ground radiation, monitoring will have to be by wipe test[8]. The area of interest (1000 cm^2 for walls floors and ceilings and 300 cm^2 for other surfaces) is wiped using a moistened swab. The wipe may then be assessed qualitatively by one of the instruments described above or quantitatively in a well counter used for sample counting. For tritium it is necessary to use fibre glass filter paper moistened with methanol and assess the wipe using a liquid scintillation technique. It is generally assumed (in the absence of evidence to the contrary) that in a wipe test, one tenth of the removable contamination is transferred to the wipe.

c) Calibration

Monitoring equipment which is used for environmental monitoring of controlled and supervised areas must be thoroughly examined and tested at least every 14 months (IRR Reg 24). These tests must be carried out by or under the supervision of a 'qualified person' usually appointed by the employer. Equipment is also legally required to be properly maintained and also to have its initial

Table 7.3 Contamination monitoring equipment

Equipment	Use
Geiger-Mueller tube	Beta emitters—High energy: side window adequate Low energy: thin end window essential
Scintillation detector	Gamma emitters: High energy betas by detection of bremsstrahlung
Proportional counter	Beta and gamma emitters

performance established. The 'first use' tests required will frequently be undertaken by a qualified person appointed by the equipment manufacturer. When monitoring equipment is bought, users should ensure that it is accompanied by appropriate test certificates and manuals explaining the maintenance procedures. The RPA should be consulted about the best way of carrying out the routine tests. Records of maintenance and tests of equipment must be kept for at least two years from the date of entry (IRR Reg 24).

7.5.2 Procedural considerations

Routine monitoring of the workplace is intended to show whether the environment is safe and that no change has taken place calling for a reassessment of operating procedures. Sometimes special monitoring is required to determine radiation levels and contamination arising from a particular procedure. ACOP (1/146) recommends that in order to establish whether adequate monitoring is being achieved the following questions should be considered:

a) What kind of measurements should be made?

b) Where should the measurements be made?

c) How frequently or on what occasions should measurements be made?

d) What method of measurement is appropriate?

e) Who should carry out the measurements?

f) What records should be kept?

g) What are the reference levels and what action should be taken if they are exceeded?

h) When should the monitoring procedures be reviewed?

The answers to these questions will be considered for external radiation monitoring and contamination monitoring of both nuclear medicine departments (including unsealed radionuclide therapy) and laboratory departments.

7.5.3 Nuclear medicine departments

a) External radiation monitoring

In the clinical areas of the department the main contributions to external radiation dose will arise from radiopharmaceuticals prior to their administration to patients, e.g. loaded syringes, radionuclide generators, and from the patients themselves once radionuclides have been administered. For example immediately after the administration of 500 MBq of Tc-99m labelled radiopharmaceutical to a patient the dose equivalent rate at one metre from the surface of the patient is of the order of 6.5 μSv h^{-1}. Thus if there is a receptionist situated near to the patient waiting area it may be advisable to measure integrated dose in the area over a representative period using, for example, a film badge.

The radiopharmacy has locations where the radiation dose rate will be relatively high and may change quickly with time, for example when eluting a generator. The environment should therefore be monitored continuously. It may be useful to have an audible alarm when a predetermined dose rate is reached. Dose rates around source and waste stores should also be measured at regular intervals at a frequency commensurate with changes in stored activity.

These measurements within the department should be supervised but not necessarily performed by the departmental RPS. (The RPA may carry out some spot checks at the time of an annual visit). Records must be made and should include the date, time, place and the radiation level found. Usually the RPS should keep the departmental monitoring records. They have to be kept for a minimum of two years from when they were made (IRR Reg 24).

Records kept must demonstrate that the demarcation of controlled and supervised areas remains correct. The reference levels at which action should be taken are therefore ultimately determined by 7.5 μSv h^{-1} and 2.5 μSv h^{-1} for controlled and supervised areas respectively. However, there is an additional requirement to keep radiation levels as low as reasonably practicable so if circumstances arise in which dose rate measurements are unexpectedly high (even if they do not exceed a reference level) they should be investigated and remedial action taken if possible.

The RPA would expect to inspect the records and review monitoring procedures at the time of an annual visit. Monitoring procedures should also be reviewed if there is a substantial change in working practices or revisions in relevant legislation. The employer should be informed, on at least an annual basis, of the results of monitoring which should demonstrate that the dose rates in the working environment are acceptable.

b) Contamination monitoring

Contamination monitoring is necessary on a routine basis and after spills have occurred. It will mainly consist of direct surface monitoring although in some circumstances wipe tests may be used; occasionally air monitoring may be desirable. Experience shows that there is not necessarily a correlation between surface contamination of working areas and the exposure of workers. However if surface contamination remains below some suitably low defined level it usually indicates a high standard of containment of the activity and provides evidence that there is likely to be no significant internal contamination of employees. Routine individual monitoring for internal contamination and air monitoring are generally unnecessary. The only circumstance under which air monitoring may be required is when handling large (greater than 1 GBq) quantities of I-131 (in non-capsule form). The administration of aerosols to patients may be thought to be another situation where air monitoring is advised though measurements at present show activity levels not to be a problem. However in departments where either of these procedures is performed to any great extent it should be established that air contamination levels are not significant. A device suitable for air monitoring is shown in *figure 7.10.*

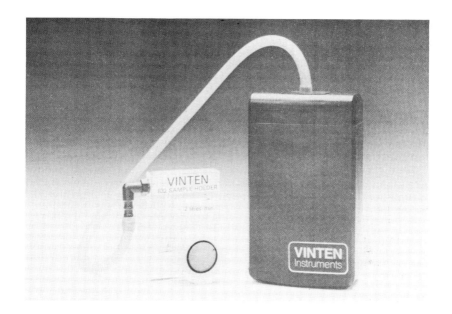

Figure 7.10 Air sampling device (no longer commercially available) (*courtesy* Vinten Instruments Ltd, Weybridge).

Surface contamination levels should be checked regularly by monitoring at least a representative fraction of the surface in question at a frequency determined by the nature of the work being done. In the radionuclide imaging department, surfaces used for handling radionuclides and those designated for paperwork etc, should be monitored regularly. Floors should also be monitored on a routine basis and particularly before being cleaned by general domestic staff. Drains and exhaust systems of fume cupboards etc must be monitored before they are made accessible to maintenance staff. Surface contamination monitoring should be carried out after cleaning up a spill (see Chapter 8). Surface contamination monitors should also be available for staff to monitor their hands and clothes before leaving a radioactive handling area. In areas with a high background countrate (e.g. a radiopharmacy) it may be desirable to install a dedicated hand monitor which incorporates environmental shielding.

A thorough survey should be made of wards or rooms occupied by I-131 therapy patients immediately after the patient has been discharged and before a new patient is admitted to the room. The toilet and wash hand basin must be included in the survey as should surfaces such as door handles. It is also advisable to monitor the patient's belongings before they are discharged to ensure they are taking no highly contaminated articles home with them (see Chapter 2). Surface contamination monitoring is also necessary in ward and clinic areas where radionuclides are administered to patients on an occasional basis. Monitoring should be carried out at the completion of the procedure to ensure the area can revert to its normal usage. Similar monitoring may also be required in operating theatres and occasionally in port mortem rooms.

All contamination measurements should be carried out under the supervision of the RPS but they can be organised so that the person working in a particular area actually makes the measurement. For routine measurements it is sometimes helpful to have a plan indicating, for the benefit of all staff involved, the areas where surface monitoring should be carried out. These areas can be lettered or numbered so that the weekly record can be kept in the form of a chart and undesirable trends identified as soon as they occur (an example of one such record sheet is given in *figure 7.11*. Less regular monitoring should be recorded in a monitoring book. As for external radiation monitoring, it is necessary to record the date, time, place and contamination level and records must be kept for at least two years from the date on which the measurements were made.

There is no level of contamination specified in the Regulations as being satisfactory. However, the Guidance Notes specify 'derived levels' (*table 7.1*)

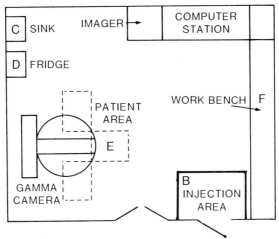

Week beginning:

POSITION		GROSS COUNTS PER SECOND				
		Mon	Tues	Wed	Thurs	Fri
BACKGROUND						
INJECTION AREA	B					
SINK	C					
FRIDGE	D					
FLOOR	E					
BENCH	F					
OTHER						

Figure 7.11 Contamination monitoring report sheet.

which may be used in practice. All the non-fixed contamination should be removed where practicable and designation of a controlled or supervised area must not be used as an alternative to decontamination. Thus, in monitoring for contamination, a surface should be monitored and cleaned sequentially until further cleaning fails to reduce significantly the contamination. As for external radiation monitoring a review of the monitoring programme should be made with the RPA at least annually or more frequently should circumstances or relevant legislation change.

7.5.4 Laboratory departments

a)   External radiation monitoring

It will be highly unlikely that laboratories using only small activities of low energy gamma and beta emitters will contain areas designated as controlled or supervised on the grounds of external radiation dose. However dose rates within a department should be checked annually and this could be done by the RPA, the Radiation Protection Service (if there is one) or suitable agents thus making it unnecessary for the individual laboratory to acquire its own doserate meter. Source and waste stores are the most likely places requiring checking for external radiation dose. Records of the results of monitoring should be sent to and retained by the RPS. A suitable summary report to the effect that conditions are satisfactory should be sent to the employer.

b)   Contamination monitoring

Although radionuclide activities being handled in laboratories are generally small, monitoring is required to show that working procedures are such as to keep radiation levels as low as reasonably practicable. Much of what was contained in Section 7.5.3 (b) on contamination monitoring in nuclear medicine departments is also relevant in laboratories. This applies to the method of monitoring (direct or wipe), acceptable levels and the requirement to keep contamination levels as low as reasonably practicable, the keeping of records and monitoring after spills. The routine monitoring frequency will depend on how work schedules are arranged. Often, in smaller laboratories, areas are used one or two days a week for radiation procedures, the rest of the time reverting to use for non-radioactive procedures. It is therefore important that monitoring is carried out at the end of the session before the area is returned to general use. The same applies to areas used for occasional iodination procedures.

For areas in regular use for work with radionuclides (including particularly those areas around disposal sinks) monitoring should be on a weekly basis. Centrifuges, door handles (especially fridges), and floors should also be monitored.

The results must be recorded. No level of contamination is deemed to be satisfactory and the aim should be to keep contamination levels as low as reasonably practicable (*table 7.1*). As in nuclear medicine departments, it is useful to set an investigation level based on the expected consistency of results during normal working conditions.

Some laboratories use tritium for which it is difficult to carry out environmental monitoring (Section 7.5.1 (b)). Details of various aspects of the use of tritium, including its monitoring, are given by Martin[9] who suggests that only occasional monitoring is necessary when activities up to about 1 GBq tritium are handled routinely. Laboratories in hospitals are generally handling quantities much less than this. Monitoring, when it is required, will normally be by wipe test and liquid scintillation counting.

7.6 Personal Monitoring

7.6.1 Equipment

A dosemeter to be used for monitoring external radiation received by an individual must be capable of permitting the estimation of dose equivalent with reasonable accuracy over the range of radiations, energies, dose equivalents and dose equivalent rates likely to be encountered.

For whole body dose measurements these specifications will be met by film badges or thermoluminescent dosemeters available from an Approved Dosimetry Service. Such a service must be used for classified employees but there are advantages of using such a service for other employees as well. (The RPA will be able to advise on these services). Both types of dosemeter are able to measure down to about 0.1 mSv with an accuracy of the order of ± 15 per cent (dependent on dose and energy).

Where an immediate reading is required, there is a variety of personal dosemeters available. Some of these have an audible warning as well as a visual display and are useful in a potentially high dose rate situation or where a new technique is being tested. Some commercially available devices use energy compensated GM detectors which are capable of measuring dose equivalent rates of between 0 and 100 mSv h^{-1} up to an integrated dose of 1 Sv. The energy range covered (with accuracy of $\pm$ 20 per cent) is 50 keV–3MeV (*figure 7.12a, b*).

The dose to extremities (particularly the fingers) is of major interest when handling unsealed radionuclides. This monitoring could be carried out using an Approved Dosimetry Service or, if employees are not classified, it may be carried out 'in-house'. In this case the dosimetry service must conform to the same standard. Dosemeters which are capable of adequately estimating skin dose (i.e. doses received at a depth of between 5 and 10 mg cm^{-2}) must be used. Thermoluminescent dosemeters which measure dose at about 7 mg cm^{-2} deep are

Figure 7.12a Personal dose meter (*courtesy* Radiation Components Ltd, Twickenham).

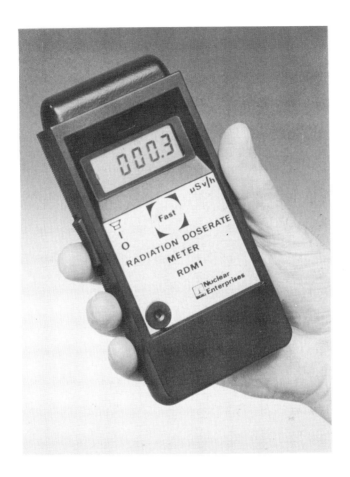

Figure 7.12b Personal dose meter (*courtesy* NE Technology, Reading).

commercially available; these dosemeters are capable of measuring dose down to 0.15 mSv with 15 per cent accuracy (*figure 7.13*). Thicker dosemeters (e.g. LiF 'chips') significantly underestimate doses arising from beta emitters.

Skin contamination may be monitored using one of the monitors described in the environmental monitoring equipment section 7.5.1 (b).

Measurement of internal contamination presents some problems but can be attempted using equipment normally used for clinical purposes e.g. whole body monitors, scintillation (thyroid uptake) detectors, sample counters. In non-clinical departments (see section 7.6.3), thyroid uptake of radioiodine may be simply assessed using an appropriate gamma contamination monitor. In some circumstances it may be necessary to measure air contamination levels in order to estimate the activity that may be inhaled by a person working in such an environment. Air sampling monitors (*figure 7.10*) draw air through a filter at a known rate and the filter may subsequently be counted in a sample counter.

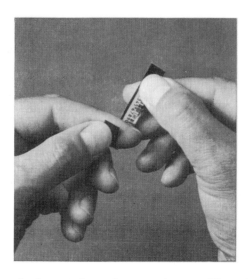

Figure 7.13 Thermoluminescent finger dosemeter (*courtesy* Vinten Instruments Ltd, Weybridge).

7.6.2 Nuclear medicine departments

a)   External radiation monitoring

Classified persons must be individually monitored by an Approved Dosimetry Service (IRR Reg 13). With the possible exception of personnel dispensing radiopharmaceuticals, who may be classified on the grounds of their finger doses, it is unlikely that there will be any classified persons in these departments. However employees regularly entering controlled areas should normally be individually monitored to demonstrate the efficacy of the system of work in force. This monitoring can best be done on a monthly basis by an Approved Dosimetry Service. Controlled areas, either permanent or temporary, are likely to be radiopharmacies, areas where administration of radiopharmaceuticals takes place, wards where radioiodine therapy patients are accommodated, waste stores and possibly waiting rooms. Thus, staff to be routinely monitored are scientific and technical staff, radiopharmacists, clinicians working regularly within the department, nursing staff (both those in the department and those on the therapy ward) and portering staff (if they are regularly assigned to nuclear medicine). Whether domestic staff require monitoring will be a matter for local discussion but in most cases monitoring will be unnecessary. Clerical staff also should not require individual monitoring. In practice decisions on who is to be monitored should always be taken on the advice of the RPA. A suggested monitoring scheme is given in *table 7.4*.

The dose received by the fingers of radiopharmacists (or staff working in that capacity) should be monitored[10]. A thin thermoluminescent dosemeter should be worn around the finger in a position which does not interfere with the procedure being carried out but yet will give a result representative of the dose received (*figure 7.13*). Monitoring will often have to be done on a weekly rather than a

Table 7.4 Personnel to be monitored on grounds of external radiation dose received

Work place	Monitored staff	Whole body monitoring	Extremity monitoring
Radiopharmacy	Radiopharmacist, technicians, scientists, domestics	Regularly for all	Regularly for radiopharmacist and those routinely handling large activities
Clinical areas	Medical staff, nurses, scientists, technicians, porters	Regularly for all	Occasionally for those administering radionuclides
Waste stores	Scientific, technical	Regularly for both	—
Therapy wards	Nursing staff	Regularly	—
Laboratories	Scientific and technical staff	Regularly for those carrying out labelling procedures	Occasionally for those carrying out labelling procedures or using high activities P-32

monthly basis because of the lack of durability of the dosemeters (this is a particular problem when they are worn under frequently changed gloves). If monitoring shows doses to be consistently low (less than 1 mSv per week on average) then monitoring may be carried out on an occasional basis — say for one month each year. If doses are higher than expected, working methods must be investigated and where possible modified. Further monitoring must be carried out to show that modifications have had the desired effect. If improvements cannot be made in working procedures and measured doses exceed one tenth of the dose limit, monitoring must be carried out on a regular basis (Guidance Notes 1.20(4)).

Finger monitoring should also be carried out occasionally on staff who regularly prepare and administer radioactive substances to patients, (particularly those involved in injection of radiopharmaceuticals, therapy administrations and the priming of aerosol systems).

Monitoring should be carried out when new procedures are introduced, or new staff (or trainees) appointed. The workload should be kept under continuous review since significant increases may necessitate the introduction of routine monitoring where it had previously been only occasionally necessary.

b)   Skin monitoring

After handling unsealed radionuclides the hands must be monitored whether contamination is suspected or not. It may be convenient to mount a suitable contamination monitor above the sink where hands are washed. Care must be taken to ensure that the monitor itself does not become contaminated. In high background areas it will be necessary to shield the detector, and it may be convenient to have a foot or elbow operated switch to activate the monitor. The measurement may be averaged over an area not exceeding 300 cm^2 (ACOP 1/32) although it is still necessary to clean all areas of contamination.

c) Monitoring for internal contamination

Monitoring for intake of radionuclides is the subject of ICRP Report 54[10]. In practice, monitoring for internal contamination in radionuclide imaging departments is rarely necessary on radiation protection grounds but it may be useful in providing staff reassurance. However staff who come close to therapeutic doses of radioiodine, e.g. radiopharmacists, scientific and technical staff, nurses in radiotherapy wards, require this form of monitoring on a regular basis. A suggested monitoring scheme is given in *table 7.5*.

Table 7.5   Personnel to be monitored for contamination

Work place	Whole body monitoring	Thyroid	Hands
Radiopharmacy	Regularly	2 weekly if I-131 regularly in use 2 monthly if I-125 regularly in use 24 h after incident of irregular use of above	On leaving controlled area after working with unsealed sources
Clinical areas (not therapy)	Occasionally	Occasionally	On leaving controlled area after handling unsealed sources
Therapy wards	Regularly	2 weekly if I-131 regularly used 24 h after incident or irregular use	On leaving controlled area after handling patient or patients belongings
Laboratories	Occasionally (regularly for high activity users)	2 monthly for regular users of I-125 in excess of 1 MBq	After handling unsealed sources

The two methods available for monitoring internal contamination are the assessment of radionuclides in the body by external measurements and the analysis of excreta or samples of body fluids. The former method is appropriate for gamma or X-ray emitters or bremsstrahlung radiation from high energy beta emitters (provided there are no interfering gamma or X-ray emissions). Such monitoring may be carried out using a whole body monitor or, specifically for the thyroid, appropriate thyroid uptake equipment. A sensitive scintillation detector normally used for surface contamination measurements can also be used to detect activities of the order of 1 kBq in the thyroid. Sample analysis is appropriate for beta emitters. Either of these methods (external measurement or sample analysis) enables an estimate of activity in the subject at the time of measurement to be made.

Internal contamination of any significance is most likely to arise from ingestion of radioactive iodine which localises in the thyroid. In the normal (euthyroid) individual the effective half-life of I-131 in the body is about 7 days. It is important that if large quantities are used infrequently monitoring is carried out at a suitable time (but usually not sooner than 1 to 2 days after the possible intake). If a significant accidental intake of iodine is suspected, monitoring should take place as soon as possible. If I-131 is used regularly then monitoring should be carried out at intervals of a maximum of 14 days; any uptake can then be assumed (without undue error) to have taken place in the middle of the monitoring interval. The longer half life of I-125 means that the monitoring interval can be extended to 120 days although it will generally be more advisable, organisationally, to monitor more frequently, say every 60 days.

When considering internal contamination it is helpful to use the quantity annual limit on intake (ALI)[12]. The ALI of a particular radionuclide is that activity which, if taken into the body, will give rise to an annual committed dose equivalent limit. Thus if intake each year is restricted to less than the ALI the maximum annual committed dose equivalent from that source will always be less than the dose limit. For both I-131 and I-125 the ALI for ingestion is 1 MBq and for inhalation is 2 MBq. It is generally assumed, in the absence of evidence to the contrary (e.g. thyroid abnormality), that about 30% of any iodine activity ingested is taken up into the thyroid. It therefore follows that if 300 kBq is assessed as having been in the thyroid, 1 MBq (i.e. an ALI) was ingested. For monitoring related to a known time of intake or suspected intake, the ICRP[11] recommend a recording level of one thirtieth of the ALI and an investigation level of one tenth of the ALI. For routine monitoring the recording level is one tenth of the ALI pro rata and the investigation level three tenths of the ALI pro rata (i.e. $1/10 \times$ ALI $\times$ t/365 and $3/10 \times$ ALI $\times$ t/365 respectively, where t is the monitoring interval in days).

The chief problem in monitoring for internal contamination is in interpretation of the measured activity in terms of dose equivalent. It is necessary to establish a metabolic model to relate the measured quantity to the dose limit. The model must take into account the chemical form in which the radionuclide was taken into the body and the route of intake. Furthermore the final calculation must allow for any delay between the time of measurement and the time of intake which may be unknown and will have to be assumed. For these reasons care must be exercised when applying the annual limits on intake

Table 7.6   Dose equivalents from iodine radionuclides deposited within the thyroid

Nuclide	Committed dose equivalent mSv Bq^{-1}
I-123	1.5×10^{-5}
I-125	1.1×10^{-3}
I-131	1.6×10^{-3}

from Prime (1985)[13].

published in ICRP 30[12]. Iodine activity in the thyroid may be converted to a committed dose equivalent using the data given in *table 7.6*. A helpful summary of the dosimetry of radionuclides of iodine is given by Prime[13]. It is recommended in ICRP 54[11] and it is generally accepted that if the activity is assessed at less than the derived recording level no dose calculation is required. Derived levels are specified for several radionuclides, in particular those of iodine. (Derived levels have been calculated making certain assumptions about intake, deposition, metabolism and retention.) Using a suitable scintillation detector it is possible to detect down to a kilobecquerel of I-131.

7.6.3   Laboratory departments

a)   External radiation

Many laboratory departments use only commercially available kits to carry out radioimmunoassay and other low activity procedures. Activities and consequent dose rates are sufficiently low not to require the designation of controlled areas (except possibly for stores on the grounds of activity contained therein). As long as environmental monitoring (7.5.4) is carried out regularly and results are satisfactory whole body monitoring for external radiation using a film badge or thermoluminescent dosemeter is unnecessary. However staff may require the reassurance provided by such monitoring. Occasionally a film badge will detect splashes of contamination indicating a poor laboratory technique.

In departments where larger quantities of radionuclides are handled, for example in the process of 'in house' manufacture of kits and protein labelling, routine external monitoring, including periodic finger monitoring, should be carried out. The monitoring requirements in this case are the same as for employees in nuclear medicine departments (7.6.2(a)).

b)   Skin contamination

The hands must be monitored after working with unsealed radionuclides. The laboratory monitor used for surface contamination measurements will be suitable. Frequently this will be the only form of personal monitoring regularly taking place in a laboratory and the fact that it has taken place, with a successful outcome, should be recorded.

c)   Internal contamination

Details of some of the problems encountered in monitoring for internal contamination have been given (section 7.6.2(c)). Fortunately, for laboratories where only kilobecquerel activities of radionuclides are handled, monitoring for internal contamination is unnecessary. However, for staff reassurance, some measurements may be advisable.

Many laboratories will be using I-125 and the procedures outlined for nuclear medicine departments may be used (7.6.2(c)). However a thin window scintillation detector, which should be available in all laboratories using I-125, held up against the front of the neck should be able to detect activities down to one kilobecquerel in the thyroid. This should provide the necessary reassurance for staff and any unduly high results can then be referred to specialist facilities for more accurate assessment.

Some laboratories use tritium labelled compounds and the annual limit on intake for tritium is 3 GBq for tritiated water. This is based on the assumptions that the intake is immediately evenly distributed among the soft tissues and that tritium is excreted exponentially with an effective half-life of ten days[9]. However for some tritium labelled compounds these assumptions are not true; in particular tritiated thymidine is incorporated selectively into the nuclear DNA of dividing cells. Therefore the annual limit on intake for tritium in this form is as much as a factor of fifty less than that for tritiated water. C-14 is also used in some laboratories and for labelled organic compounds the annual limit on intake is 90 MBq. It is inconceivable that staff, through working with these materials (tritium or C-14) in hospital laboratories, will become internally contaminated to anywhere near the ALI (or even 10 per cent of it). Thus monitoring for internal contamination is, in general, unnecessary.

7.6.4 Combining internal and external doses

Guidance on how to combine doses arising from external radiation and internal contamination is given in ICRP 35[1]. For classified persons this will be the province of the record keeping Approved Dosimetry Service. In the case of non-classified persons who are monitored it will normally be sufficient to assess the internal and external exposures separately.

7.7 Conclusions

It is important that departments in which radionuclides are used set up a comprehensive monitoring programme for both personal radiation doses and environmental measurements. Staff carrying out the monitoring should be aware of why it is being done and should know the procedures involved, and the records to be kept. They should know the action required in the case of unexpectedly high results. The departmental RPS should retain overall supervision for the monitoring procedures. The RPA should give advice in setting up the programme and from time to time carry out a review of the procedures and the results. The employer must be adequately informed of the results in order that he may fulfil his legal obligations.

References

1 International Commission on Radiological Protection 1982 *General Principles of Monitoring for the Radiation Protection of Workers* Publication **35** (Pergamon Press, Oxford)
2 *The Ionising Radiations Regulations 1985* (SI 1985 No 1333) (HMSO, London)
3 Approved Code of Practice 1985 *The Protection of Persons against Ionising Radiation Arising from Any Work Activity* 1985 (HMSO, London)
4 *Guidance Notes for the protection of persons against ionising radiations arising from medical and dental use* 1988 (HMSO, London)
5 *The examination and testing of portable radiation instruments for external radiations* 1990 Health and Safety Series booklet HS(G)49 (HMSO, London)
6 International Commission on Radiological Protection 1977 *Recommendations of the International Commission on Radiological Protection* Publication **26** (Pergamon Press, Oxford)
7 Cardarelli G, Campbell C and Evdokimoff V 1986 The superiority of a NaI survey meter over a GM counter in detecting ^{32}P contamination *Health Physics* **50** 138–9

8   Clayton R F 1970 *Monitoring of Radioactive Contamination on Surfaces* Technical Report Series No **120** (International Atomic Energy Agency, Vienna)

9   Martin E B M 1982 *Health Physics Aspects of Tritium* Occupational Hygiene Monograph No **6** (Science Reviews Ltd, Leeds)

10 Williams E D, Laird E E and Forster E 1987 Monitoring radiation dose to the hands in nuclear medicine: location of dosemeters. *Nucl Med Commun* **8** 499–503

11 International Commission on Radiological Protection 1988 *Individual Monitoring for Intakes of Radionuclides by Workers: Design and Interpretation* Publication **54** (Pergamon Press, Oxford)

12 International Commission on Radiological Protection Part 1 1979 Part 2 1980, Part 3 1981 *Limits for Intakes of Radionuclides by Workers* Publication **30** (Pergamon Press, Oxford)

13 Prime D 1985 *Health Physics Aspects of the Use of Iodine* Occupational Hygiene Monograph No **13** (Science Reviews Ltd, Leeds)

CHAPTER 8

Incidents

C B Clayton

8.1 Introduction

Even efficient establishments should anticipate that incidents will occur occasionally when unsealed sources of radioactivity are used and therefore the purposes of a radiation safety programme are: (i) to reduce the likelihood of incidents; (ii) to minimise the detrimental consequences of incidents when they occur, and (iii) to ensure that any experience gained as a result of an incident is used to further reduce the likelihood or consequences of subsequent incidents.

8.2 A Cautionary Tale

It may be helpful, in considering the hazards that may arise, to relate an account of an actual incident which involved employees using high specific activity I-125. An employee, who regularly labelled proteins with I-125, became pregnant. She did not wish to inform her supervisor of her condition but was concerned about her work with radioiodine. She discussed the matter, in confidence, with a colleague who agreed to carry out the protein labelling. On the first occasion that their informal arrangement was put into effect, the pregnant member of staff supervised the procedure.

During the protein labelling procedure, the initial reaction is performed in a cold room using extremely small volumes of reagent in order to avoid denaturing the protein; typically, a few microlitres of sodium iodide solution containing several tens of megabecquerels of I-125. The reaction is stopped and the mixture is passed through a gel filtration column to obtain a purified specimen of the labelled protein.

An incident occurred at the purification stage. The reaction mixture was being driven down the gel filtration column by means of a peristaltic pump. The delivery tube became blocked, probably as a result of kinking. The operator tried to restore the flow but in doing so the tube became disconnected from the top of the column and its contents were projected towards the observer. Although a perspex splash barrier was in use to protect the operator, it provided no protection for the pregnant observer who was peering intently at the defective apparatus and was splashed in the face.

The two employees immediately left the cold room and went into the staff changing room where they began washing in the hand washbasin. At this stage the department's radiation protection supervisor (RPS) was called and monitoring indicated persistent skin contamination. The group moved to a nurses' changing room, reached by walking the length of a ward block corridor and through the nurses' home. The contaminated employee showered and shampooed her hair.

At this stage the radiation protection adviser (RPA) became involved. He went first to the nurses' changing room where no surface contamination was detected. However, about 1.5 kBq of residual activity was found equally on the

129

observer's head above the hairline, in the region of the inner canthus of one eye and near the corner of the mouth. Her eyes had been protected by spectacles which were retained for decontamination. The only residual activity found on the operator was about 4 kBq on her left thumb.

The pregnant woman was given an iodine mouthwash. A five-day course of potassium iodide (60 mg per day) was prescribed, on medical advice, to block thyroid uptake of radioiodine. Four hours after ingestion, activity in the neck was measured to be 12 kBq. Two days later thyroidal activity was 2.2 kBq. The operator had no significant thyroidal uptake.

The laboratory coats being worn by the two women were both found to be contaminated with about 400 kBq of I-125. These coats were effectively laundered with a procedure designed for the cleaning of biologically contaminated linen. In this procedure articles are sealed into alginate-stitched plastic bags by the decontamination team and the bags are transferred, still sealed, into an automatic washer. The alginate stitching readily dissolves in hot water and the contents of the plastic bag are released for washing in a strong detergent solution.

Entry to the cold room and the female staff wash/changing room had been restricted by the RPA as soon as he was apprised of the circumstances of the incident. Subsequently, checks in the wash/changing area revealed slight contamination of taps; these were cleaned and the room was re-opened for normal use. Contamination monitoring in the cold room was complicated by the presence of radioactive materials which had not been involved in the spill. These items were removed and the contamination of surfaces assessed. The congestion in the room, and the presence of radioactive debris, made an accurate assessment of surface contamination impossible. However, it was unlikely that radioactivity on the bench exceeded 2 MBq. Several spots of activity were found on the floor, each of about 10 kBq. The room was padlocked pending decontamination and final inspection by the RPA.

Estimates based upon published data[1] indicated that the observer's thyroid dose was unlikely to have exceeded 7.5 mSv. At the time of the incident she was in the eighth week of her pregnancy. Since foetal thyroid does not begin to produce thyroid hormone until about 20 weeks gestation and is not structurally complete until about 16 weeks, there would have been little likelihood of specific organ uptake and the radiation dose to the foetus would have arisen solely from circulating I-125. This dose would be similar to the maternal whole body dose and would be unlikely to have exceeded 1 mSv.

This account illustrates many of the factors which can exacerbate an incident. Firstly, it is important that an individual working with ionising radiation should inform a responsible person, such as her project supervisor or her RPS, when she becomes pregnant so that any necessary revision of duties can be arranged formally. In the incident described, no-one with supervisory responsibilities was aware of the informal arrangement that had been made and therefore had no opportunity of reviewing the detailed implementation.

Secondly the maternal and, particularly, foetal irradiation was potentially much more serious than transpired. Although 40 MBq of radioactivity was being used in the protein labelling procedure, fortunately no more than a tenth of this was dispersed in the spill. Furthermore, foetal development had not reached the stage of thyrogenesis and so there was unlikely to be a target organ for I-125 within the foetus.

Several operational factors contributed to the nature of the incident and the resulting distribution of contamination:

(i)   The pump and its associated connectors were mounted at eye level.
(ii) The competence of the flow path had not been checked immediately before use.
(iii) The operator was not wearing protective gloves.
(iv) There was no disposable cover or drip tray on the bench.
(v)   An observer was present.
(vi) There was no splash barrier between the observer and the apparatus.
(vii) Congestion of the work space resulted in several incidental items becoming contaminated.

Had a proper hazard assessment been undertaken before work with radioactive material commenced, procedures could have been laid down so that the majority of these factors could have been eliminated.

The movements of staff should have been much more restricted. The two employees could have moved from the cold room to the operator's laboratory immediately opposite, where a sink was available for washing and to where assistance could have been summoned. Fortunately, there was very little contamination of the departmental wash/change facilities, the nurses' changing rooms or the intervening circulation areas. However, this fortunate outcome could not have been predicted. A decontamination kit, kept in the area where radioactive materials were used, would have been very useful.

The use of an overhead shower is generally not appropriate in instances of radioactive contamination of the face. The objective is not to achieve rapid dilution, as would be the case if chemical contamination was involved, but to remove the contaminating substance without spreading it to other parts of the body, especially facial orifices. Therefore, local irrigation and cleansing are the most suitable procedures.

In this episode some potentially serious mistakes were made, although the worst of the possible consequences did not materialise and subsequently there appeared to be no foetal injury. The remainder of this chapter seeks to give guidance on how an incident of this type may be prevented or, if it does occur, its effect minimised.

8.3 Hazard Assessment

Employers must not allow work with radioactive materials to be carried out on their premises unless, in accordance with the Ionising Radiations Regulations 1985 (IRR)[2] they have identified the possible radiation hazards and the appropriate level of response (IRR Reg 25). Staff who work with radionuclides must be informed so that they develop an appreciation of the potential hazards. The possibility that accidental dispersal of radioactivity may lead, by contamination, to unacceptable doses of ionising radiation should be appreciated. However, for the purpose of improving radiation safety, incidents with potential detriment which may not materialise should also be taken into account. Furthermore, it should not be assumed that significant incidents will always involve the dispersal of radioactivity.

Much of the guidance in previous chapters has been concerned with the prevention of the dispersal of radioactive materials through the routine use of technical and administrative procedures. Good practice, based on that advice, should have the effect of reducing the risk of accidents. In the main, this chapter is concerned with providing guidance on how to respond when routine safety measures have been frustrated or overwhelmed by events. However, it is pertinent to define, firstly, what is meant by an incident.

An incident is taken to be a discrete occurrence which could give rise to any of the following:

(i) The receipt, by a patient, of a dose of radiation significantly greater than intended.
(ii) The contamination or unintended irradiation of any person.
(iii) An actual or potential dose of radiation, as a result of external exposure, skin contamination or intake of radioactivity, to an occupationally exposed individual, in excess of any relevant dose limit, or of the established normal dose for the task.
(iv) The unaccountable disappearance of a source, or of activity from a source.

Few occurrences falling within these definitions will need to be treated as major emergencies although prompt action, which must be specified in the local rules, is required. Furthermore, notifiable occurrences, as defined in IRR Reg 31[2] and relating to the accidental release of radioactivity, will be extremely rare in hospitals. The most common radionuclides used as unsealed sources in UK hospitals are Mo-99/Tc-99m, I-125 and I-131. For these radionuclides, the Health and Safety Executive must be notified if loss or dispersal occur involving activities greater than those given in *table 8.1*. The values quoted in column 2 of the table, for which notification of loss to the Executive would be required (IRR Reg 31[2]), serve to emphasise the need for vigilance in the custody of radioactive sources. Column 3 indicates that occurrences notifiable to the Executive (IRR Reg 31[2]) may typically involve the accidential dispersal of an entire consignment of I-131 intended for several treatments of thyroid carcinoma (i.e. 4 to 6 GBq per treatment) or the contents of a large capacity of Tc-99m generator. For an exhaustive tabulation of radionuclides refer to IRR Schedule 2.

Table 8.1 The activity levels at which the Health and Safety Executive must be notified.

1. Radionuclide	2. Quantity for notification of loss (MBq)	3. Quantity for notification of dispersal (GBq)
Mo-99	0.5	20
Tc-99m	5.0	20000
I-125	0.05	20
I-131	0.05	20

Below such levels, incidents may occur which range from the minor to the very serious. A minor occurrence is one which requires only simple remedial action and consequent radiation doses should not exceed a few per cent of any relevant dose limit. If the incident involves the accidental dispersal of radioactivity, contamination can be efficiently reduced below contamination limits by extension of routine procedures. Derived limits for surface contamination from the Guidance Notes[3] are given in Appendix VI. If contamination persists, the RPA should be consulted.

Incidents other than minor occurrences must be the subject of a report to the RPA. Those which are likely to result in the release of activities in excess of 10 times an Annual Limit on Intake (Appendix III) or to give rise to external dose rates greater than 240 μSv h^{-1}, persisting for several hours, should be dealt with in accordance with a written emergency action plan. It may be necessary to designate an area affected by an incident as a temporary controlled area, until acceptable conditions have been restored. Designating a controlled area requires clear demarcation of boundaries and restriction of access which therefore reduces the possibility of spread of contamination.

Data useful in assessing the hazard potential of procedures and incidents are given in Appendix III. The list of radionuclides selected includes those which are routinely used.

Wherever work with radioactive materials is being performed, an assessment should be made to determine the designation of the work area. Many area designations will be made with reference to external dose rates. Except in enclosed work stations, such as fume cupboards or glove boxes, the assumption will be that very low levels of air and surface contamination are present under normal circumstances. However, in the event of an accidental release of radioactivity, contamination may increase and designation of a controlled area become necessary. The total activity dispersed when an incident occurs may be uncertain. If an accident occurs involving fire, or damage to equipment, then dispersal of additional radioactive materials may occur.

Having made a hazard assessment the employer in conjunction with his RPA must ensure instructions are included in the local rules so that the occurrence of such accidents is minimised. However, in the event of an accident these instructions should limit the consequences of the incident and provide staff with adequate information to restrict their exposure.

8.4 Planning for Contingencies

Specific contingency plans have to be prepared for dealing with any reasonably foreseeable incident in which persons are likely to receive a radiation dose in excess of any relevant dose limit or in which an area not already a controlled area (IRR reg 27) requires designation. The Guidance Notes suggest that a list should be maintained of the places where significant amounts of radioactive materials are held; notices should be posted where accidents may occur, indicating how to contact the RPS, RPA, medical or fire services in an emergency and where to find emergency equipment; the local Chief Fire Officer should be supplied with information about the layout of the premises, warning notices, signs and the type and location of radioactive sources.

In most cases the hospital use of unsealed sources will not require the writing of a specific contingency plan. However local rules should be written in such a way that they provide adequate practical guidance for users in all safety aspects of the handling of unsealed sources of radioactivity, both of a routine and of an incidental nature. Sections should be included on minor spills and on action during an emergency.

The following two sections are presented in the form of rules which could be included in Local Rules and issued to every user of unsealed sources.

8.4.1 Minor spills

Most incidents involving spills of unsealed sources of radioactivity in the hospital environment require only simple remedial action by local staff for the control of the spread of contamination. Decontamination of personnel will usually take precedence.

133

(i) If a spill occurs on a tray, wear disposable gloves and remove any objects from the tray, decontaminating them to acceptable levels before depositing them elsewhere. If decontamination is not effective, items should be placed in plastic bags and stored in a suitable secure shielded area. No attempt need be made to decontaminate disposable items which can be transferred to a plastic bag for later disposal by the appropriate route. Rinse the tray carefully over a designated sink unless the spill is estimated to exceed 5 MBq, when the advice of the RPS must be sought. Include an estimate of the radioactivity disposed of through decontamination procedures in the waste disposal records. Use a contamination monitor or wipe test to assess progress during decontamination. A final check for residual contamination should be made using a monitor or by performing a wipe-test: the result must be recorded.

(ii) If a spill occurs on a bench or floor:

   a) Drop paper tissues/towels onto the site of the spill to limit spread of contamination.

   b) Wear disposable gloves (and overshoes if appropriate). Note that it may be necessary to change disposable gloves etc if they become contaminated during lengthy decontamination procedures.

   c) Mop up the spilled material, working from the periphery inwards, and wash the affected surface, placing contaminated articles in plastic bags for later disposal or cleaning.

   d) Monitor the surface. If unacceptable level of contamination persists, further cleaning and monitoring will be required.

   e) Report the incident to the RPS.

8.4.2   Action during major emergency

The response to an incident can be divided into two phases. During the first phase the people involved will assess the situation, trying to ensure that the effects of the incident are restricted as much as possible; the Local Rules concentrate on this aspect. The second phase will generally be much more prolonged and may involve more 'expert' assistance. During this phase attempts should be made to restore normal conditions.

In some circumstances, involving fire or injury, the most urgent need will be to raise the fire alarm or to summon medical assistance; otherwise the priorities will be as follows:

(i) Avoid spread of contamination and isolate area, as appropriate.

(ii) Warn persons in the immediate vicinity of the accident.

(iii) Render first aid, or such other urgent assistance as is necessary, to involved persons.

(iv) Notify the RPS who may decide to issue further warnings and summon additional assistance if required.

(v) Deal with the emergency or evacuate the area as circumstances dictate. Until an appropriate course of action has been worked out by the RPS and/ or RPA, only the minimum immediate action should be taken. Except where the person in charge decides that it is necessary to evacuate the area immediately, attempts should be made, in the case of radioactive solids or liquids, to limit their dispersal or, in the case of radioactive gases or vapours to disperse them as quickly as possible.

(vi) Protective and outer clothing which is contaminated with radioactive material should be removed and left in the affected area. When removing clothing, take care not to transfer radioactivity to the skin.

(vii) All functioning apparatus should be made safe; ventilation and other services, except lighting, should be switched off and all doors and windows closed to reduce the spread of contamination by draughts and to restrict access. However, where the radioactivity is in the form of a gas or vapour, and there is no risk of explosion, the mechanical ventilation should be left on (as long as there is no possibility of the extracted air being recycled) and, according to discretion, doors and windows should be opened.

(viii) Contaminated persons should not move far from the site of the incident until they have been monitored and, if necessary, decontaminated. However, the treatment of serious injuries must take precedence over decontamination and containment of contamination.

(ix) Persons entering the affected area to carry out emergency procedures should wear protective clothing.

(x) Entry to the affected areas (including areas used for treatment of contaminated casualties) must be restricted until all the appropriate actions have been taken to clear the contamination from the area and environmental surveys have satisfied the RPA that it may be reoccupied.

(xi) In the event of fire, radiation hazards are likely to be negligible compared with the risk of an uncontrolled conflagration and the prime requirement is to follow the standard fire alarm procedure. Staff should not exaggerate the radiation hazards and thereby cause fire-fighting operations to be inhibited.

The foregoing rules, reinforced by suitable training, should ensure that users of radioactive materials respond in an adequate way when incidents occur. They are not expected to be able to cope with all aspects of an unusual occurrence, nor to restore normal conditions after a substantial incident without trained assistance. In an emergency their immediate concern, from a radiation protection point of view, must be containment.

8.5 Decontamination

An important part of the plan for dealing with radiation incidents is instruction on the decontamination procedures that should be used on people and on surfaces.

In any area where radioactive materials are used, it is advisable to have a decontamination kit containing simple cleaning materials, protective clothing and an instruction sheet to deal with incidents. Possible contents of the kit are given in *table 8.2* and the level of sophistication of the kit will depend on the nature and activities of the radionuclides in use. For example in a pathology laboratory carrying out radioimmunoassays, detergent (e.g. Decon), absorbent towels, plastic bags and plastic gloves will be sufficient.

The body may become contaminated with radioactivity as a result of deposition on skin, inhalation or ingestion. Absorption may then take place through the skin (including open wounds), alveolar membranes in the lung, or through the mucosal surfaces of the gastrointestinal tract, leading in each case to transfer of radio-

Table 8.2 Contents of decontamination kit

Plastic overshoes and gloves, plastic aprons.
Paper tissues for absorbing spills.
Polythene bags.
Labels (luggage type for waste bags) and radiation warning tape.
Soap.
Detergent (e.g. Decon).
Soft nail brush.
Barriers or means of demarcating and roping off affected area.
Remote handling tools.
Warning notices.

activity into the bloodstream and, possibly, its concentration within body organs. The transfer of radioactivity into the bloodstream, following inhalation of soluble contaminants, is particularly rapid.

Radioactive contamination of body surfaces, including those of the respiratory and gastrointestinal tracts, may be susceptible to removal by decontamination processes. The degree of urgency for removal will depend on the amount of the contamination, the radiotoxicity of the material and the likelihood of its being incorporated. Whereas the skin provides a barrier against the penetration of substances, the respiratory and alimentary systems provide the major routes of intake. Therefore, an important step in the process of ingestion is the transfer of radioactive contamination from the skin to the mouth or nose and measures should always be taken to limit such transfers. It may also be necessary to take measures to inhibit the uptake of ingested radioactivity by particular body organs and to hasten the processes of elimination (See 8.5.8).

Measures to reduce the amount of radioactivity on or within the body must be accompanied by monitoring. The purpose of preliminary monitoring is: (i) to establish the level and distribution of contamination; (ii) if necessary, to identify the type of contamination; and (iii) to estimate the degree of incorporation.

On the basis of these early data, a strategy for minimising the consequences of bodily contamination can be devised. During decontamination and decorporation procedures monitoring is useful to gauge progress. Subsequent analysis of the monitoring results is crucial in the estimation of the radiation dose received by the contaminated individual. Techniques of monitoring for contamination have been discussed in Chapter 7.

8.5.1 Removal of contamination from the skin

Penetration of substances through the skin increases markedly if the horny layer is damaged or removed. Such damage must be avoided during decontamination procedures. Contaminated parts of the body should be washed or scrubbed gently using warm water, soap and a soft nail-brush. After rinsing and drying with paper towels, the washed areas should be monitored for residual contamination. If necessary, the areas may be washed again. However, there is a danger that vigorous scrubbing or excessive washing will break the skin, thus allowing contamination to enter the bloodstream. The spreading of contamination to other areas particularly internal organs must be avoided. Where possible, damaged but uncontaminated skin should be covered with a waterproof dressing before washing commences.

As indicated in Section 8.2 it is inappropriate to stand the contaminated subject under a shower because of the possibility of spreading the contamination. However, if the skin has been contaminated by a strongly acidic or alkaline radioactive chemical, the affected areas should be irrigated immediately with a strong flow of water without regard to the spread of contamination.

8.5.2 Persistent skin contamination

If gentle scrubbing does not reduce contamination to an acceptable level then the following chemical method may be attempted. The affected area should be painted with a 4% (saturated) solution of potassium permanganate and allowed to dry. This procedure should be repeated. When dry, the dark brown stain should be removed with a 5% solution of sodium metabisulphite and the area rinsed, dried and monitored for residual contamination. If necessary repeat the entire process. This method should not be applied to hair on the head or face. All skin decontamination procedures should be discontinued if the skin shows signs of developing damage such as smarting, reddening or swelling, and medical advice should be sought.

8.5.3 Hair contamination

To remove contamination from the hair a shampoo should be used taking care not to spread radioactivity to other parts of the body. It is important to monitor for residual contamination and the procedure can be repeated perhaps twice. If an unacceptable level of contamination persists it may be necessary to trim off the affected hair, collecting the clippings for assay and subsequent safe disposal.

8.5.4 Finger nails and nail margins

It may be beneficial to cut the nails carefully. Radioactive material which has lodged under or beside the nails may be removed by the use of calamine lotion. The lotion should be applied generously, allowing it to become thoroughly dry, before brushing or rinsing away. Absorption onto the surface of the colloidal particles can result in the removal of the offending material. However, care should be taken not to disperse the powder into the atmosphere; it may be advisable to brush the nails with the hands inside a plastic bag.

8.5.5 Eyes, mouth and ears

The eyes should be irrigated with sterile normal (0.9 per cent w/v) saline if available; otherwise tap water can be used. Great care should be taken to ensure that radioactivity is not spread to other parts of the face, especially the nose and mouth.

In the event of intra-oral contamination the subject should be warned not to swallow; any dentures should be removed and copious mouth washes administered. Swabs can be used to monitor progress. The teeth can be brushed gently with a soft toothbrush, sweeping away from the gums with each stroke. Dentures should be scrubbed with a soft brush until free of contamination.

Ears can be syringed with water at body temperature but this should only be carried out by appropriately trained hospital staff.

8.5.6   Nasal contamination

The subject should be asked to blow his or her nose into a paper tissue and to expectorate into a disposable cup. The products should be monitored and if, after repeated nose blowing, the level of contamination remains high or is still suspected then nasal swabbing and irrigation will be necessary. This procedure should be done under medical supervision.

At the beginning and end of the procedure and whenever inhalation of radioactivity (other than a gas) is suspected, nasal smears should be obtained. This should commence by removing or covering any extensive contamination in the vicinity of the nostrils and the smears taken on strips of filter paper coiled around swab sticks. The subject should take the smears using first a dry smear strip and then a wet one inside each nostril. The paper strips should then be unrolled and placed smear side uppermost on a clean surface and monitored for contamination. The strip may also be assayed by well or liquid scintillation counting. Cotton wool 'buds' will serve equally well if the inhalation of gamma emitters, only, is suspected.

8.5.7   Minor wounds

Any contaminated wound, however trivial, should be thoroughly irrigated with water or normal saline solution, care being taken to limit the spread of contamination to other parts of the body. Any wiping should be away from the edges of the wound.

8.5.8   Internal radioactivity

Where it is known or suspected that an intake of radioactivity probably exceeding 10 per cent of an ALI has been taken into the body, immediate action should be taken to limit its concentration in body organs and to increase its rate of removal[4]. Incorporation is most likely to occur by translocation from the respiratory or digestive tracts. Therefore, relevant measures of general application include mouth wash, nasal irrigation and expectoration.

Simple remedial action is available in only a few instances once incorporation has occurred. Prompt administration of potassium iodate will block the thyroidal uptake of radioiodine; a 170 mg dose should be given with water.

Antacids will inhibit the absorption of some contaminants; in particular, the absorption of radiostrontium can be substantially reduced by administration of aluminium combined with alginates, in the form of Gaviscon granules, at a dose of 1 sachet (3g to 4g) every six hours for two days. Since the preparation contains glucose the advice of a medical practitioner should be sought if the subject is diabetic. The use of activated charcoal can also reduce uptake in the GI tract and is available as Medicoal (a suspension of 5 g in 100 ml of water should be given as soon as possible and the dose repeated after an interval of 20 minutes).

Where an intake of radioactivity in excess of 10 times the ALI is likely, specialised advice must be sought from one of the hospitals listed in the NAIR handbook as being prepared to give advice on the treatment and admission of casualties exposed to large doses of radiation.

Tritium, in aqueous and many organic forms, is quickly absorbed from the lungs and GI tract and, as water, is one of the few substances which is readily absorbed through the intact skin. Once incorporated, it is rapidly distributed throughout the body and is then excreted in urine with a biological half life of about 12 days. The rate of excretion can be substantially increased by maintaining a high fluid intake (4 litres per day) for several days. Chelating agents, especially CaDTPA, have been found effective in the removal of some radionuclides present in the body in chelatable form, but the administration of such medication requires careful clinical control. The uptake of caesium and thallium from the gut can be reduced significantly by the use of potassium ferric cyanoferrate (Prussian blue) but preliminary use of an emetic is recommended and the medication must be administered by duodenal tube. The efficacy of all attempts to reduce internal radioactivity must be monitored by *in vivo* measurement and specimen assay as appropriate.

8.6 Clinical Incidents

There is an ever-present risk that a radiopharmaceutical preparation will be administered to the wrong person. Patients, or visitors to hospital, cannot be relied upon to question what is happening to them and an extreme example is the case of a woman who was prescribed a drink of radioiodine after her name and address had been confirmed. It subsequently transpired that the drink should have been given to the woman's mother who happened to have exactly the same name and lived at the same address; the error would not have occurred if a check had been made of the patient's age.

The delivery of radiation dose for medical purposes is acceptable if there is a net benefit for the irradiated individual. However, circumstances should be identified which would render a radionuclide investigation abortive or lead to an unacceptable radiation dose. For example, iodine containing radiographic contrast media will interfere with the thyroidal uptake of radioiodine and pertechnetate, and blood transfusions may invalidate haematological studies.

Most radioactive tracers used for diagnostic procedures are administered by intravenous injection. This normally simple procedure can be affected by a variety of complications (e.g. fluid may leak out of the vein in the vicinity of the needle and suffuse the surrounding tissues). Solutions will usually disperse rapidly from the site of injection and re-enter the bloodstream. However, particulate materials may be sequestered for a much longer time. One incident involved the intravenous injection of red cells labelled with 550 MBq of Tc-99m. The injection was deposited in the tissues outside the target vein and an attempt was made to accelerate the dispersal of the radioactivity by dilation of the local blood vessels with a hot compress. The local dose was calculated to be about 1 Gy.

Incidents leading to the spread of contamination may also arise in the clinical situation and these are potentially much more serious when therapeutic quantities of radioactivity are involved. Examples include leakage around the bladder catheter of a patient undergoing radioiodine therapy for thyroid carcinoma, regurgitation or failure to swallow radioiodine after drinking a solution and the escape of infusion colloids from delivery tubes or faulty plastic collection bags. Such incidents can result in considerable contamination of the environment. The detriment to the patient will be generally reduced efficacy of treatment and the likelihood of skin contamination. Spills in the clinical environment can be managed in a similar manner to laboratory incidents except that in taking prompt action the patient should not be unnecessarily distressed.

8.7 Recording and Reporting Incidents

Under the provisions of the Health and Safety at Work etc Act (1974) (see Chapter 1) every worker has a responsibility for the safety of him/herself and others. This principle applies to radiation safety as to any other aspect of employment and individual workers must comply with the relevant local rules. It is undesirable to impose unnecessary paperwork onto employees whose duties are of a practical nature. Nevertheless, it is a legal requirement that users of radioactive materials keep records of their utilisation and disposal of radioactivity and of the results of monitoring for contamination. Records should include details of any spills of radioactivity and any other incidents that relate to radiation safety.

The use of an incident report form will ensure that the necessary information is recorded with the minimum of trouble. A suitable form is shown in *table 8.3.*

The RPA and RPS should review incident reports at regular intervals, so that lessons can be learned and procedures amended as necessary. Entries will include those relating to clinical incidents involving radioactivity and the personnel involved.

Table 8.3   Report of an incident involving radioactivity

Date: Location:
Nature of incident:

Factors which precipitated the incident:

Radionuclide(s) involved:
Total activity present:
Estimate of activity dispersed:
Immediate action taken:
Details of personal contamination or intake:
Details of personal decontamination procedures undertaken and outcome:
Assessment of initial environmental contamination:
Decontamination measures taken:
Results of final monitoring for environmental contamination:
Continuing measures required:
Commentary:
Signature of person reporting the incident:

The report should be sent to the RPS, RPA and Departmental Manager.

8.8   The NAIR Scheme

The National Arrangements for Incidents Involving Radioactivity (NAIR) scheme was set up in 1964 to provide advice and assistance to the police, at their request, when an incident occurs involving radioactive substances. The arrangements are intended to cover incidents in public places or involving the public on premises where radioactive substances are not normally handled. The scheme is not intended to cover incidents at places where radioactive substances are normally handled and where competent staff should be available to cope. The NAIR scheme is fully explained in a handbook compiled by the National Radiological Protection Board[5] and supplied to participants.

8.9 Admission of Casualties to Hospital

As a result of an incident outside the hospital, e.g. on the road or in a local factory, there may be casualties who are suspected of being, or are known to be, contaminated with radioactivity[6]. They should be taken to a hospital listed in the NAIR handbook as designated to receive such casualties. Information on the handling of casualties contaminated with radioactive substances is given in a Health Circular[7].

The admission of a contaminated patient to one of these hospitals will ideally be via a decontamination unit where the hazards to patient and staff from radioactive contamination can be assessed and, as far as possible, eliminated. However, when immediate life-saving measures are necessary, they must take precedence over all other procedures. A good understanding between the medical emergency staff and health physics staff is essential if the correct priorities are to be determined in a crisis.

The special admissions facility should be as close as possible to the Accident and Emergency Department and have an independent entrance from the outside with good access for ambulances. Within the facility, the floor should have a welded PVC covering and a floor drain, and the walls should be washable. Installed features should include WC, shower, low-level sink, washbasin and storage cupboards. An inventory of other equipment and materials required in addition to the basic decontamination kit (*table 8.2*) is given in *table 8.4*.

Table 8.4 Inventory of supplementary equipment and materials for decontamination procedures.

Decontamination agents:	Calamine lotion
	Mouth wash
	Saline for eye irrigation
	Potassium permanganate and sodium metabisulphite
	Shampoo
Equipment:	Eye bath
	Toothbrushes
	Irrigation bottle and tubing
	Large plastic bins
	Waterproof aprons
Disposable materials:	Cotton tipped applicators
	Cotton wool balls
	Nasal swabs (filter paper strips)
	Safety razors
Monitor:	Surface contamination probes for beta and gamma radiation
	Sample counting attachments
	Doserate meter

Arrangements should be made to ensure that the reception facility is opened and prepared as soon as notice is received of casualties at the incident. A medical physics team will be called in to join the medical staff waiting to receive the casualties. When the ambulance arrives, and if the condition of the casualty allows, monitoring staff should enter to make a preliminary assessment. It may be possible, at this stage, to declare the patient free of contamination in which case admission to the Accident and Emergency Unit becomes straightforward. Alternatively, appropriate containment measures against the spread of contamination can be put in hand and the patient transferred to the decontamination facility. Ambulance personnel should be asked to remain in their ambulance until they can be assessed for possible contamination.

It is not envisaged that a large number of contaminated individuals, requiring admission to hospital, would be involved. Designated hospitals should be prepared to allocate sufficient resources to enable one or possibly two contaminated casualties to be admitted at the same time. It would usually be reasonable to require that other contaminated individuals wait for detailed attention after an initial assessment.

While it is clearly desirable that a decontamination facility, of the kind described above, should be provided, it will rarely have to be called into use for its primary purpose. In this situation two questions arise; how can it be maintained in a state of permanent readiness and can its range of uses be extended? The answers to these questions are closely related. A programme should be devised involving regular, say six monthly, inspections of the facility to be carried out. Inspections should not be made by a physicist alone but by a multi-professional team, at least some of whose members change each time. In this way an inspection can incorporate a larger element of training and rehearsal. During the inspection, access arrangements should be reviewed, equipment functions checked and stock taken of stored materials including chemicals which may require replacement. Without impairing its state of readiness, the facility could be used for the training of users of radioactive materials in monitoring and decontamination techniques. Furthermore, there is no reason why the facility should not also be used for the decontamination of chemically contaminated individuals. By these means the area can become familiar and functional.

The following information could be issued to doctors and nurses working in Accident and Emergency:

Information for Doctors and Nurses

1. If a patient arrives at the hospital and there is reason to believe that he/she may be contaminated with radioactive material, a medical physicist should be summoned immediately.
   (Include here a list of names for contact, with daytime and home telephone numbers).

2. A doctor wearing protective overalls, gloves and mask should examine the patient in the ambulance. If possible, the patient should remain in the ambulance until the physicist arrives to assess the severity of the contamination.

3. Severe injury may make it imperative to remove the patient from the ambulance without delay. All personnel who assist in carrying the patient

must wear protective clothing (i.e. overalls which can be disposed of if necessary, gloves and mask). The stretcher should be protected with a polythene sheet and it should remain in the Decontamination Unit until it has been monitored by the physicist. Similarly, protective clothing worn by porters or other assistants must remain in the Unit for monitoring and disposal.

4. Although the patient may be heavily contaminated there is unlikely to be a significant risk to staff handling him/her provided protective clothing is worn.

5. The ambulance should not be allowed to leave until it has been checked by the physicist. The ambulance driver and anyone else who may have made physical contact with the patient or his/her clothes must also be checked for contamination.

6. In the treatment room, the floor and surfaces with which the patient comes into contact must be covered with a non-porous covering. Staff must wear waterproof aprons and boots if there is a risk of clothing becoming wet and thereby contaminated.

7. Radioactive contamination is similar in some ways to bacteriological contamination so that the general principles of aseptic surgical techniques are a good guide to safe procedures.

8. The physicist will determine the extent of contamination on the patient and will define the areas affected.

9. Contamination must be removed because: (a) its spread can endanger people with whom it comes into contact; (b) local irradiation of the skin may cause long-term radiation injury; (c) internal contamination from ingestion or inhalation may result in long term damage and, ultimately, malignancy.

10. Because of these risks from intake of radioactivity, great care must be taken in cleaning the patient's face.

11. Maximum safe levels of radioactivity on the body surface may be defined approximately in terms of the count rate from an appropriate radiation monitor.

12. Contamination dangers vary, depending upon the area of the body affected as well as the type and energy of the radionuclide and the degree of contamination. The greatest hazard generally arises when the head, and particularly the mouth, becomes contaminated.

13. Where internal contamination is suspected this must be recorded with a view to further detailed examination.

14. During reception and checking of the patient everything thought to be contaminated must be stored or disposed of under the supervision of the physicist. This also applies to any secretions and waste from the patient.

15. Soiled swabs and similar materials must be deposited in the bin for contaminated waste. Linen must be placed in a separate bin for later checking and, if necessary, total disposal. Equipment and implements will also require monitoring for radioactivity after use.

16. Decontamination of the patient requires the application of the relevant decontamination procedure as described on the instruction card which should accompany the decontamination kit.

17. Every effort must be made to detain the patient in the Decontamination Unit until the physicist has been able to make an assessment of the situation. If, through extreme urgency, it is necessary to remove the patient to an operating room before freedom from contamination is established, his/her clothing should be removed completely in the decontamination room and the trolley and operating table should be protected by disposable covers. Theatre garments will provide adequate protection for those performing the operation.

18. The patient should not be taken into the X-ray department before having been certified free of contamination. If radiographs are required sooner, a mobile or portable X-ray machine should be brought to the Decontamination Unit.

References

1. International Commission on Radiological Protection 1977 *Limits for intakes of radionuclides by workers* Publication **30** (Pergamon Press, Oxford)
2. *The Ionising Radiations Regulations 1985* (SI No 1333) (HMSO, London)
3. *Guidance Notes for the Protection of Persons Against Ionising Radiations Arising from Medical and Dental Use* 1988 (HMSO, London)
4. International Atomic Energy Agency 1978 *Manual on early medical treatment of possible radiation injury* Safety Series No 47 (IAEA, Vienna)
5. *NAIR Handbook* 1987 (National Radiological Protection Board, Chilton)
6. International Commission on Radiological Protection 1988 *The principles and general procedures for handling emergency and accidental exposures of workers* Publication 28 (Pergamon Press, Oxford)
7. HC(89)8 1988 *Health Services Arrangements for Dealing with Accidents involving Radioactivity* (Department of Health, London)

CHAPTER 9

Waste Disposal

M J Myers

9.1 Introduction

9.1.1 Definitions of radioactive waste

A formal definition of radioactive waste is radioactive material which has been discarded because it is either not required or not usable. In a hospital context waste would thus include radioactive material left over from preparations used for patient or laboratory work; radioactive material that has been used in patient or laboratory procedures; radioactivity excreted by patients and radioactive material resulting from cleaning up after accidental spillage of radioactivity.

For general hospital work purposes, any radioactive substance that has an activity concentration less than 100 Bq g^{-1} would not be considered, under the Ionising Radiations Regulations 1985 (IRR), as radioactive waste unless it presented a radiation hazard[1]. Such a hazard could arise if the material contained an alpha emitter.

Solid waste appearing as a collection of contaminated articles each associated with a small amount of radioactivity can be treated as ordinary, non-radioactive waste. The activity of this 'low level' solid waste is defined in section 9.4.1.

9.1.2 Legal and safety aspects

The problem of dealing with radioactive waste involves not simply disposal of useless and potentially hazardous products of hospital work. It should be considered as an intimate component in the cycle of reception, storage, utilisation and disposal of radioactive material in which the activity is tracked and accounted for at all stages.

It is important to note that accounting for radioactive waste products is a legal requirement and that prosecution could therefore follow if the regulations are seen on inspection to have been ignored. Two legal instruments (both currently under review) are of relevance in this context: The Radioactive Substances (Hospitals) Exemption Order (1990)[2] which allows disposal and storage of limited amounts of waste and the Radioactive Substances Act 1960 (RSA)[3] which makes it necessary for a hospital to obtain authorisation from the Department of the Environment before disposing of radioactive waste above the exempted limits. The amounts of different forms of waste that may be stored and disposed of are set on an individual hospital site basis by agreement, usually between the RPA and the Department of the Environment (DoE). The latter has to be consulted if levels for disposal or storage times are likely to be exceeded. The legislative aspects and practical implications are covered in more detail in Chapter 1 and section 9.3, respectively.

The hospital use of radionuclides does not of course entail the scale of potential dangers from radiation inherent in the operations of the nuclear industry; the radiation levels involved are very much less and/or the radioactive substances that are handled differ greatly in their pathogenic properties. However, public perception of radioactivity does not allow this distinction to be made and environmental issues have to be taken into account in deciding on routes for hospital radioactive waste disposal. Care must also be exercised in the methods used to deal with and remove radioactive waste to ensure that the operations themselves do not lead to further unnecessary exposure of personnel. A further consideration is that hospital radioactive waste will often have other hazardous properties. From the point of view of radiation safety, the handling of waste must be considered in relation to a number of different groups of persons:

a) those working with and handling radionuclides directly as part of their work

b) those members of ancillary staff who, as part of their duties, must come into contact with radioactive waste

c) those members of the public inside the hospital, either as patients or visitors

d) those members of the public totally unconnected to the hospital use of radionuclides who must be protected from potential contamination of common resources (e.g. drinking water, atmosphere, etc).

9.1.3 Classification of hospital waste

Radionuclides are used in many different ways in the hospital and give rise to different types of waste products. Hospital usage will generate waste from both laboratory and diagnostic patient work (e.g. residues from laboratory preparations, radioactive excreta and blood samples, soiled hospital supplies, etc). Such waste will appear, at a higher activity level, in the therapeutic use of unsealed radionuclides. Laboratory work is generally performed with a relatively low level of radioactivity although some preparations such as radio-iodination, for example, do lead to problems in disposing of large activities.

The method of disposal that is chosen will depend not only on the physico-chemical state of the radioactive product but also on properties such as its half-life, types of emissions and activity level. Efficient management of the waste may involve categorising the disposal into management of 'solid', 'liquid' and 'gaseous' waste and grouping of the radionuclides involved as, for example, 1-125/1-131, H3/C14/S35 etc.

9.2 Regulations Governing Management of Waste

9.2.1 Legal requirements

The keeping and disposing of radioactive waste is regulated by law and is subject to the following requirements:

a) registration of use of radioactive substances under the RSA, although some hospitals in England, Scotland and Wales are exempt[2]. All hospitals do, however, need to register with the Health & Safety Executive (HSE) under the IRR.

b) official authorisation for the accumulation of waste for a specified time and its disposal, or

c) exemption orders providing for the accumulation and disposal of small amounts of radioactivity. These specify the exempted activities of specified radionuclides that are disposed of by incineration, waste collection and discharged to a public sewer.

d) systems of record keeping and local rules covering the handling of waste.

Although IRR Regulation 31 requires that the HSE be notified under certain conditions where activities larger than those detailed in column 7 of IRR Schedule 2 are, in effect, disposed of except under an authorisation, these levels (e.g. 2×10^7 MBq Tc-99m) are unlikely to be exceeded in hospital work and notification would hardly ever be called for.

9.2.2 Sources for official guidance

The Ionising Radiations Regulations 1985[1] and the accompanying Approved Code of Practice (ACOP)[4] do not deal with the practical aspects of radioactive waste disposal. Discussion of waste in these two publications is confined to a short discussion (IRR Reg 19) of the need to keep records of waste in the general process of accounting for radioactive substances. This dearth of information contrasts with the practical guidance given in the Guidance Notes (1988)[5] which include short descriptions of types of waste occurring in medical practice, legal requirements and methods of disposal of various forms of radioactive waste.

Her Majesty's Inspectors of Pollution (HMIP) in the Department of the Environment and the equivalent agencies in Scotland and Northern Ireland are themselves a very useful source of information. Modifications or updates of the hospital authorisation may be arranged in consultation with the Inspector and the RPA. One-off disposals of unusually large amounts of activity may be performed following official authorisation.

Another excellent, though rather indirect, source of information to personnel involved in hospital waste management is from the DoE. In providing the answers to the list of questions asked in completing form RSA3(88) about the choice and justification of disposal routes much can be learnt about the safe handling of radioactive waste and its implications to the public. A useful guide to completion of the RSA3 (88) form has been produced by the Association of University Radiation Protection Officers[6] and an abbreviated version of the form, listing many of the questions required to be answered, is included in section 9.8.

The IAEA booklet, Safety Series 70[7] (Management of Radioactive Wastes Produced by Users of Radioactive Materials), is a useful practical guide. It covers subjects such as applications of radionuclides and their corresponding waste products, methods of treatment and disposal of waste material, solid and liquid waste management, including storage and treatment, and airborne discharge. The concept of the Annual Limit on Intake (ALI) is used to define the activity of many of the common radionuclides in hospital waste that may be disposed of safely. Thus, for example, Tc-99m has an ALI of 3000 MBq and Mo-99 an ALI of 300 MBq. For waste released to the sewage system or sent to a radioactive refuse disposal plant it is suggested that the total monthly activity must be less than $10 \times$ ALI, i.e. the amount of Mo-99 released must be less than 3000 MBq in any one month. The environmental hazards associated with a particular mode of disposal may also be related directly to the ALI. For example, a figure of 0.1 per cent of the ALI may be acceptable to HMIP as a 'safe' threshold in calculating the effect of discharge from the point of view of the amount that may possibly be ingested by a member of the public.

A Health and Safety Commission publication[8] on 'The safe disposal of clinical waste' is a valuable source of practical information on the disposal of waste in general, some of which may be radioactive. It details various categories of clinical waste (e.g. group A — soiled dressings etc, group B — discarded needles etc), disposal procedures (handling of waste etc), segregation, storage and containment of waste. This information is often of use in handling those items that constitute both clinical and radioactive waste.

9.2.3 Authorisation certificates and exemption orders

Disposal of radioactive waste must be carried out in accordance with either an authorisation certificate or an exemption order. The disposal of wastes, arising in hospitals, e.g. from the administration of very low levels of radioactive materials to patients is at present exempted from complying with the specific conditions of an authorisation certificate. This covers such items of waste as syringes and vials, patient excreta and residual ash. Waste containing alpha emitters is excluded but the following are currently allowed:

a) waste activity less than 400 kBq in a volume at least 0.1 cubic metres or 40 kBq as a single article in that volume, for disposal as inactive refuse. One-tenth of a cubic metre corresponds roughly to a cylindrical bin of 45 cm diameter and 60 cm height. (The 'dustbin' limit.)

b) waste activity less than 25 MBq of C-14 and H-3, taken together, and 5 MBq of all other radionuclides, for disposal by incineration on the premises per month, with activity in 0.1 m^3 of ash not exceeding 400 kBq.

c) waste activity in human excreta, less than 1 GBq of Tc-99m and 500 MBq of other radionuclides in any month, for disposal via the drains to a public sewer, and less than 50 MBq of other aqueous liquid radioactive waste.

Clear, legible and up-to-date records should be kept of all activity, estimated as well as possible, disposed of by these different routes.

A Certificate of Authorisation for the disposal of larger activities than those given above and accumulation of radioactive waste is issued by the Department of the Environment after a completed application form, RSA3, has been approved. A copy must be prominently displayed in a permanent location conveniently sited in the department. An example of a Certificate of Authorisation is shown in section 9.9. (The wording of the official document has been simplified.)

9.3 Types of Waste

9.3.1 Solid waste

Listed below are examples of the variety of sources of hospital radioactive waste with some general comments of how each category is dealt with. More specific descriptions of methods of waste removal are detailed in section 9.4. The methods discussed are unsuitable for biologically hazardous material (see section 9.3.5).

a) Waste arising from preparation of radiopharmaceuticals

Much of the radioactive waste generated in the hospital preparation and administration of radionuclides may be considered, from the operational point of view, as solid waste. It includes radioactive gloves, paper sheets, swabs, tissues and polythene bags; sealed glass vials, plastic syringes and tubing containing liquid radioactive material are also included under solid waste. For the shorter lived radionuclides that make up the bulk of the workload, there is rarely a necessity to dispose of the contents of the vials or syringes into the drainage system. This process would involve extra manipulation and generation of more contaminated waste (e.g. syringes) and would increase the risk of spreading activity and add to personal radiation exposure.

An important aspect of the preparation and administration of radiopharmaceuticals is the generation of radioactive syringe needles and broken glass vials. These 'sharps' should be collected in a specially marked container and are usually disposed of by incineration or collection by an authorised waste disposal agency.

b) Patient-generated waste

Examples of this type of waste are excreta, syringes containing blood samples, catheters, dressings, food and disposable eating and drinking utensils. Disposal is usually via the sewer system (for liquids), by collection for landfill (for solids) or by incineration. The waste should also fulfil the requirements governing the disposal of clinical waste[8].

c) Waste arising from decontamination following a spill or similar accident

The material used to clean and decontaminate will appear as miscellaneous solid radioactive waste.

9.3.2 Liquid waste

Since most diagnostic use involves Tc-99m, large activities of this radionuclide will appear as waste in liquid form (notably in the urine of patients and in material left over from preparation and administration). Similarly, therapeutic usage of I-131 will result in large activities accumulating in excreta and body fluids. Installation of radioactive colloids into patients can give rise to liquid waste if subsequent leakage and drainage occurs.

a) Liquid waste from preparation of radiopharmaceuticals:

This can arise from active syringe contents and supernatants from blood samples and is usually discharged into sinks. Dilution of high activities to a level less than $1 \, MBq \, l^{-1}$ is recommended.

b) Organic and scintillant material labelled with C-14, H-3 and other beta emitters.

The radionuclides C-14 and H-3 very often appear mixed with liquid scintillator. This may be immiscible with water and toxic even if not flammable and so should not be disposed of via the drains. Biodegradable versions of premixed liquid scintillation cocktails are now available and are suitable for counting aqueous (and some non-aqueous) samples with acceptable efficiency. These scintillators have a low toxicity, are non-flammable, do not penetrate plastics and are biodegradable, and are therefore disposable via the drains. However, there may be some opposition to their introduction because of cost, possible loss of counting efficiency and changes in working procedures. In addition, permission will have to be obtained from the local water authority. Disposal via the drains is also an acceptable route for agreed levels of aqueous forms of C-14 and H-3 and other beta emitters such as S-35.

c) Radioiodine and other volatile substances

If these are of high activity then the vapour hazard must be taken into account, for example by using a sink inside a fume cupboard.

d) Washings from laboratory hardware and low level waste

Unless the washings contain immiscible liquids, in which case they should be collected, direct disposal to the sewers is allowed.

9.3.3 Gaseous or airborne waste

Airborne discharge of gas or vapour can take place as a result of (i) an investigation on a patient involving a radioactive gas or aerosol such as Xe-133 or Tc-99m DTPA aerosol; (ii) the handling of a gas or volatile radioactive substance, such as tritium, C-14 dioxide or monoxide, I-125 or I-131, in a fume cupboard or non-recirculating laminar flow cabinet; (iii) emissions from incinerators; (iv) exhaust from a radioactive decay store or radium store.

A number of radioactive gases are used in diagnostic hospital work including Xe-133, Kr-81m, Xe-127, Kr-85 and a range of positron emitters such as N-13, O-15 and C-11 and their derivatives. The radiation hazard associated with these gases is very much a function of their half-lives. Some are so short lived as to make dealing with them before decay virtually impossible. An example is Kr-81m with a half-life of 13 seconds. The limit to the amount of their discharge is, in practice, controlled more by detrimental effects on background radiation levels that could affect instrumentation than on personnel exposure.

9.3.4 Radioactive generators

Molybdenum-99 generators are employed for the daily production of Tc-99m in the majority of hospitals offering diagnostic nuclear medicine services (other hospitals are usually supplied with centrally generated technetium labelled products). These are in use for a period of a week or two after which time the generator is considered a waste product and a new generator is supplied. Also employed to a significant extent are Rb-81/Kr-81m systems, used over the period of a day, Sn-113/In-113m systems which are renewed after a 6–9 month period. Problems of waste disposal occur with the relatively long-lived parent radionuclides.

9.3.5 Infected and biohazard material

Incineration is necessary for this form of waste. Recommendations of the 'Howie Code'[9] for the safe disposal of clinical waste should be followed (see section 5.6). Some pathology laboratories autoclave this waste and then dispose of low level material as ordinary waste.

9.4 Methods of Disposal of Waste

In view of the above regulations practical steps in dealing with waste can be outlined. All the methods must be described in the Local Rules and must be drawn to the attention of users.

9.4.1 Disposal of low level solid waste as non-radioactive waste

Bags of solid waste material containing in aggregate less than 0.4 MBq of radionuclides (excluding alpha emitters) and, if permitted by HMIP, 4 MBq of

C-14 or H-3 per 0.1 m³ may be disposed of as non-radioactive waste on condition that no single item contains more than 0.04 MBq of any radionuclide (or 0.4 MBq of C-14 or H-3). To avoid misinterpretation of the status of the waste, all labels referring to the radioactive nature of the contents of the bags should be removed.

9.4.2 Disposal via drains

Most of the radionuclide material used in hospitals has a short half-life (i.e. less than a few days) and is in aqueous form. This can be easily disposed of directly into the sewer system via a sink specially designated and labelled for this purpose. The sinks should, as far as possible, be connected directly to the sewer system and avoid passing near working areas where people might be irradiated. Any trapping of the radioactive effluent and passage to open drains should be avoided. The routes by which radioactive waste reaches the sewer system should be known and labelled in order to help reduce possible exposure to workers dealing with the plumbing and sewerage system.

The waste should be poured directly into the sink outlet with the tap running steadily throughout the discharge and for 10–15 minutes afterwards, without any splashing that would cause the spread of the activity outside the sink. The container should be rinsed, also in a manner that avoids splashing. Special care must be taken with large amounts of activity, e.g. urine collections from I-131 therapy patients.

A record of the type and amount of activity and its time of disposal should be kept for inspection by Her Majesty's Inspectorate of Pollution who periodically check the complete site records for evidence of compliance with the disposal authorisation. Periodic recorded contamination monitoring of the sink and the associated nearby pipes and outlets is also advisable.

The amount of radioactivity that may be authorised for disposal via drains is often large, perhaps up to several gigabecquerels per month, even for tritium which in other European Community countries is more strictly controlled. The Local Rules should indicate the amount of discharge allowed per day and over a period of a month. Thus it might be stated that beta emitters and gamma emitters with half-lives of less than a year might be discharged via the drains if the amounts involved are less than, say, 2 MBq per day (for each individual user) or, say, 200 MBq per month with amounts greater than these allowed to be discharged only after consultation with the RPA. Significant long term changes in patterns of disposal will, however, have to be authorised by the DoE.

Some distinction is made in the UK between the different chemical forms of the liquid waste (such as acid or alkaline) since there exist the possibilities of precipitation or exothermic reactions and associated aerosol production. The effect of the different forms should be discussed with the Inspector. It is not standard procedure to further treat the waste (such as with ion exchange resins, chemical coagulants, filtration of suspended solids or through a process of evaporation) in order to separate the activity since this might lead to the possibility of unnecessary operator irradiation or further accidental contamination. Conversion of small volumes of aqueous liquid waste to a solid form by adsorption onto diatomaceous earth for disposal inside a plastic bottle as solid waste may also be unnecessary.

Liquid scintillator material is flammable or toxic and unless biodegradable (see section 9.3.2) should not be disposed of in the same way as aqueous material. The preferred route for disposal will often be by incineration, although burning quantities of scintillant poses problems for some incinerators. Alternatively, special arrangements for its collection and storage in drums that are subsequently removed from the site have to be made. Provided that the levels of radioactivity are low enough, and this is generally the case since only small amounts are able to be counted in a liquid scintillation counter, the scintillant may be stored in the hospital solvent store and removed by a commercial company along with the other solvents.

Disposable counting vials containing liquid scintillator materials should be firmly capped and placed in a plastic bag which is sealed and placed inside another heavy duty plastic bag again sealed. The volume of liquid should not exceed about one litre. Leaching of toluene through plastic vials should be checked; this is not a problem with glass vials although leaks through the vial caps may be a problem common to both sorts of container.

Liquid scintillant not in disposable vials should be stored in a metal drum inside a flame proof cupboard until a set volume agreed for collection (say ten litres) has been accumulated. The total activity should be less than 400 kBq for C-14 and H-3.

Disposal via the sewer system is the easiest way to dispose of radioactive excreta. Toilets exclusively for patients undergoing diagnostic tests should not be necessary since levels of activity in the patient are generally less than those detailed in the Guidance Notes for patients leaving hospital (less than, for example, 1 GBq Tc-99m). However an individual department may find it preferable to provide special toilets near the waiting area. Toilets must be allocated to patients undergoing therapy with radioiodine or radiolabelled antibodies and outlets should have easily identified and maintained routes to the main sewers. The WC facilities used by radionuclide therapy patients should be designated and monitored periodically because of the relatively large amounts of activities that may be involved. Any repairs to the drains associated with these WCs should be carried out only after activity and radiation dose rate levels have been checked. Patients who have received diagnostic levels of short-lived radioactivity should generally be free to use any of the toilet facilities in the hospital.

At sites where small animals containing radioactivity have to be disposed of, a macerator connected directly to the sewer system is the most convenient facility. The waste is converted to a finely dispersed mass that can be washed away. Care should be exercised in the operation of the macerator to prevent its jamming and the need for subsequent attention to remove a radioactive blockage. Where there might be local difficulties in disposing of solid waste (e.g. the storing of contaminated eating utensils used by a patient undergoing radionuclide therapy) the waste may have to be separated and as far as possible converted into liquid form using, for example, a macerator.

Radioactive toxic or other 'special' waste material must not be released into the sewers without authorisation from the local water authority.

9.4.3 Incineration

Combustible low-level waste is conveniently dealt with by incineration. The waste may include animal carcasses, animal excreta, specimens, biologically toxic material, a limited amount of plastic vials and combustible material. The activities of the various radionuclides involved that are able to be dealt with by incineration vary from site to site and must appear on the Certificate of Authorisation (for waste disposal) for a particular establishment.

Strict monitoring of the resulting ash and debris is necessary since much of the activity may be concentrated here while the main bulk of the material is removed by the incineration process. Sufficient volume dilution of the remaining activity must take place for it to be removed with the ordinary hospital waste. A chronological record of the activities of the radionuclides that have actually been incinerated should be kept. This record may be kept centrally at the site of the incinerator if the waste is presented there in bags with labels showing details of the activity, reference date and radionuclide and will enable the amount disposed of in a set period to be kept within the locally allowed limits.

The design of the incinerator and its suitability for burning the required amount of solid material or solvent, if liquid scintillant is to be burnt, should be considered. The combustion rates in kg h^{-1} of solid material, or litres h^{-1} of solvent, should be ascertained for the particular position of the exhaust gas discharge of the incinerator. Other details, such as the height of the stack, its relation to other buildings or areas used by the public, the presence of an after burner or water scrubber, the temperature and completeness of combustion should also be known.

9.4.4   Airborne discharge

Traditionally, longer lived gases such as Xe-133 have been dealt with by discharge into the atmosphere through an exhaust pipe leading out of a window chosen to prevent re-entry to occupied areas. Systems for trapping the waste gases have also been employed, sometimes in order to re-utilize an expensive product. Aerosols used for diagnostic imaging purposes would not appear as gaseous waste as they are trapped by the body or by the dispensing equipment before entering the atmosphere. Volatile compounds, especially those labelled with I-125 or I-131 should be considered as potentially forming gaseous waste.

Emissions from incinerator stacks or from the exhaust stacks of fume cupboards are a potential form of radiation hazard if there is a possibility that they may enter a building before sufficient dilution has taken place; outlets to stacks should be of a height and position that this is avoided.

Where filters are involved, as in a microbiological safety cabinet, they must be checked periodically and replaced. The old, contaminated, filters are treated as solid waste.

9.4.5   Storage until decay

Storage of exempt waste before disposal should not normally exceed two weeks without special authorisation. With the increase in the difficulties of disposal due to increased public awareness of radioactivity in the environment there has been a move towards longer periods of storage and decay on site. However, much of the radioactive waste generated in hospital use is of a relatively short half-life. It can therefore be stored until the activity has decayed to low levels such that the material can be defined as inactive (see 9.2.3) and disposed of as any other form of waste. This method of disposal will apply very readily to the products of Tc-99m use including unused doses, sharps, syringes, paper towels etc.

It is desirable and usually possible to sort waste into bags according to radionuclide. This will allow separation of short-lived from long-lived waste and help assessment of the activity of each bag of waste. A practical technique of measuring the activities in the bags should be established. The exact method of monitoring will depend on the instrumentation commonly available such as one or more of the several types of hand held monitors equipped with geiger or scintillation detectors (see Chapter 7). This technique will apply to many of the methods of disposal and should be simple and rapid enough that a number of bags can be measured without excessive personal exposure. A check or calibration of the technique can be based on simulations with known activities and distributions of commonly used radionuclides in the bags. Checks should be made of:

a) the suitability of the detectors for the specific radionuclide handled. It is invariably impractical to check for C-14 or H-3.

b) ability to detect the low level radiation in relation to background levels.

c) independence on the distribution of radionuclide in the bag.

However, in many cases, reliance has to be placed on the data supplied by the users who, working with an initially known (calibrated) activity can assess the proportion in the waste.

Items that have become contaminated with radioactivity and are required to be used again (e.g. laboratory equipment, patients belongings, linen, etc) will be stored in the same way although with recycling rather than disposal as the ultimate aim. Clothing and bedding may be washed as a special washing machine load or in a washing machine dedicated to washing radioactive material of this sort and specially plumbed in.

Compaction of bagged medium term waste in order to conserve storage space is possible with a dedicated compactor. This can reduce the volume of the waste to a half or a third but involves some risk of escape of liquid or vapour and exposure of personnel in the process. In addition items such as flexible plastic syringes are rather difficult to compact with standard machines.

9.4.6   Collection by manufacturer or supplier

This usually applies in the case of disposal of Mo99/Tc-99m and other radionuclide generators. Two methods of dealing with expired molybdenum radionuclide generators which are also applicable to the other generator systems are available in hospitals:

a) storage for an agreed period of decay (negotiated with the supplier and also with the Inspector of Pollution), often a few weeks, followed by collection by the supplier. This method is generally to be preferred and as short a turn around time as can be arranged is desirable to avoid storage and handling of large numbers of expired generators.

b) storage until the activity on the column has decayed sufficiently to be disposed of as low level solid waste following the dismantling of the generator to separate the lead. This method is more time consuming and may involve a long storage period on site.

9.4.7   Disposal through waste disposal services

Disposal of medium and long half-life activity such as solid waste containing I-125 and S-35 and scintillator material containing C-14 and H-3 through an authorised disposal service is a recognised method of disposal. However, the costs of this service may be prohibitively high so that it may be a last resort if storing the waste to decay or other means of disposal are not possible. Radioactive solvents or toxic substances that have effectively decayed away to acceptably low levels may, with the exception of C-14 or H-3 products, be disposed of as solvent waste through the local authority waste disposal service under the control of the Control of Pollution Act (1974)[10] with the approval of the Chemical Inspectorate.

9.4.8 *Disposal of radioactive corpses and carcasses*

Animal carcasses containing more than the minimum levels of radioactivity defining non-active waste would be incinerated or macerated and subsequently disposed of via a sluice plumbed directly into the waste system.

Disposal of radioactive corpses from the hospital would normally be by burial or cremation which might follow post-mortem examination. The Guidance Notes[5], give recommendations on the maximum activities of commonly used radionuclides such as I-131, P-32 and I-125 for burial and cremation of corpses without special permission. The relative effects of the presence of other radionuclides should be estimated with respect to the more common ones in establishing a 'safe' activity limit by the RPA. When the radioactive corpse has to be subject to more handling as in embalming or post mortem examinations the automatically allowable levels of activity are reduced. In the case of I-131, for example, the maximum activities for post mortem/embalming, burial and cremation are, respectively, 10 MBq, 400 MBq and 400 MBq.

9.4.9 *Other radioactive waste*

Alpha emitters need special authorisation for disposal and should be disposed of only after consultation with the RPA who would consult with HMIP. For pathological or biologically hazardous radioactive material, the advice of both the RPA and an expert in the biohazards involved should be sought.

9.4.10 *Summary of disposal methods*

Before storage of solid active waste it should be sorted to exclude non-active material if storage space is at a premium and no unnecessary irradiation is incurred. Waste sent for storage and decay should always be labelled with the name of the departmental laboratory, the radionuclide(s), the activity(activities) and the date.

A scheme such as that illustrated in *table 9.1* is suggested as a working model for laboratories involved in handling radionuclides.

9.5 Storage of Radioactive Waste Material

General recommendations for the storage of radioactive materials as distinct from radioactive waste may be found in the Guidance Notes[5]. The following applies specifically to radioactive waste.

A room on the hospital site should be set aside for the short-term storage of radioactive waste. This room serves as a collection point where waste is monitored and made ready for disposal rather than a place where long lived radionuclides are allowed to decay over indefinite periods. A common problem in the use of technetium generators is safe storage of a few 'decaying' generators awaiting collection by the supplying company. It is difficult to dispose of the previous generator, when the new one is supplied, because of the high radiation levels. The requirements for the decay store will depend on the amount and nature of the waste. Sometimes large volumes of linen contaminated with I-131 used in therapy may be generated. There might be contaminated labware associated with I-125

Table 9.1 The disposal of radioactive waste from laboratories

Route	H-3 or C-14	Other radionuclides
Aqueous solutions- dispose into drains via designated sink	<4 MBq 1^{-1} (for greater activities make prior arrangements with RPS or RPA and HMIP)	<0.4 MBq 1^{-1}*
Solid waste — dispose as general laboratory waste	<4 MBq 0.1 m^{-3}	<0.4 MBq 0.1 m^{-3}
Solid radioactive waste — allow to decay or dilute as radioactive waste in waste store to 'dustbin' limits	>4 MBq 0.1 m^{-3}	>0.4 MBq 0.1 m^{-3}
Waste organic solvent — dispose in waste solvent store	<75 MBq 1^{-1}	allow to decay or dilute in store to the limits above as appropriate

* A concentration is suggested in the table as this implies a dilution of the activity before its disposal. Although an *activity* rather than a *concentration* should be stated here the absolute amount will be determined by the authorisation certificate and the total amount of water discharged from the premises into the public or private sewer system. If a fairly conservative final dilution of 100 Bq per litre of effluent is sought and the total daily discharge is 400,000 litres per day (say 550,000 litres for a large and 250,000 litres for a small hospital site) then 40 MBq per day (1.2 GBq per month) could be disposed of in this way.

labelling. Often there could be relatively small amounts of waste associated with Ga-67 (3.2 d half-life), Se-75 (120 d), P-32 (14 d), In-111 (2.8 d), Sn-113 generators (115 d) and Co-57 (271 d) flood and marker sources.

Attention has to be paid to the siting and design of the store in order to reduce the radiation hazards associated with handling the activity. Although it is desirable to site the store away from areas with personnel and patients it should, nevertheless, be near enough to the source of the waste not to involve long journeys carrying bags of active material. The room should be secure to prevent loss or theft. The entrance should be clearly marked with a radiation warning sign showing the nature of the activity and the names and telephone numbers of persons responsible for the store. The interior should be well lit and should conform to good laboratory practice with washable and impervious walls, ceiling, floor and work surfaces. Good ventilation, with outlets away from any occupied area, is necessary because of the possibility of having to store decaying organic radionuclide material (such as that associated with eating utensils used by therapy patients) as well as volatile radionuclides. The storage racks or shelves should allow easy access and efficient organisation (with e.g. moveable date labels) of the items of waste during their passage through the store in order to minimise the operator time in the store. A 'filing' system should be organised with the waste contained in bags and a label showing the reference date of the activity and the type and amount of activity clearly visible so that stored waste can be moved out for disposal on a sequential basis. Recording of the material deposited and leaving the store is important together with the nature, activity and history of the material.

Some shielding of the racks may be necessary and monitoring equipment should be available to measure the radiation dose levels as well as the activity levels in the room, individual items or bags. Contamination monitoring and recording should be carried out regularly. The dose rate outside the room should be low enough not to constitute any significant hazard to members of the public.

Medium term liquid waste, with half-lives of weeks to months, should be stored in leak proof containers and precautions taken against the evaporation of contents into the atmosphere of the decay room. Long term storage of biological material is possible if a freezer is installed.

9.6   Economics of Waste Disposal

As the public awareness of radiation increases so the social and environmental effects of radioactive waste disposal must increasingly be taken into account.This has led to an increased demand for avoiding the pollution of the environment and a consequent limitation of access to traditional facilities such as local authority waste tips or National Disposal Service land burial sites. The cost involved in alternative methods of disposal of radioactive waste, especially private disposal services, has therefore to be taken into consideration.

Since many of the practicalities of actual disposal will be dealt with automatically by the nature of the radioactive decay process itself, storage for a sufficiently long time, if permitted, will solve many of the problems. It is the longer lived radionuclides such as I-131 and I-125 where the problem arises of storage until decay has occurred or until disposal can be undertaken. Increased costs of waste disposal apply to the running of established departments and the planning of new ones where adequate provision of space for decay of contaminated items has to be provided. Such a facility, described in section 9.5, involving relatively easy access for authorised users, security against unauthorised use and safety aspects such as adequate ventilation, shielding and space for movement is usually at a premium on a hospital site. The alternative of removal of storable waste by a specialist company involves more direct costs. In budgeting for the use of radionuclides, a factor must be included to cover the cost of disposal as well as purchase of radionuclides.

9.7   Waste Record Keeping

HM Inspectorate of Pollution, through the authorisation granted to a site, requires an up-to-date record of all the waste activity on site classified according to activity generated, activity removed, radionuclides involved,chemical forms and modes of removal from the site. Since waste is associated with accumulation of activity on site these records should include the activities of the various radionuclides being used. Invariably there is a time lag introduced in the collection of waste returns or numbers of patient administrations from the different users on a site. This may mean that waste accounts, as with dosimetry records, are retrospective.

One method available to audit radionuclides as they are received, utilised and subsequently appear as radioactive waste is by using one of the many simple spreadsheet programs on a microcomputer.

An important factor in such a scheme is an agreement with the Inspectorate on how much waste is attributed to each patient procedure. The amount of associated waste is nominal and takes little account of detailed knowledge of metabolism or rate of elimination or decay *table 9.2*.

Table 9.2 Suggested proportions of activities of radionuclides commonly administered to patients that may be attributed to waste

Tc-99m for imaging (if excreted)	30%
I-131, I-123 for general thyroid imaging	70%
I-131, I-123 in thyrotoxicosis	40%
I-131 for ablation therapy	90–100%
Other imaging (Ga-67, Tl-201 etc)	30%
Gases (Kr-81m, Xe-133)	90–100%

Records associated with radioactive waste that are kept include those for:

a) radioactive material received and issued on site (as an approximate balance on input and waste output); this is simplified if centralised ordering is carried out; if not, then a monthly return from each department of how much of each radionuclide has been received is necessary.

b) administrations of radionuclides to patients (in association with *table 9.2*, leading to amounts appearing ultimately as waste). This will require a monthly return from users which may be integrated into the type of record shown in *table 9.3*.

c) disposal of radioactive waste, categorised by radionuclide, physical or chemical form, activity, and route of disposal (sinks, incinerator, collection etc). Returns are required by users in order to compile the records. A separate log of activity disposed of via a particular designated sink would also have to be maintained. In the case of radioactive waste contained in the corpse of a human patient, records should be kept of whether the corpse was buried or cremated, the date of removal from the premises, the details of activity and type of each radionuclide involved, at the time of removal.

9.8 Applying for Authorisation to Accumulate and Dispose of Radioactive Waste

In order to apply for authorisation to keep radioactive material and deal with the waste products a form, RSA 3[11], available from the DoE entitled 'Application for authorisation to accumulate and dispose of radioactive waste' has to be completed. It is useful to review what is required for the form in case a new application is needed, or a change of requirements or procedures is envisaged.

The application form asks a series of questions on how waste is proposed to be dealt with and the justification for these methods. It is a very practical document and goes into great detail about, for example, the equipment actually used in the procedures. For each route of disposal (incineration, via a public sewer, etc) the application form requires:

CENTRAL RECORD OF RADIOACTIVE WASTE DISPOSAL

MONTH   December
YEAR   1990

					Tc-99m	I-131	I-125	Misc r/a liquids	Misc r/a gases	C-14/H-3
TOTAL ACTIVITY ACQUIRED ON SITE IN MONTH (GBq)					37	5	2	10	2.5	0.5

RADIOPHARMCL	ARSAC CODE	MBq/Test	No.Tests	%Waste	Tc-99m	I-131	I-125	Misc liquids	Misc gases	C-14/H-3
HOSPITAL USAGE										
Cr51 RCVol	24.a.1.i	.8	1	30				.24		
Cr51 RCSurv	ii	2	2	30				1.2		
Cr51 RCSeque	iii	4	1	30				1.2		
Fe59 Metabol	26.b.1.ii	.4	3	30				.36		
Ga67 Tumour	31.a.1	150	1	30				45		
Se75 Adrenal	34.a.2	10	3	30				9		
Kr81m Gas/Aq	36.a.1	40	39	100					1560	
Tc04-ThyU/T	43.a.1.i	40	16	30	192					
Tc04-Imaging	ii	80	2	30	48					
Tc04-Brain	v	500	5	30	750					
Tc04-Haem	vi	800	9	30	2160					
TcHSA Perfn	43.a.3	100	39	30	1170					
TcMDP Bone	43.a.4	600	76	30	13680					
TcDTPA Renal	43.a.5.i	300	24	30	2160					
TcDMSA Renal	43.a.6	80	3	30	72					
TcSC Liver	43.a.7	80	2	30	48					
TcHIDA	43.a.8	150	8	30	360					
TcRBC Spleen	43.a.9	100	10	30	300					
TcRBC Cardio	43.a.10.ii	800	10	30	2400					
Tc04- Gastro	43.a.11	80	8	30	192					
TcDTPA Aersl	43.a.12	80	2	30	48					
In111 WC	49.a.3	40	13	30				156		
I131-Thy U/T	53.c.6.i	.2	5	70		.7				
I131-WB Mets	53.c.6.ii	400	3	70		840				
I131 MIBG	53.c.7	20	2	70		28				
Xe133 Perfn	54.a.1.i	200	3	100					600	
Tl201MyoPara	81.a.1	80	9	30				216		
THERAPY		Activity(MBq)								
I-131 (Total MBq)		3700		100		3700				
P-32 (Total MBq)		200		100				200		
LABORATORY WASTE DISPOSAL		Activity(MBq)								
organic solvent		10		100						10
solid(I-125)incind		40		100			40			
solid(others)incind		10		100					10	
solid(H-3,C14)incind		200		100						200
Misc.Liquid(I-125)		400		100			400			
Misc.Liquid(others)		670		100				670		
Misc.Liquid(H-3,C-14)		220		100						220
Misc I125 Disposal Service		250		100			250			
TOTAL LIQUID WASTE TO DRAINS					23580	4569	400	1309		220
TOTAL GAS WASTE TO ATMOSPHERE									2160	
TOTAL SOLID WASTE INCINERATED							40			200
TOTAL MISC I125 TO DISPOSAL SERVICE							250			
TOTAL WASTE DISPOSED OF FROM SITE IN MONTH (GBq)					23.58	4.57	.69	1.31	2.16	.43

Table 9.3 Example of use of a spread sheet to record waste arising from hospital and laboratory usage. Radionuclides are grouped as Tc-99m, I-131, I-125 etc. A sample of the available clinical tests is shown with the assumed waste from each test in the "% Waste" column.

a) the radionuclides involved, expressed in terms of the groups C-14/H-3, short lived beta/gamma, other beta/gamma and alpha radiation

b) the activity per month of the waste at the time of disposal

c) the method of estimating or measuring this activity

d) reasons why that method of disposal has been chosen

e) an assessment of the consequences of the proposed disposals in terms of the maximum likely radiation dose to a member of the public.

This assessment usually involves a calculation by the RPA based on the situation found at the particular site. A rule of thumb that would have to be agreed with the appropriate inspector is that the consequences to the public are negligible if, at the point of exit of the activity (e.g. the top of the incinerator chimney, outlet of the hospital sewer system etc) the activity that would be ingested there is less than 0.1 per cent of the ALI or DAC for a particular radionuclide. Obviously this rule involves some unusual calculations. For example, the activity of each radionuclide leaving the site in a volume of drain water equal to the yearly consumption of water by reference man (0.8 m³) should be less than 0.1% of the ALI or DAC. However, if such conditions are fulfilled, it does remove any doubt about the radiation hazard attributable to that method of waste disposal.

A brief description of the details required and the arrangement of the form are as follows:

1. Applicants details.

2. The premises; National Grid map reference, name of individual responsible for compliance, authorities in whose areas premises are located, reasons why radioactive materials are used.

3. Radioactive waste; how produced, steps taken to minimise its production, source of waste products, general nature and radioactivity of waste.

4. Solid radioactive waste disposal

   4.1 Disposal with normal refuse; volume per month, radioactive group, Bq m⁻³.

   4.2 Incineration; details of incinerator, height, distance from public access point, methods of dealing with ash, alternative disposal method if incinerator breaks down.

   4.3 Burial at a specified location.

   4.4 National Disposal Service; details of agreement with UKAEA (Harwell) or BNFL (Drigg) to accept waste.

   4.5 Assessments of maximum radiation dose to member of public.
   One method of calculation might be based on:

      (i) estimation of annual output, in m³, of active gases issuing from stack outlet.

      (ii) annual activities of principal radionuclides incinerated.

      (iii) dilution factor at nearest point of public contact; at its simplest this might be an inverse cube dependence. A graph showing ground level concentration against distance from a stack is given in reference 6.

      (iv) the time a member of public stays at this point.

(v)   total volume inhaled based on average minute ventilation.

(vi)   total activity ingested compared with 0.1 per cent of ALI.

The dispersion of radioactive gases from an incinerator may be calculated from semi-empirical formulae using assumptions that are greatly dependent on atmospheric conditions. Some of the parameters that have to be taken into account are the emission rate ($MBq\ min^{-1}$), the effective height of the chimney (greater than the physical height if the gases exit with a significant velocity), the wind speed and empirical diffusion factors. Details of some approaches to airborne contamination calculations are given by Cember[12].

5. Aqueous radioactive waste disposal

    5.1 Public sewer; monthly volume of water discharged from premises, names of sewage works, water authority, details of discharge point.

    5.2 Direct watercourse or waterbody.

    5.3 Premises' own sewage treatment works.

    5.4 Septic tank or cess pit on premises.

    5.5 Assessment of maximum radiation dose to member of public.

       As an example, this calculation may be based on:

       (i)   the annual output of water.

       (ii)   the activity of each radionuclide disposed of annually via the sewers.

       (iii)   the average activity concentrations at the point of exit of the drain from the site.

       (iv)   an estimation of how much liquid is drunk annually by a member of the public.

       (v)   comparison of the activity that would be contained in this volume with 0.1 per cent of the ALI or with the derived water concentration.

6. Organic liquid radioactive waste disposal

    6.1 Incineration on the premises or at other local premises; details of incinerator, details of ash, alternatives used when incinerator out of action.

    6.2 Incineration by a national contractor.

7. Aerial disposal of radioactive waste

For discharge in the form of gas, mist or dust, estimate maximum daily activity and presence of tritium, details of discharge point(s), height, distance from point to which public has access. The assessment of the radiation dose to the public will be based on a calculation similar to that outlined in part 4.5 of this section.

8. Accumulation of radioactive waste

Reasons for accumulation, physical nature of waste (e.g. inflammable, biologically hazardous etc), maximum activity of each radionuclide, containers to be used.

Details of building, room, security measures, fire alarm systems for place of storage, maximum period of waste accumulation, methods of recording and labelling waste, radiological assessment of proposed accumulation of radioactive waste.

The assessment of the maximum radiation dose to members of the public might be based on the dose rate, averaged over the year for a particular pattern of storage, measured at a distance close to the storage point and extrapolated to the nearest point of public access.

9.9 Sample Waste Authorisation Certificate

A simplified model of a typical Waste Authorisation Certificate is presented here.

DEPARTMENT OF THE ENVIRONMENT

RADIOACTIVE SUBSTANCES ACT (1960)

CERTIFICATE OF AUTHORISATION FOR THE DISPOSAL AND ACCUMULATION OF RADIOACTIVE WASTE

1. This is to certify that the XXXXXXXX Health Authority are authorised under section 6 (1) and 6 (3) of the Act, with effect from Day Month Year to dispose of radioactive waste on or from XXXX Hospital, XXX Road, City, subject to the conditions specified in paragraphs 3, 4, 5, 6 and 7 of this Certificate.

2. The waste referred to in the preceding paragraph is solid, liquid and gaseous waste which contains neither Sr-90 nor any radionuclide which emits alpha particles.

3. The disposal of solid waste is authorised subject to the conditions specified in paragraph 7 [note: this deals with records and samples of waste] of this Certificate, and to the following conditions:

   a) that the waste is disposed of by any of the following:

      (i) removal as refuse by a waste collection authority

      (ii) by burning on the premises and disposing of the residual ash through a waste collection authority; or

   b) that where the waste is disposed of through a waste collection authority, at the time of removal

      (i)   the waste is with non-radioactive refuse

      (ii) in any 0.1 cubic metre of the whole mass of the waste and refuse the sum total of tritium and C-14 does not exceed 4 MBq and the sum total of all other radionuclides does not exceed 400 kBq; and

      (iii) in any one article of the waste the sum total of tritium and C-14 does not exceed 400 kBq and the sum total of all other radionuclides does not exceed 40 kBq; and

   c) that if the waste is disposed of by burning it on the premises:

      (i)   in all the waste burnt on the premises in any one calendar month the sum total of tritium and C-14 does not exceed A MBq and the sum total of all other radionuclides does not exceed B MBq; and

      (ii)   the waste is burnt at a place and in a manner such as to ensure that the gas or vapour arising from the burning is discharged into the open air at such points and in such a manner as to prevent, so far as is reasonably practicable, the re-entry of the gas or vapour into any part of the premises.

4. The disposal of liquid waste, other than organic solvent, is authorised subject to the conditions of paragraph 7 and to the following conditions:

   a)   that the waste is disposed of, on or from the premises, by discharging it to a drainage system; and

   b)   that, in all the waste disposed of in one calendar month

      (i)   the sum total of Tc-99m does not exceed X GBq

      (ii)   the sum total of I-131 does not exceed Y GBq and

      (iii) the sum total of all radionuclides other than Tc-99m and I-131, when taken together, does not exceed Z GBq.

5. The disposal of liquid waste consisting of organic solvent is authorised subject to the conditions of paragraph 7 and to the following conditions:

   a)   that the waste contains no radionuclide other than tritium or C-14

   b)   that the waste is disposed of by either of the following means

      (i)   by burning on the premises and disposing of the residual ash as in paragraph 3.(a)(i) or

      (ii)   by disposing it to a contractor authorised to deal with this type of material.

   c)   that if the waste is disposed of as in 5.(b)(i).

      (i)   in all the waste burnt on the premises during any one calendar month the sum total does not exceed C MBq.

   d)   that if the waste is disposed of as in 5.(b)(ii).

      (i)   in all the waste disposed of to a contractor the sum total of all radionuclides does not exceed D MBq during any period of 3 calendar months; and

      (ii)   that each consignment of waste removed from the premises is accompanied by a Certificate signed on behalf of the Health Authority showing the total estimated activity of tritium and C-14 taken together contained in the waste at the time of its removal from the premises.

6. The disposal of gaseous waste is authorised subject to the conditions specified in paragraph 7 and to the following conditions:

   a)   that the waste is discharged into the atmosphere at places and in a manner such as to prevent as far as reasonably practicable, its reentry into any part of any premises; and

b) that in all the waste discharged in any one calendar month, the sum total of gases having a half-life of less than 30 minutes does not exceed E GBq and the sum total of gases having a half-life greater than 30 minutes does not exceed F GBq.

7. The further conditions subject to which the disposal of waste is authorised are:

a) That the Health Authority keep and retain for inspection by any person authorised by the Secretary of State, records of disposal showing:

(i) the description of the waste disposed of and the means of disposal and the sum total of becquerels of all the radionuclides (excluding those that are decay products of those present) contained in the waste at the time of its disposal, and

(ii) the means of and date of its disposal; and

b) that, if the Secretary of State so dictates, the Hospital Authority takes samples of the waste and keeps them for examination by authorised persons.

8. This is also to certify that the Health Authority are authorised with effect from **DD MM YY** to accumulate on the premises, solid and liquid organic waste containing Sr-90 and any radionuclide which emits alpha particles, with a view to subsequent disposal by burning or removal by an authorised waste collection authority subject either:

a) to the condition that if the waste is to be disposed of through a waste collection authority within a period of two weeks beginning with the date upon which its accumulation began, it is in a closed container or containers; or

b) if the waste is disposed of by burning, within a period of 1 calendar month beginning with the date upon which its accumulation began it is done in a closed container or containers; or

c) to the conditions that:

(i) all necessary measures are taken to prevent any person having access to the waste without the permission of the Health Authority;

(ii) all necessary measures are taken to prevent, so far as reasonably practicable, the accumulated waste from contaminating any other substance or article; and

(iii) the disposal of the waste is not unduly delayed and is in any case effected within a period of 26 weeks from the date upon which it arose.

9. In this Certificate

'the Act' means the Radioactive Substances Act 1960;

'disposal', 'dispose of', 'radioactive waste' and 'contamination' have the same meanings as in the Act;

'drainage system' means any drainage system normally used for the disposal of foul water arising on the premises;

'liquid waste' means waste consisting of a liquid with or without solid matter in suspension;

'waste collection authority' means a local authority with statutory powers/ duties relating to the removal of refuse;

'residual ash' includes cinders and other debris;

and the activity in Becquerels is measured by any generally accepted method or, where it is impractical to measure the activity, is estimated in any generally accepted manner

signed by authority of the

Secretary of State for the Environment

Date

The authorisation does not authorise the accumulation or disposal of waste in contravention of any other enactment or rule of law.

In particular, if the waste authorised for disposal is also special waste as defined by Regulation 2 of the Control of Pollution (Special Waste) Regulations 1980, [this refers to combustible waste with a low flashpoint and to drugs and prohibited substances which require special documentation and authorisation] the requirements of these regulations will also need to be met.

References

1   *The Ionising Radiations Regulations 1985* (SI No 1333) (HMSO, London)
2   *The Radioactive Substances (Hospitals) Exemption Order 1990* (SI No 2512) (HMSO, London)
3   *Radioactive Substances Act 1960* (HMSO, London)
4   Approved Code of Practice 1985 *The protection of persons against ionising radiation arising from any work activity.* (HMSO, London)
5   *Guidance Notes for the protection of persons against ionising radiations from medical and dental use 1988* (HMSO, London)
6   *Completion of RSA3 forms* Association of University Radiation Protection Officers Guidance Note 3
7   *Management of Radioactive Wastes Produced by Users of Radioactive Materials* IAEA Safety Series 70 (IAEA, Vienna)
8   Health and Safety Commission 1982 *The Safe Disposal of Clinical Waste* (HMSO, London)
9   *Code of Practice for the prevention of infection in clinical laboratories and post-mortem rooms 1978* (HMSO, London)
10 *Control of Pollution Act 1974* (HMSO, London)
11 Department of the Environment Application Form RSA 3 *Application for authorisation to accumulate and dispose of radioactive waste* (DoE, London)
12 Cember H 1969 *Introduction to Health Physics* (Pergamon Press, Oxford)

CHAPTER 10

Transport and Movement of Radioactive Materials

A E Simpson

10.1 Introduction

Although the transport or movement of unsealed radioactive material, when appropriately contained, is in general a relatively non-hazardous procedure, there is always the risk of accidental damage to the container or its shielding while it is being moved. Such accidents may range from simply dropping a package onto the floor to a major traffic accident or fire. It is therefore the responsibility of those transporting radioactive material to ensure that it is sufficiently well contained, shielded and packaged so that there is minimal danger to members of the public in the event of an accident occurring. The package must be adequately labelled so that anyone dealing with such an accident is made aware of the possible hazards involved, and so that the package and its contents can be readily identified in the event that it is mislaid. The use of suitable packaging and labelling will also allow for safe handling and proper stowage during transport.

For movement of radioactive sources within a hospital site, the necessary precautions and procedures are largely a matter for local agreement and may form part of the Local Rules required under The Ionising Radiations Regulations (1985) (IRR)[1]. However, when radioactive material is transported off the hospital site (even if it is only to another nearby hospital or laboratory) such movements become subject to the statutory provisions of various regulations. These regulations require a well established formal structure of documentation and labelling and a high standard of packaging capable of withstanding common accident conditions. Under these transport regulations, hospital staff may act not only as consignors, but also sometimes as carriers and drivers with each having their own legal responsibilities.

All regulations and codes of practice covering the transport of radioactive material are based on the safety standards set by the International Atomic Energy Agency (IAEA), as set out in various publications. The 1973 edition of these regulations, as amended in 1979, forms the basis for the current UK legislation. However, the IAEA published a revised set of regulations in 1985 ('the IAEA Regulations') with the provision for both sets of regulations to be operated in parallel for a transitional period extending no later than 1990[2]. Current UK legislation and Codes of Practice are being revised to conform with the IAEA Regulations, and full harmonisation is expected by 1990. In particular, it is anticipated that the values of 'A_1' and 'A_2', the maximum activities of a specified radionuclide permitted in a Type A package, and from which the exempt activity limits are derived (10^{-4} A_2 for radioactive liquids), will be revised to harmonize with the 1985 revision.

In all the regulations covering the transport of radioactive material there is a general exemption for patients who contain radioactive sources (whether for radiotherapy, diagnosis or the power source for a cardiac pacemaker). Such patients are, however, still subject to restrictions on their movements under the

IRR, and these restrictions are clarified in the Approved Code of Practice[3] (ACOP 2/30-33).

The various transport regulations should not be regarded as just another series of restrictions to be tolerated reluctantly and circumvented where possible. They form a sensible and coherent system of procedures to ensure that the high standards of radiation safety maintained in the hospital uses of ionising radiation are extended into situations, outside the direct control of radiation workers, where members of the public could otherwise be exposed to a possible radiation hazard.

10.2 Definitions

It is helpful to clarify some of the technical terms that are used throughout the various regulations and some of the special meanings attributed to common words.

Transport means the carriage of a radioactive substance on a **road**, or through another public place (whether on a conveyance or by hand), or by rail, inland waterway, sea or air, but does not include transport by a pipeline, nor when the radioactive substance is an integral part of the conveyance and used in its operation[1]. Since safety in transport necessarily depends upon actions taken prior to the actual movement, the definition of 'transport' in the IAEA Regulations[2] is more extensive. It includes the design, fabrication and maintenance of packaging and the preparation, consigning, handling, storage in transit and receipt at the final destination of packages.

Road means either 'a road within the meaning of section 196(1) of the Road Traffic Act 1972'[1] or 'any highway, and any other road to which the public has access'[4]. These definitions are essentially identical, though there has been more case law to establish the interpretation of the Road Traffic Act definition, which is taken to include public footpaths and bridleways and bridges; 'access' is generally taken to mean access by right, and the provisions of the Act still apply to vehicles which are only partly on the road and partly on private land.

Radioactive material or **radioactive substance** means any material having an activity concentration or specific activity greater than:

100 Bq g^{-1} (IRR[1])
74 Bq g^{-1} (Carriage by Road Regulations[4])
70 Bq g^{-1} (IAEA Regulation[2])

The IRR extend the definition to cover any other substance where radioactivity cannot be disregarded for the purposes of radiation protection and include a sealed radioactive source.

The specific activity of a material in which the radionuclide is uniformly distributed, means the activity of radionuclide per unit mass of the material[2]. In calculating the specific activity in relation to an article, only part of which incorporates or has on its surface any radionuclide, account is taken only of the part of the article which incorporates or has on its surface that radionuclide.

The **consignor, carrier** and **driver** have the meanings generally understood for these terms, but it should be noted that they may, in some cases, overlap. For instance, the consignor may be an individual or a hospital department. The carrier may be a commercial carrier (who could be a single taxi driver or a large firm) or may be a hospital department or a Health Authority. The driver could be an employee of the carrier or the carrier himself, and in some cases will also be the consignor.

Type A and **Type B** packages are defined by the IAEA[2]. Type A packages are designed to withstand the minor accidents anticipated in normal transport, whereas Type B containers, which are designed for the transport of very high activity sources, must satisfy much more stringent conditions so as to withstand even severe traffic accidents and must be specifically approved by the national **Competent Authority** (in Great Britain, this is the Secretary of State for Transport). Examples of containers meeting the various requirements are given in a British Standard, BS 3895[5]. In general, hospital users of unsealed radionuclides will only require to use Type A packaging.

Special form material means either an indispersible solid radioactive material or else a sealed radioactive source meeting certain provisions of the IAEA Regulations[2] and certified as such by the **Competent Authority**. It is allowed to be transported at higher activities in a Type A container. This will not generally be applicable to hospital users of unsealed radionuclides. It should be noted that the transport of certain sealed sources (e.g. some bone densitometry sources) may come into this category.

A_1 and A_2 values are the maximum activities for a specified radionuclide that may be transported in a Type A container for, respectively, **special form** and other material. For unsealed radionuclides A_2 will always apply. These values are tabulated for most radionuclides in the IAEA Regulations[2], but the tabulation in the earlier (1973) IAEA Regulations differs for some radionuclides, and some transport regulations may still refer to the earlier IAEA Regulations. However, all transport regulations should be harmonised with the (1985) IAEA Regulations[2] by 1990. A_1 and A_2 values are also used as the basis for the exempt limits of activity, below which many provisions of the various regulations will cease to apply. A list of A_2 values for radionuclides in common hospital use is given in *table 10.1*.

The **transport index** for a package not containing fissile radioactive material is the numerical equivalent of the maximum doserate in air at one metre from the external surface of the package when expressed in the units of mrem per hour (mrem h^{-1}). When the doserate is expressed in SI Units of microsievert per hour (μSv h^{-1}), the transport index is the numerical equivalent of one tenth of this doserate.

e.g. Maximum doserate at 1 m from the external surface = 0.5 mrem h^{-1}
or 5 μSv h^{-1}
Transport Index = 0.5

The number expressing the transport index should be rounded up to the first decimal place, except that a value of <0.05 may be regarded as zero.

White and **Yellow Labels** are an internationally recognised design of warning labels affixed to radioactive packages to identify their contents and to indicate the conditions under which they may be stowed in a vehicle or store. The designs are specified in both the Code of Practice for the Carriage of Radioactive Materials by Road (1986)[6] and by the IAEA[2]. It should be noted, however, that for carriage of radioactive material by passenger train in the UK, British Rail require an adapted form of the yellow Category II and III labels, as specified in specific British Rail regulations.[7]

The **Competent Authority** is the national authority designated to carry out various statutory functions under the IAEA Regulations[2]. In Great Britain, this is currently the Secretary of State for Transport, and his powers are exercised through the Radioactive Materials Transport Division of the Department of Transport. For Northern Ireland, these functions devolve upon the Department of

Table 10.1 A_2 values for radionuclides in common hospital use:

Radionuclide	A_2 (1986 UK 'Road Code')	A_2 (1985 IAEA Regulations)
	Ci	TBq
Au-198	40	0.5
C-14	100	2
Ca-45	40	0.9
Ca-47	20	0.5
Co-57	90	8
Co-58	20	1
Cr-51	600	30
Fe-59	10	0.8
Ga-67	100	6
H-3 (as tritiated water)	1000	40 (and concentration < 1 TBq l^{-1})
I-123	50	6
I-125	70	2
I-131	10	0.5
I-132	7	0.4
In-111	30	2
In-113m	60	4
K-42	10	0.2
K-43	20	0.5
Mo-99	100	0.5
Na-22	8	0.5
Na-24	5	0.2
P-32	30	0.3
Rb-81	30	0.9
S-35	300	2
Se-75	40	3
Sn-113	60	4
Sr-85	30	2
Sr-89	40	0.5
Tc-99m	100	8
Tl-201	200	10
Xe-133	1000	20
Y-90	10	0.2

the Environment for Northern Ireland. These statutory functions include the approval of Type B packages, the certification of special form material and the implementation of a compliance assurance programme to ensure that the provisions of the IAEA Regulations are met.

10.3 Internal Movements

Many movements of unsealed radioactive sources by hospital workers are confined within the hospital grounds and are not subject to the various transport regulations (except where public roads cross these grounds). Such internal movements will include the transfer of radioactive material between laboratories, conveying radiopharmaceuticals to a ward or clinic and the removal of radioactive waste to a temporary store. These movements, while exempt from all transport regulations, are nevertheless subject to the IRR.

There is a requirement (IRR Reg 21 (3)) that all radioactive substances must be kept in a 'suitable receptacle' while they are being moved, so far as is reasonably practicable. Guidance on the suitability of a receptacle is given in the Approved Code of Practice[3] (ACOP 1/128–130). Any package satisfying the requirements of the IAEA Regulations[2] will be adequate (for instance the original manufacturer's packages used to send radioactive material to the hospital, if they are unopened or re-usable). If some other form of container is used, it should provide adequate shielding for the carrier (who will be the individual most exposed). It should be suitable for the physical and chemical form of the source and able to withstand any likely hazards that could be encountered during the movement (particularly the hazard of being dropped or knocked over). Account should be taken of the distance over which the source is to be moved (long distances or the need to move up or down stairs can increase the risk of an accident) and also of the possible consequences of an accident (e.g. therapeutic activities of unsealed radionuclides are potentially serious hazards). This regulation does not apply to patients or corpses containing unsealed radioactive material, although they are covered by the provisions (IRR Reg 8) concerning mobile controlled areas which will generally apply only to patients who have received a therapeutic dose of I-131.

In instances when the radioactive material is contained in a live animal, there will generally be no serious external radiation hazard. However, the animal's cage should have sufficient absorbent material to contain any radioactive excrement, and both this material and the animal must be securely contained.

The provision of adequate shielding is essential for protection of the person(s) carrying or accompanying a radioactive source other than a very low activity source or patient's specimen. For low energy beta emitters (e.g. C-14, H-3) sufficient protection will generally be provided by the walls of a glass vial, but higher energy beta emitters (e.g. Y-90, P-32) may need additional shielding against both the beta radiation and the bremsstrahlung, especially if present in therapeutic activities. Gamma emitters will generally require some degree of lead shielding, though if space is not a problem it may be cheaper and lighter to make at least some use of the rapid decrease of doserate with distance. Some examples are given below:

1. 800 MBq Tc-99m in a type P6 vial:
   doserate at surface of unshielded vial $\cong$ 130 mSv h^{-1}
   doserate at surface of 5 mm thick lead pot $\cong$ 20 μSv h^{-1}
   doserate at surface of 10 cm diameter 'fruit tin' containing the lead pot $\cong$ 2.5 μSv h^{-1}

2. 100 MBq Na-24 in a type P6 vial
   doserate at surface of unshielded vial $\cong$ 500 mSv h^{-1}
   doserate at surface of 35 mm thick lead pot $\cong$ 5 mSv h^{-1}
   doserate at 1 metre outside the lead pot $\cong$ 11 μSv h^{-1}

3. 500 MBq I-131 therapy capsule:
   doserate at surface of unshielded capsule $\cong$ 1.2 Sv h^{-1}
   doserate at surface of 13 mm thick lead pot $\cong$ 1.8 mSv h^{-1}
   doserate at surface of outer cardboard box (23 cm sides) containing the lead pot $\cong$ 190 μSv h^{-1}

4. 5000 MBq I-131 therapy capsule:
   doserate at surface of unshielded capsule $\cong$ 12 Sv h^{-1}
   doserate at surface of 29 mm thick lead pot $\cong$ 3.2 mSv h^{-1}
   doserate at surface of outer cardboard box (23 cm sides) containing the lead pot $\cong$ 300 μSv h^{-1}

There is no specific requirement (IRR Reg 21) for radioactive sources to be suitably labelled while they are being moved internally, although this is clearly good practice. There is a general duty for employers, however, to ensure that adequate information is given to all persons directly concerned with work with ionising radiation to enable them to comply fully with the requirements of the regulations and to ensure their health and safety (IRR Reg 12). This duty implies that all radioactive sources must be readily identifiable, with a clear indication of the extent of the radiation hazard; the most sensible way of complying with this requirement will be to use suitable labels. Labels complying with the IAEA Regulations[2] will be adequate, but more compact labels will be required for individual vials, syringes and small containers. Such labels should include the radiation trefoil symbol, the word 'RADIOACTIVE' as a general warning, the radionuclide and its activity at a reference time, and also the chemical form of the radioactive material. It may also be convenient to have the consignor's details on the label (e.g. 'Medical Physics Department, City Hospital; ext 1234'). Although simple 'radioactive' adhesive tape may be adequate within a laboratory, when a radioactive source is moved outside the laboratory from which it originated a more explicit identification is desirable. Examples of suitable labels are shown in *figure 10.1.*

It is generally unnecessary to label specimens from patients receiving diagnostic levels of radiopharmaceuticals (e.g. urine or blood samples), but if such specimens are to be sent to another laboratory they should be labelled or documented so that the receiving laboratory is aware of their radioactive content. This is essential to avoid interference with the receiving laboratory's own radioactive measurements and contamination monitoring.

The final test of whether the packaging of an unsealed radioactive source is adequate will be to monitor it directly. Monitoring the external doserate at the surface of the package will determine whether it can be handled directly (IRR Reg 6(5)a implies that the surface doserates should be kept below 75 μSv h^{-1}). The doserate at one metre from the surface will indicate the hazard involved in transporting the package and should preferably be kept below 7.5 μSv h^{-1}. In all cases, the radiation dose to the carriers, as expressed by the external doserate, should be kept as low as reasonably achievable (the ALARA principle). Special attention should be paid to reducing this doserate if the movement is likely to take an appreciable length of time, or if the person carrying or moving the source is involved in such movements frequently. It would be good practice, wherever reasonably practicable, to keep doserates to within the limits for a category I White Label transport package (i.e. surface doserate <5 μSv h^{-1}). Monitoring of the outer container and shield for radioactive contamination, after the movement of the source has been completed and the source removed, will indicate whether the primary (inner) container (e.g. test tube, vial or syringe) was adequate for the task, and this should be performed routinely for any parts of the packaging that are to be reused.

Particular problems may be encountered in nuclear medicine when moving Tc-99m generators and recently filled Tc-99m flood sources (used to monitor the

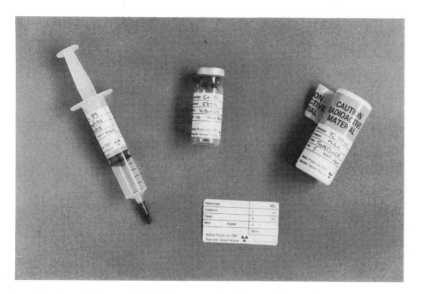

(a)

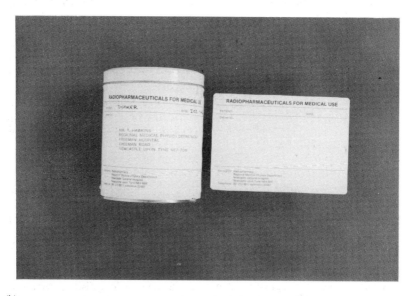

(b)

Figure 10.1 Examples of suitable labels for radioactive packages and containers: (a) for vials, syringes, or lead pots (b) for outer packaging

172

uniformity of response of a gamma camera). These may be very inconvenient to shield adequately and any such shields would probably be impracticably heavy for movement purposes. In such cases, the duration of handling and movement should be kept to a minimum and full use should be made of trolleys or wheel chairs when carrying the source so as to gain the maximum benefit from the decrease of doserate with distance.

There are requirements (IRR Reg 19; ACOP 1/116) for records to be kept showing the quantity and location of all radioactive sources having a half life >3 hours, and having activities in excess of those specified (IRR Schedule 2 Column 2). All movements of such sources must be recorded and it may be convenient to keep such records with the central register of radioactive material which is required under the Radioactive Substances Act (1960)[8].

The requirement to designate a controlled area (IRR Reg 8) around a radioactive source while it is being moved is clarified in ACOP 1/41. In general such a controlled area would affect only the person(s) accompanying the source and not bystanders. A controlled area would not exist outside a package which satisfies the category I requirements of the IAEA Regulations[2]. It should be possible to shield containers used for the internal movement of radioactive sources so as to keep the external surface doserate below the exempt limits specified (IRR Schedule 6 section 3 (c)) i.e. below 240 μSv h^{-1} for short duration movements totalling not more than 1 hour in any 8 hour working day. However, it will usually be necessary to designate a controlled area around a patient who has received radioiodine therapy if the activity remaining within the body exceeds 400 MBq, although the same exempt limits of IRR Schedule 6 (section 3 (c)) given above may allow more latitude.

Although the IRR[1] and ACOP[3] establish a statutory framework for radiation safety, most radiation protection measures are based on common sense and care. This is as true for the movement of radioactive sources as it is for laboratory handling procedures. The following recommendations may be taken as a guide to good practice in the internal movement of unsealed radioactive sources:

1. All unsealed radioactive material must be securely contained in a closed container (e.g. a screw top vial or capped specimen tube; the use of 'cling film' or 'parafilm' alone is not adequate). If the container is a syringe, it should be capped with a blind hub.

2. The container must be clearly labelled with the radionuclide, its chemical form, and the activity at a specified reference time.

3. Adequate shielding must be provided for the protection of the person(s) carrying or accompanying the source.

4. If the container in paragraph 1 above is not adequate against accidental dropping, a further, more robust, outer container is required. For the movement of liquid sources, containers should be watertight (e.g. a resealable tin or a plastic 'picnic box'), with shock and water absorbent packing. For higher activities (e.g. therapeutic doses of liquid I-131 or Y-90), and especially if there is a greater risk of an accident (e.g. a long distance to travel, movement outside in bad weather, travel up or down stairs or along busy corridors) consideration should be given to using a full Type A container.

5. The outer container should also be labelled, with details of the radionuclide and the activity at a specified reference time, and also with details of both consignor and consignee.

6. The radioactive source must be delivered without delay.

7. The source must not be left unattended while in transit.

8. If the doserate at the external surface of the outermost container exceeds 240 μSv h^{-1}, it will be necessary to designate a controlled area, and the RPA should be consulted before moving the source. However, the precautions needed to comply with a system of work are likely to be broadly similar to the guidance given in paragraphs 1–7 above.

Some examples of suitable containers for internal movements of unsealed radionuclides are shown in *figure 10.2*.

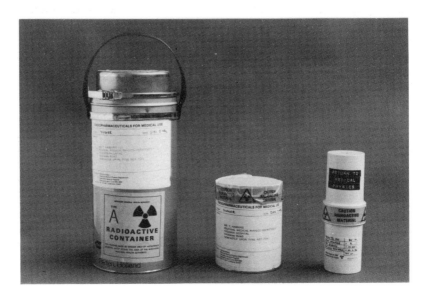

Figure 10.2 Suitable containers for internal movements

10.4 Carriage by Road

Many hospital users of unsealed radionuclides will never be concerned with movement of radioactive material outside the hospital bounds, but for those who are involved with external transport of radionuclides the most common mode of transport will almost certainly be by road.

Transport of radioactive material by road in Great Britain is governed by the Radioactive Substances (Carriage by Road) (Great Britain) Regulations (1974)[4], with some minor amendments in 1985 to convert to SI units of activity and doserate.[9] Very similar regulations cover the transport of radioactive material in Northern Ireland[10]. The Regulations are exceedingly general in their formulation and more explicit and detailed guidance is given in the Department of Transport's Code of Practice[6]. This Code ('Road Code') is currently being revised to harmonise with the IAEA Regulations[2], and a new edition is anticipated for use with the new Carriage by Road Regulations in 1990. Transport of radioactive materials which is covered by these Carriage by Road Regulations is specifically excluded from the scope of IRR Regulation 21, but the other IRR Regulations continue to apply, particularly as concern the designation of controlled areas and the health and safety of road transport workers. Any hospital worker intending to transport radioactive material by road will need to refer in detail to the 'Road Code'[6] and should consult with the RPS and RPA before commencing such procedures. A brief summary of the main provisions of the Carriage by Road Regulations is given below.

10.4.1 General

These Regulations cover all roads to which the public has access, and this may include some internal hospital roads. The most important prohibition (Reg 6) for hospital workers is against carriage of radioactive material in a public service vehicle. Transport between hospitals, therefore, could be by taxi, ambulance, private car, hospital van or commercial carrier, but not by bus. There is a general duty imposed on both consignor and carrier to exercise reasonable care to avoid injury to the health of any person.

10.4.2 Consignor's responsibilities

It is the consignor's responsibility to ensure that all radioactive sources are packaged so that they are safe to be carried. Generally a Type A container will be required. Packages must be appropriately labelled with either White or Yellow Labels, as detailed in Appendix VIII of the 'Road Code'[6]. The consignor must also provide a document stating that the packages comply with the Regulations (Reg 12; section B.1.6 of the 'Road Code'[6]) which is known as a 'consignor's certificate' or 'shipper's certificate'. An example of a form of certificate satisfying these requirements has been given in BS 3895[5] Appendix J. The IAEA Regulations[2] require certain extra information to be incorporated (Section 447) including use of the United Nations Number and proper shipping name (*table 10.2*). A specimen consignor's certificate is shown in *figure 10.3*.

10.4.3 Carrier's responsibilities

No passengers are allowed in the vehicle carrying the radioactive source unless they travel with the carrier's consent and in a 'personnel compartment' (e.g. driver's cab) which is separate from the 'goods compartment' in which the sources

Table 10.2 Excerpts from the list of United Nations Numbers, Proper Shipping Names and Descriptions.

UN No.	Name and description
2910	Radioactive material, excepted package
	— Instruments or articles
	— Limited quantity of material
	— Empty packaging
2912	Radioactive material, low specific activity (LSA).
2913	Radioactive material, surface contaminated objects (SCO).
2982	Radioactive material (not otherwise specified).

```
                    CONSIGNOR'S CERTIFICATE
                           FOR THE
              CARRIAGE OF RADIOACTIVE MATERIAL BY ROAD


    This is to certify that the goods listed below are properly described and
    are packed and marked in accordance with the applicable regulations of the
    Radioactive Substances (Carriage by Road) (Great Britain) Regulations 1974,
    or of the International Regulations, and are in a proper condition for
    transport.

    Consigned by:  Regional Medical Physics Dept
                   Newcastle General Hospital
                   Westgate Road
                   Newcastle upon Tyne  NE4 6BE
                   tel: 091 273 8811 x22487

    Consigned to:




    Consignment No:_____

    Date of dispatch:_____

    Carrier:_____


    Description of radioactive material:

    Radionuclide:_____

    Chemical name:_____

    Physical form:_____

    Activity of contents:_____ MBq

    Delete as appropriate:

    UN No:    2910 Radioactive material, excepted package(s)
           or 2974 Radioactive material, special form, not otherwise spec'd
           or 2982 Radioactive material, not otherwise specified

    Package type: A  or  B(U)  or  B(M)

    Category: Exempt  or  I (White)  or  II (Yellow)  or  III (Yellow)

    Transport Index (Category II or III only):_____

    Maximum surface doserate:_____ μSv h⁻¹



    Signed (on behalf of consignor):_____ date:_____
    RMPD CONSCERT 31/10/89
```

Figure 10.3 Specimen Consignor's Certificate

176

are carried. No passenger under 18 years old is permitted unless only White Label packages are being carried and the doserate in the personnel compartment is everywhere $<20~\mu\text{Sv h}^{-1}$. The sum of all the Transport Indices of all the Yellow Label packages carried must in any case not exceed 50.

The vehicle must bear warning placards to indicate the presence of radioactive material ('Road Code', Appendix VIII), as well as a fireproof notice in the cab giving details of the consignor in case of accident ('Road Code', Appendix IX). In the event of such an accident, the carrier must ensure that both the police and the consignor are notified immediately. The load must then be examined as soon as reasonably practicable to check for possible radioactive contamination and damage to the sources. If any contamination is found this must be reported to the Secretary of State through the Transport Radiological Adviser at the Department of Transport. A contaminated vehicle must be withdrawn from service within 48 hours of the incident and not used for any further loads until it has been decontaminated.

All radioactive packages must be kept secure against unlawful removal from the vehicle.

10.4.4 Driver's responsibilities

The driver of a vehicle conveying radioactive packages should take reasonable care against the theft, loss or escape of the radioactive material carried, and should not leave the vehicle unattended in a public place. The vehicle should not be left parked in one place for longer than one hour, unless either there is a clear space of 2 metres all around the vehicle or it is carrying only White Label packages. No passengers are permitted in the vehicle unless authorised by the carrier for that journey. Both the police and the carrier must be informed as soon as reasonably practicable of the loss, theft, or escape of or damage to any of the radioactive material carried.

10.4.5 Exemptions

Both the Carriage by Road Regulations[4] and the IAEA Regulations[2] permit certain packages, with which there is associated only a very low level of hazard, to be exempt from all or part of the respective regulations. In the IAEA Regulations these are referred to as 'excepted packages'. Packages containing only low activities and which meet the conditions and activity limits specified ('Road Code', Appendix II) are exempt from the transport regulations, though they must still be declared on transport documents as 'exempt radioactive materials' and must be identifiable as radioactive when the packages are opened. Empty packages are also exempt subject to the conditions in Appendix II. It should be noted, however, that the IAEA Regulations[2], in addition to using amended values of A_1 and A_2 for some radionuclides, require a consignor's certificate to be provided for all radioactive shipments, including excepted packages (paras 415, 447–452). Some radioactive liquids, of very low specific activity ($<10^{-5}~A_2~\text{g}^{-1}$), may be transportable as Low Specific Activity material (class LSA-II), but this is unlikely to be widely useful in hospital practice, and in most such cases the material would also be excepted under the provisions for the overall quantity of radioactive material in the package.

Medical radioactive sources which are sealed and undamaged, and which are or have been carried in or about a patient for his treatment, are exempted from the regulations. The 'Road Code' (para A.3.6.1) interprets this to include any radioactive substance so carried by a patient or being returned to a hospital immediately following treatment. A similar exemption applies to live animals or carcasses which have been made radioactive during experiments or treatment.

Low activity radioactive waste (generally < 0.4 MBq in any 0.1 m^3) which is being transported to a refuse disposal site for disposal in accordance with a Certificate of Authorisation or an Exemption Order issued under the Radioactive Substances Act[8], which is not subject to any special precautions, is exempted from the Carriage by Road Regulations[4]. However, higher activity waste disposed of under conditions imposed in a Certificate of Authorisation is subject to these Regulations, although such waste will often be exempt under the conditions specified in Appendix II of the 'Road Code'.

Finally, there is currently a partial exemption granted to professional hospital users subject to certain conditions. The carriage of properly packaged and labelled radioactive sources by professional users experienced in handling radioactive material is exempted from the regulations covering consignor's certificates, passengers in the vehicle, placards, fireproof notice and stowage of packages provided that:

a) not more than 10 packages are carried.
b) the sum of all the Transport Indices of any Yellow Label packages is < 10.
c) in the case of a vehicle other than an ambulance, all occupants are at least 18 years of age.
d) if the vehicle is an ambulance, the carriage of the radioactive material has been authorised by a Radiological Safety Officer for that hospital, and the professional user is acting under his instructions.

However, it would be good practice to have some form of documentation in the vehicle to indicate that radioactive material is being transported. It would be reasonable to assume that the term 'Radiological Safety Officer' may be taken to refer now to a Radiation Protection Supervisor or Radiation Protection Adviser appointed under the IRR.

10.5 Carriage by Rail

Transport of radioactive material by rail within the UK is subject to British Rail's Conditions of Acceptance[7]. A new edition is in preparation and is expected to harmonise with the IAEA Regulations[2]. All consignments of radioactive material must comply with the provisions of the (1973 revised) IAEA Regulations, with the following amendments and additions relevant to hospital users:

1. The yellow Category II and III labels for packages carried on a Passenger Train (i.e. by Rail Express Parcels Service) have an additional panel carrying instructions for stowing the package, and Category III is subdivided into III A (Transport Index < 1.5 and containing no fissile material), and III B (Transport Index < 10 and including fissile material).
2. Each package must bear a securely attached label showing, in legible and durable characters, the name and full address of both consignor and consignee, and the station of destination.
3. A Dangerous Goods Consignment Note must be completed for each consignment which includes radioactive material of specific activity > 74 Bq g^{-1} even if the packages are exempted from other provisions of the regulations by virtue of their low activities. Such exempt materials must be declared as 'Exempt Radioactive Material', though further details (e.g.

radionuclide, activity, transport category etc) may be omitted. However the IAEA Regulations[2] require certain additional information to be given including the United Nations Number and proper shipping name.

4. For carriage by Passenger Train (hospital users are unlikely to use freight trains), one full day's notice is required for despatch of Categories I, II and IIIA packages, and four full days for Category IIIB.

5. All radioactive packages, other than those exempted under the IAEA Regulations[2], must be sealed and despatched under either the Recorded Parcels Transit Scheme on a station to station basis, or the Red Star Parcel Service.

6. Cartage of radioactive materials beyond the destination station, and consignments with either a surface doserate > 2 mSv h^{-1} or a Transport Index > 10, will only be accepted by special arrangement with the British Railways Board.

10.6 Carriage by Inland Post

The carriage of radioactive material by inland post is available only for very low activities per package, and is subject to the conditions laid down in the current edition of the Post Office Guide[12]. The latest (1986) edition is still based on the 1973 Revised Edition of the IAEA Regulations, though this may be expected to be changed in subsequent editions to harmonise with the 1985 Regulations[2].

The limits on activity for carriage by post are 1/10 of the IAEA exempt limits for carriage by other modes of transport (i.e. 10^{-5} A$_2$ for liquids and 10^{-4} A$_2$ for solids or gases), and the surface doserate must be < 5 μSv h^{-1}. *Prior approval of all containers must be obtained from Postal Headquarters in London and sample packaging, together with information on the chemical nature of the radioactive substance, must be provided for inspection.* It may be assumed, however, that approval will be forthcoming if the activities comply with the IAEA limits and the container meets the specifications of BS 3895[5] for a Type A container.

In addition, the following conditions will apply.

1. Approved packets must bear the name and address of the consignor on both the inner and outer wrappings.

2. The inner wrapping must also show clearly the description of the radioactive material.

3. The outer wrapping must display a conspicuous request for the package to be returned to the consignor in the event of non-delivery.

4. In addition to the radioactive properties of the contents of the package, any other dangerous properties (e.g. flammability, toxicity, pathogenicity) must also be taken into account.

5. Non-fixed contamination of any external surface must not exceed the levels specified in the IAEA Regulations (0.4 Bq cm^{-2} for beta and gamma emitters).

6. The package must retain its contents under conditions likely to be encountered in routine transport (this condition will automatically be satisfied if a Type A container is used).

Enquiries and applications for approval should be addressed to Royal Mail Parcels Marketing, Post Office Headquarters (see Appendix VII).

10.7 Carriage by Air and Sea, and International Movements

It is unlikely that many hospital users will be involved with these modes of transport, though there may be a limited use of internal air transport for the movement of some short lived radionuclides (such as Kr-81m generators used for lung ventilation imaging). It is not intended to provide any detailed descriptions in this publication of the various statutory requirements and Codes of Practice, but a brief list of relevant documents is given below for reference.

10.7.1 Air

Air Navigation Order (SI 1985 No 1643).
Air Navigation (Dangerous Goods) Regulations (SI 1985 No 1939).
International Air Transport Association (IATA) Dangerous Goods Regulations (reissued annually).
International Civil Aviation Organisation (ICAO) Technical Instructions for the Safe Transport of Dangerous Goods by Air (reissued annually).

10.7.2 Sea

Merchant Shipping (Dangerous Goods) Regulations (SI 1981 No 1747).
Merchant Shipping (Dangerous Goods) (Amendment) Regulations (SI 1986 No 1069).
Code of Practice for the Carriage of Radioactive Materials through Ports (1975).
Carriage of Dangerous Goods in Ships — Report of the Standing Advisory Committee 1978 (the 'Blue Book').
International Maritime Dangerous Goods Code 1981 (IMDG).

10.7.3 International movements

(International movements by air and sea are covered above).

European Agreement concerning the international carriage of dangerous goods by road, 1986 edition (ADR).
International Convention concerning the carriage of goods by rail (CIM).
International Regulations concerning the carriage of dangerous goods by rail, 1985 edition (RID).

In all cases, reference should also be made to the IAEA Regulations[2] as well as the local regulations in force in the countries through which the consignment will pass (including the UK) and to which it is consigned. There will also be a need to comply with any relevant Customs regulations.

10.8 Packaging and labelling

10.8.1 Package types

The IAEA Regulations[2] define three types of packaging for radioactive materials: industrial (for Low Specific Activity material or Surface Contaminated Objects), Type A (for activities less than A_1 or A_2) and Type B (for higher activities). In addition there are some general provisions for all packaging of radioactive material (including exempt packages). These requirements for packaging are also incorporated into the UK Regulations.

In general, the 'industrial packaging' will not be applicable to hospital users of unsealed radionuclides. Similarly, Type B packaging, although quite common for sealed radioactive sources used in radiotherapy, is not likely to be needed for unsealed sources. These types of packaging will not, therefore, be considered further here.

10.8.2 General provisions

All packages containing radioactive material, even if it is below the exempt limit, must conform to certain standards (IAEA[2] para 505-517).

It is required that the package is designed to be easily and safely handled and transported, and can, where necessary, be properly secured in the transporting vehicle. The package should generally be free of protruberances from the external surface, except for handles, where applicable, which should be capable of supporting the full weight of the package. The outer layer of the packaging should prevent the collection and retention of water, and should be easy to decontaminate. The package should be able to withstand unimpaired the effects of acceleration, vibration and resonance encountered in routine transport, particularly with regard to nuts, bolts and other securing devices. The materials used in the packaging should be physically and chemically compatible both with each other and with the radioactive contents. Finally any valve through which the radioactive contents could escape must be protected against unauthorised operation (this may be applicable to some radionuclide generators where the contents are in either liquid or gaseous form).

In addition to the above requirements, which take account of the radioactive properties of the contents, it will be necessary to take full account of any other dangerous properties which the contents may have (e.g. flammability, corrosiveness or toxicity) and to comply also with any relevant regulations controlling such hazards.

If packages are to be transported by air, they must also be capable of withstanding temperature changes ($-40°C$ to $+55°C$) and a pressure reduction of 95 kPa without leakage or other impairment of their integrity. In particular, this implies for aqueous solutions either a high standard of thermal insulation or the ability of the primary container (e.g. a glass or plastic vial) to withstand freezing of the contained liquid. If a plastic vial provides the sole containment, consideration should be given to the possibility of greatly increased brittleness of the plastic at low temperatures. Attention should also be given to the possibility of loosening of seals due to different degrees of thermal contraction or expansion, and to the loss of effectiveness of some adhesive tapes and labels at very low temperatures. These considerations of low temperature effects are also applicable to the transport of frozen material (e.g. therapy doses of I-131-mIBG, which may be packed in dry ice).

10.8.3 Type A packages

Full details of the requirements for a Type A package are given in paragraphs 524-540 of the IAEA Regulations[2]. It is intended that a Type A package should be capable of withstanding routinely all the rigours of normal transport, including loading and off-loading, and also of surviving a minor accident without loss or dispersal of the radioactive contents and without more than a 20% increase in the radiation level at the external surface of the package. Although not subject to prior approval or certification by the Competent Authority, any package purporting to be Type A must be capable of satisfying the various tests specified (IAEA[2] paragraphs 619-625). In most cases, the consignor may satisfy himself that a package design fulfills these test requirements by complying with the provisions of BS 3895[5]. Alternatively, it may be possible to reuse the packaging in which radioactive material has been received from a reliable manufacturer; in this case great care must be taken to ensure that the packaging is suitable for reuse, is undamaged, and is not missing any necessary components, such as the absorbent material for liquids or the expanded polystyrene foam blocks (used to provide a shock absorber and thermal insulation and to immobilise the radioactive source in the centre of the package).

If, however, a consignor wishes to use packaging of his own design, he should demonstrate and document the compliance of the design with the statutory requirements, and keep a record of this documentation to show to the competent authority if so required.

Some examples of Type A packaging are given in Figure 10.4.

10.8.4   Labelling

The inner containers of any radioactive package (e.g. glass vial, lead pot, sealed can) should all be labelled clearly with the details of the radioactive material (see Section 10.3). This is to ensure that at all stages of handling and unpacking, the nature and extent of any radioactive hazard is made apparent to anyone handling the package. This will be required whatever the mode of transport used for the package. Examples of suitable labels are shown in *figure 10.1*.

Labelling of the outer container will consist of two types of label:

a) the address label, which must specify the full address of the consignee and a return address for the consignor in case of non-delivery or accident in transit. An example of a suitable label is given in *figure 10.1*.

b) For non-exempt packages, two transport category labels must also be affixed to the outer packaging. This label specifies the external radiation hazard, and allows radioactive packages to be handled and stowed safely in accordance with the relevant transport regulations. The two labels must be affixed to two opposite sides of the outer surface of the package.

Exempt packages do not require transport category labels, but should still bear appropriate labels on the inner containers and an address label as in (a) above.

The IAEA Regulations[2] specify three Transport Categories (paragraphs 440–445), with distinctive labels, that are used for all modes of transport except post (for which the permissible radioactive packages are well within the exempt limits and therefore will not require such labels) and UK rail (for which the Category II and III labels are adapted for carriage by passenger train). These exceptions have already been detailed (Sections 10.5 and 10.6).

The external radiation hazard is quantified by two parameters in order to assign a package to the appropriate Transport Category. The first parameter is simply the maximum radiation doserate anywhere on the external surface of the package and gives an indication of the hazard in handling the package. The second parameter, called the Transport Index (see Section 10.2) is a measure of the maximum radiation doserate at one metre from the external surface and allows the package to be stowed safely in such a position that it will not present an unacceptable doserate to the carrier. The further refinements of the Transport Index to take account of the particular hazard of criticality for fissile material are not relevant to hospital users. The limits on surface doserate and Transport Index for the three categories are given in *table 10.3*.

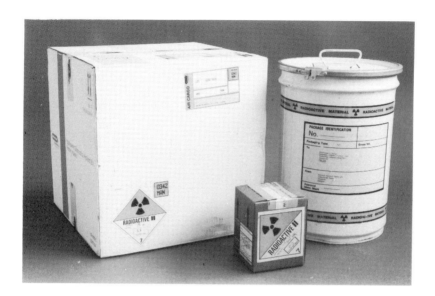

(a)

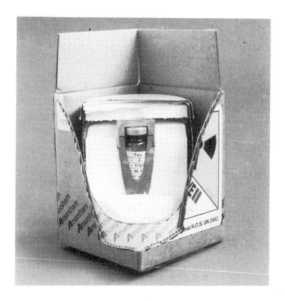

(b)

Figure 10.4 (a) Examples of Type A packages, (b) Cut-away of typical Type A packaging

Table 10.3 Transport categories for carriage of radioactive material

Category	Max. surface doserate	Max. Transport Index	Exclusions
I (white)	$<5\ \mu Sv\ h^{-1}$	—	Fissile Class II or III†
II (yellow)	$<500\ \mu Sv\ h^{-1}$	1.0	Fissile Class III†
III (yellow)	$<2\ mSv\ h^{-1}$	10	
For UK Rail only:			
IIIA (yellow)	$<2\ mSv\ h^{-1}$	1.5	All fissile material
IIIB (yellow)	$<2\ mSv\ h^{-1}$	10	–

† These restrictions on fissile material derive from the 1973 IAEA Regulations and will no longer apply when harmonisation with the 1985 Regulations[2] is achieved.

10.8.5 Quality and compliance assurance

The Regulations (IAEA[2] paragraphs 209 and 210) require that quality assurance programmes be established for all aspects of the transport and packaging of radioactive material, and that the Competent Authority implement a programme of compliance assurance to ensure that the provisions of the Regulations are met. The Department of Transport, as part of its compliance assurance programme, requires that all organisations (including hospitals, medical schools, universities and other research laboratories) involved in the transport of radioactive material should implement a programme of quality assurance to demonstrate and document full compliance with the relevant UK regulations.

Guidance on the form such a quality assurance programme should take is given in Appendix 4 of IAEA Safety Series No 37[13] and compliance with this guidance will be taken by the Department as satisfying their requirements.

The Department envisage that, for small scale users such as hospitals, an adequate quality assurance programme could consist of a simple system of visual inspection of all packaging components together with measurements of radiation levels and, if necessary, levels of surface contamination. The use of a check list would be part of this system and would also serve as a documentary record of compliance. An example of a check list appropriate for most hospital users is shown in *table 10.4*.

In addition, the Department will require all hospitals and other users involved in the transport of radioactive material to produce a documented organisational structure covering all relevant aspects of transport (e.g. packaging, documentation, calibration of measuring instruments, training and regular reviews of the system), and including lines of individual and departmental responsibility. This documentation should not only establish compliance with the regulations, but

Table 10.4 Check list for quality assurance of radioactive packaging.

This checklist must be completed before dispatch.

Consignment ref no:

Date and time of dispatch:

Carrier:

Mode of transport:

Consignee:

1. List of radioactive contents:

	radionuclide	form	activity at dispatch
(i)			
(ii)			
(iii)			
(iv)			
(v)			

2. Vial or bottle: (a) intact and sealed? ( )
    (b) correctly labelled? ( )
    (c) activity of contents checked? ( )

3. Lead pot or other shielding   (a) intact and undamaged? ( )
    (b) checked free of contamination? ( )
    (c) correctly labelled? ( )
    (d) absorbent material enclosed? ( )
    (e) securely fastened? ( )

4. Type A container   (a) intact and undamaged? ( )
    (e.g. fruit can):   (b) checked free of contamination? ( )
    (c) correctly labelled? ( )
    (d) shock absorbent packing enclosed? ( )
    (e) securely sealed? ( )

5. Outer packaging   (a) intact and undamaged? ( )
    (e.g. fibreboard box):   (b) checked free of contamination? ( )
    (c) correctly labelled? ( )
    (d) securely closed/sealed? ( )

6. Transport category:

    Exempt? ( ) Activity within limits? ( ) Surface doserate $< 5\ \mu$Sv h^{-1}? ( )

    Category I (white label)? ( ) Surface doserate $< 5\ \mu$Sv h^{-1}? ( )

    Category II (yellow label)? ( ) Surface doserate $< 500\ \mu$Sv h^{-1}? ( )
    TI < 1.0? ( )

    Category III Road (yellow label)? ( ) Surface doserate < 2 mSv h^{-1}? ( )
    TI < 10? ( )

    Category IIIA Rail (yellow label)? ( ) Surface doserate < 2 mSv h^{-1}? ( )
    TI < 1.5? ( )

    Category IIIB Rail (yellow label)? ( ) Surface doserate < 2 mSv h^{-1}? ( )
    TI < 10? ( )

7. Consignor's Certificate
    (a) Certificate completed and signed? ( )
    (b) Certificate passed to carrier? ( )
    (c) Copy of Certificate attached to this form? ( )

Checked by: Date and time:

would also enable the system to continue to operate smoothly when, for instance, staff changes occur.

10.9 Transport of Radioactive Waste

Radioactive waste is no less of a radiation hazard for being waste, and such waste originating in hospitals may indeed have extra hazardous properties such as chemical toxicity or pathogenicity. If it is transported off the hospital site for disposal, then its movement is subject to the same statutory controls as other radioactive material, and it must comply fully with all the previously mentioned requirements for packaging, labelling and documentation.

However, most radioactive waste arising from hospital use is of very low activity and may be exempted from the Carriage by Road Regulations[4] (Reg 21) subject to the following conditions:

1. The waste is being removed to a tip, dump, pit or incinerator for disposal.
2. Such removal is either permitted by a Certificate of Authorisation under Section 6 of the Radioactive Substances Act[8] or is exempted from such authorisation by virtue of an Order made under Section 5 of the Act (e.g. the Radioactive Substances (Hospitals) Exemption Order 1990).
3. All limitations and conditions specified in the Certificate or in the Order are complied with.
4. Such limitations and conditions do not require any special precautions to be taken (such as instructions to package or otherwise contain the waste, or to bury or incinerate the waste).

In general, solid radioactive waste which is within the limits (< 0.4 MBq in any 0.1 m^3), for unrestricted disposal via the domestic refuse collection service will also be exempt from all transport regulations. However, solid waste of higher specific activity disposed of under a Certificate of Authorisation (generally for landfill disposal at a designated site) will not be exempt under regulation 21[4], though it will probably be exempt under regulation 20 (and the limits specified in Appendix II of the 'Road Code') provided that the external surface doserate is everywhere < 5 μSv h^{-1}.

Radioactive waste which has other hazardous properties, such as inflammability, must also comply with any other statutory provisions governing such hazardous properties. In particular, liquid scintillant waste in which highly flammable solvent, such as toluene, often forms a major constituent, will be subject to the Petroleum Spirit (Conveyance by Road) Regulations[14] or to the Inflammable Liquids (Conveyance by Road) Regulations[15]. These regulations control the quantities of flammable liquid that may be transported by road, and the containers in which they are transported.

If the waste is being transported to a disposal site which lies outside the area of the Local Waste Disposal Authority, then it may also be subject to the Control of Pollution (Special Waste) Regulations[16] which provides for a somewhat complex system of documentation and notification of such waste movements.

10.10 Hazard Evaluation and Contingency Planning

The regulations (IRR[1] Reg 25) require that all activities (including transport or movement operations) involving radioactive sources must be assessed for any possible hazard arising from any foreseeable occurrence. Where a possible hazard is identified, all reasonable steps must be taken to prevent the occurrence and limit its consequences. A further requirement (IRR Reg 27) is that the necessary actions shall be documented in a contingency plan. Most hospital accidents will warrant no drastic action, and written contingency plans should deal with potentially serious incidents. The response required for a less severe incident (e.g. a relatively minor spill) should nevertheless be catered for in the Local Rules.

10.10.1 Hazard evaluation

Under most foreseeable circumstances, there will be little risk of significant radiation exposure or dispersal of radioactivity arising from transport incidents provided that the radioactive sources have been properly packaged and labelled in accordance with the relevant transport regulations. Internal movements will frequently be less strictly controlled but generally involve only relatively small quantities of radioactive material and will also pose little serious hazard. Special attention should be paid, however, to high activity sources, such as Tc-99m generators and therapeutic level sources (including radioiodine patients who retain activities of I-131 >400 MBq). Although the transport of therapy administrations for patients in outlying hospitals or clinics may be undertaken by both medical physics and medical staff invoking the partial exemption from the transport regulations for professional users, this exemption does not preclude the need for a hazard evaluation under the IRR, nor the need to have a contingency plan.

Theft or loss of a radioactive source should be improbable as all sources should be attended at all times when in transit. However, particular attention should be paid to the arrangements for collection and delivery of radioactive consignments, and for the security of any necessary storage facilities while in transit (this will include a vehicle which is parked and unattended during the course of a multi-delivery journey). In the event that a radioactive source does become mislaid (e.g. incorrect delivery), proper packaging and labelling will ensure both that the source can be identified and returned to the consignor and that the package can be safely handled by non-expert personnel. The hazard assessment must also consider the possible consequences of accidents, such as traffic accidents or fires, and identify reasonably practicable measures to avoid or mitigate any radiation hazards.

10.10.2 Contingency planning

The primary purpose of the hazard evaluation is to prevent any untoward occurrence that could lead to the unnecessary exposure of staff or public to radiation or to an unplanned dispersal of radioactivity into the environment. However, should such an unfortunate incident occur, it is important that remedial action be taken as soon as possible to limit its extent. It is the aim of the contingency plan to enable this response to an incident to be initiated promptly and to proceed smoothly.

Guidance on general emergency procedures, including details of appropriate equipment for an emergency kit, are given in Chapter 8. However, aspects of contingency planning that are particularly relevant to transport operations are considered further in the following sections.

The primary requirement of a contingency plan will be firstly to ensure that nobody in the vicinity is exposed to a radiation hazard (for example, by keeping them at a distance), and secondly to establish a system for notifying appropriate members of staff of the occurrence of an incident. Such personnel will then be able to assess the severity of the incident and provide such expert advice and assistance as may be required. The emergency contacts identified in the plan should be those staff who will actually perform the necessary tasks, not simply those, such as heads of department or general managers, who may assume nominal responsibility. Incidents may occur at any time, especially when external transport to distant destinations is involved, and so the plan must include a means of contacting the relevant staff outside normal working hours (for example by means of a list of home telephone numbers or the use of a radiopager). The system of communication must also be simple to operate and clearly explained to those who have to implement it (e.g. transport firms, hospital drivers, switchboard operators).

Details of all contingency plans must appear in the relevant Local Rules, and should form part of the information and training given to all staff affected by the plan, both those who may need to initiate it and those who would respond.

10.10.3 Internal movements

Most internal movements of radioactive sources will be by trained staff experienced in the handling of radioactive material who may be expected to initiate appropriate action promptly and efficiently. However, where non-expert staff are used (for example, hospital porters or messengers) particular care should be taken to ensure that, in the event of a foreseeable incident (such as the dropping of a patient's injection material in a hospital ward or corridor), the risks of significant exposure or dispersal are minimised. This is most conveniently and reliably achieved by using appropriately robust packaging to reduce damage to the source and to contain any leakage of radioactive material (most commonly in liquid form). Type A packaging will almost always be adequate, though equivalent protection can also be provided in a variety of ways (see Section 10.3).

It is essential for the proper working of contingency plans that all radioactive sources in transit (except for negligibly small activity sources, such as patients' specimens for diagnostic tests) are clearly labelled as radioactive, and that the consignor is identifiable.

In the event of an accidental dispersal of radioactive material in transit, simple containment and decontamination procedures will generally suffice. The carrier should take immediate steps to prevent or limit dispersal of the radioactivity, with help from staff in the vicinity as necessary, and then summon any further assistance and equipment needed for decontamination and monitoring, either from his own department or from the local medical physics department.

10.10.4 External transport

Movements of radioactive material outside the hospital site will inevitably require the use of robust packaging in accordance with the relevant transport regulations. Most consignments will comprise Type A packages, and this will generally ensure that there is no serious exposure of the carrier or dispersal of the radioactive contents in the event of an incident (for example a road traffic accident). It is a requirement of the various regulations that, in the event of an accident involving the possible damage to, or loss of, a radioactive package, the consignor is informed (via the driver and carrier, or directly by the attendant police). The contingency plan should ensure that this notification is speedily and efficiently carried out. This will involve clear identification of the consignor on the outside of the packaging or in the relevant transport documentation and an established system for contacting the appropriate staff at the consigning hospital or department.

The NAIR Scheme (National Arrangements for Incidents Involving Radioactivity) is a nationwide system whereby the police can summon expert advice and assistance in the event of an incident, such as a road traffic accident involving a radioactive consignment or the discovery of a radioactive source in a public place. In Northern Ireland, equivalent arrangements are provided under the RIPP Scheme. However, these are 'long stop' schemes only, and are not considered by the Health and Safety Executive (HSE) as adequate provision of a contingency plan under IRR.

Nevertheless, where a hospital medical physics department provides Stage I assistance under NAIR, it may be reasonable to use the same system for contacting expert radiation physicists and utilise a common emergency kit of monitoring equipment and decontamination materials. It must ensure, however, that the system is accessible by all relevant staff (e.g. consignor, carrier, driver, hospital porters, ambulance liaison) as well as the police and emergency services.

In order that any possible loss or accident is discovered promptly, it is prudent to advise the consignee when a radioactive consignment has been dispatched, giving details of the contents of the consignment and the expected time of delivery. Where transport is by road, the 'Road Code'[6] requires that a fireproof notice, giving details of the consignor and how he may be contacted in an emergency, is placed in the driver's cab. If a carrier is exercising the partial exemption for professional users, this notice is not statutorily required, but the code strongly encourages the provision of such a notice and this would certainly be an appropriate precaution as part of any contingency plan under the IRR.

In the event that a radioactive package is suspected of being damaged following a road traffic accident, guidance on emergency action to be taken by the driver, and any emergency services initially attending the incident, is given at the end of Section D of the 'Road Code'.

10.11 Advice and Enquiries

In the first instance, advice on transport of radioactive material should be sought from the Radiation Protection Adviser. However, if further information or guidance is required it may be obtained directly from the Transport Radiological Adviser at the Department of Transport. Enquiries relating to transport by railway may be referred to the RPA for British Rail. Details of the relevant addresses and telephone numbers are given in Appendix VII, and cover also the local variations applicable in Scotland, Wales and Northern Ireland.

Advice relating to application of the Ionising Radiations Regulations may be obtained from the HSE Inspector at the local Area Office (the address may be found in the local telephone directory).

In an emergency arising off the hospital site affecting the transport of radioactive material, the police should be notified immediately. They will, if considered necessary, obtain expert assistance through the NAIR Scheme or in Northern Ireland the RIPP Scheme. If there is a proven or suspected loss or dispersal of radioactive material, this should be notified as soon as is practicable to HM Inspectorate of Pollution.

In Northern Ireland, guidance on both transport and radiochemical matters is provided by the Department of the Environment for Northern Ireland. In Scotland, radiochemical matters are covered by HM Industrial Pollution Inspectorate at the Scottish Development Department, and in Wales by the Water and Environmental Protection Division of the Welsh Office. The Department of Transport in London, however, cover transport throughout Great Britain. Addresses and contact points are given in Appendix VII.

References

1 *The Ionising Radiations Regulations 1985* (SI 1985 No 1333) (HMSO, London)
2 IAEA Safety Series No 6 *Regulations for the Safe Transport of Radioactive Material 1985* (IAEA, Vienna)
3 Approved Code of Practice *The Protection of Persons Against Ionising Radiation Arising from any Work Activity, The Ionising Radiations Regulations 1985* (HMSO, London)
4 *Radioactive Substances (Carriage by Road) (Great Britain) Regulations 1974* (SI 1974 No 1735) (HMSO, London)
5 BS 3895: 1976 *Guide to the design, testing and use of packaging for the safe transport of radioactive materials* (BSI, Milton Keynes)
6 *Code of Practice for the Carriage of Radioactive Materials by Road 1986* (HMSO, London)
7 BR 22426 *List of Dangerous Goods and Conditions of Acceptance by Freight Train and Passenger Train 1977* (British Railways Board, London)
8 *Radioactive Substances Act 1960* (HMSO, London)
9 *Radioactive Substances (Carriage by Road) (Great Britain) (Amendment) Regulations 1985* (SI 1985 No 1729) (HMSO, London)
10 *Radioactive Substances (Carriage by Road) Regulations (Northern Ireland) 1983* (SR 1983 No 344) (HMSO, London)
11 *Radioactive Substances (Carriage by Road) (Amendment) Regulations (Northern Ireland) 1986* (SI 1986 No 61) (HMSO, Belfast)
12 *Post Office Guide* (published annually and available from any Post Office)
13 IAEA Safety Series No 37 *Advisory material for the application of the IAEA Transport Regulations* 3rd edition 1987 (IAEA, Vienna)
14 *Petroleum Spirit (Conveyance by Road) Regulations 1957* SI 1957 No 191 (amended 1966, SI 1966 No 1190) (HMSO, London)
15 *Inflammable Liquids (Conveyance by Road) Regulations 1971* SI 1971 No 1061 (HMSO, London)
16 *Control of Pollution (Special Waste) Regulations 1980* SI 1980 No 1709 (HMSO, London)

Appendix I(a) FLOW CHART (A) for identification of controlled areas under IRR Schedule 6 Pt 1 (External radiation)

Beta and Gamma emitters only

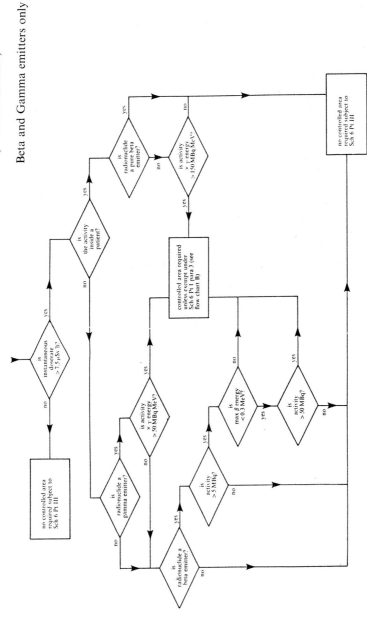

Note that if an area has to be *supervised* in relation to both internal and external radiation it must be designated a *controlled* area.

Appendix I(b) FLOW CHART (to be used if designation of a controlled area is indicated from Chart A)

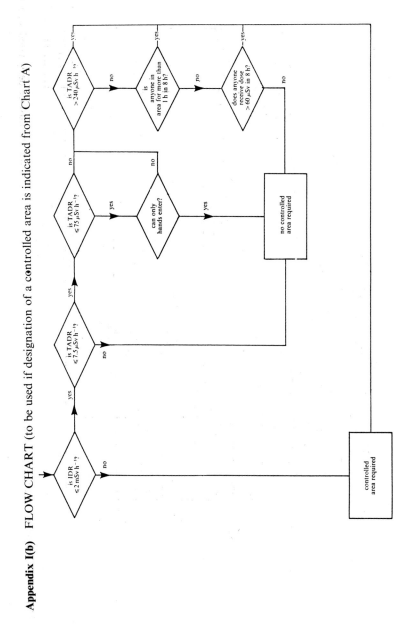

NB Use of TADR (i.e. doserate averaged over 8 hour working period) must be justified.
IDR—instantaneous doserate (doserate averaged over 1 minute).

Appendix I(c) FLOW CHART (C) for designation of controlled areas under IRR Schedule 6 Pt II (Internal radiation)

These apply only to gamma and beta emitters

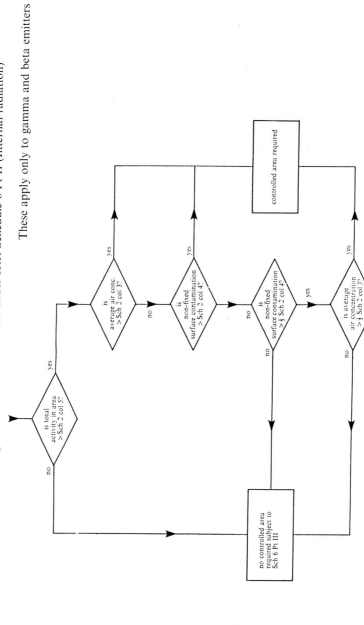

Note that if an area has to be *supervised* in relation to both internal and external radiation it must be designated a *controlled* area.

Appendix II Radionuclide decay data (principal emissions)

Radio-nuclide	$t_{\frac{1}{2}}$	$E_{\beta max}$ MeV	%	E_γ MeV	%
Au-198	2.70 d	0.961	99	0.412	95
C-14	5730 y	0.156	100	–	–
Ca-45	163 d	0.257	100	–	–
Ca-47	4.53 d	0.69; 1.99	82; 18	0.159; 1.297	70; 75
Cl-36	301 000 y	0.709	98	–	–
Co-57	271 d	EC	100	0.122; 0.136	86; 11
Co-58	70.8 d	β^+ 0.475	15	0.811	99
Cr-51	27.7 d	EC	100	0.320	10
Fe-59	44.5 d	0.274; 0.467	46; 53	1.099; 1.292	56; 44
Ga-67	78.3 h	EC	100	0.09; 0.185; 0.300	41; 24; 17
H-3	12.4 y	0.0186	100	–	–
I-123	13.2 h	EC	100	0.027; 0.159	86; 83
I-125	60.1 d	EC	100	0.035; ≈ 0.030	7; ≈ 140
I-131	8.04 d	0.606	90	0.364	82
In-111	2.83 d	EC	100	0.171; 0.245	91; 94
In-113m	99.5 m	IT	100	0.392	65
K-42	12.4 h	1.995; 3.520	18; 82	1.525	18
K-43	22.3 h	0.825	87	0.373; 0.618	88; 81
Mo-99*	66.0 h	0.454; 1.232	18; 80	0.740; 0.141	14; 84
Na-22	2.60 y	β^+ 0.546	90	1.275	100
Na-24	15.0 h	1.392	100	1.369; 2.754	100; 100
P-32	14.3 d	1.709	100	–	–
Rb-81*[1]	4.58 h	β^+ 1.05	27	0.190; 0.446	66; 19
Rb-82m[1]	6.47 h	EC; β^+ 0.80	74; 26	0.554; 0.777	63; 82
S-35	87.4 d	0.167	100	–	–
Se-75	120 d	EC	100	0.136; 0.265	59; 59
Sn-113*	115 d	EC	100	≈ 0.026; 0.393	97; 65
Sr-85	64.8 d	EC	100	≈ 0.014; 0.514	≈ 60; 99
Sr-89	50.5 d	1.463	100	–	–
Tc-99m	6.02 h	IT	100	0.141	89
Tl-201	73.1 h	EC	100	0.167; ≈ 0.075	10; ≈ 95
Xe-133	5.25 d	0.346	99	0.081; ≈ 0.033	37; ≈ 46
Y-90	64.0 h	2.274	100	–	–
Zn-65	244 d	EC	99	1.115; ≈ 0.009	51; ≈ 38

* assumed to be in equilibrium with shorter-lived daughter.

Data for all radionuclides except K-43, Rb-81 and Rb-82m taken from a compilation by Amersham International plc.

Data for K-43, Rb-81 and Rb-82m taken from the *Handbook of Chemistry and Physics 70th Edition* 1989 CRC Press, Boca Raton, Florida.

(1) In practice, the main contribution to the γ doserate from a well shielded Kr-81m generator is from the Rb-82m contaminant ($t_{\frac{1}{2}}$ = 6.47 h); this will be present in a proportion which depends on the production technique and which increases with time since production, but typically the Rb-82m/Rb-81 ratio at the end of batch production might be 25%. Although Rb-82m emits a multitude of γ energies from 0.554–1.475 MeV, the principal contribution from a shielded generator is at 0.777 MeV (82% unattenuated).

Appendix III Radiation exposure data

Radio-nuclide	ALI_{min}[1] MBq	DAC_{min}[2] kBq m^{-3}	DWC_{min}[2] kBq l^{-1}	doserate at 1 m[3] μSv h^{-1} MBq^{-1}
Au-198	10	8	0.8	0.061
C-14	40	20	3	–
Ca-45	10	4	2	–
Ca-47	10	4	0.8	0.15
Cl-36	3	1	2	–
Co-57	8	3	5	0.016
Co-58	7	3	2	0.15
Cr-51	200	80	30	0.0047
Fe-59	5	2	0.8	0.17
Ga-67	80	40	7	0.022
H-3	1000	400	80	–
I-123	90	80	8	0.044
I-125	1	0.8	0.08	0.034
I-131	0.8	0.4	0.07	0.057
In-111	50	40	4	0.084
In-113m	900	800	80	0.046
K-42	50	20	4	0.038
K-43	90	40	8	0.147
Mo-99*	10	8	0.8	0.041
Na-22	7	4	0.6	0.32
Na-24	50	30	4	0.5
P-32	5	2	0.7	–
Rb-81*[4]	400	200	30	0.093[4]
Rb-82m[4]	200	100	20	?
S-35	30	10	6	–
Se-75	9	4	0.8	0.056
Sn-113*	7	3	2	0.026
Sr-85	10	4	3	0.077
Sr-89	2	0.8	0.5	–
Tc-99m	1000	800	80	0.017
Tl-201	300	200	30	0.012
Xe-133	–	(4000)[5]	–	0.012
Y-90	5	3	0.4	–
Zn-65	4	2	0.4	0.085

* *assumed to be in equilibrium with shorter-lived daughter.*

(1) ICRP Publication No 61 *Annual Limits on Intake of Radionuclides by Workers Based on the 1990 Recommendations* (1991) Pergamon Press Oxford.

(2) Derived limits based on ICRP-61. The Derived Air Concentration (DAC) is derived from the ALI (inhalation) assuming an annual lung turnover of 2.4×10^3 m^3. The Derived Water Concentration (DWC) is derived from the ALI (ingestion); the derivation assumes an annual water consumption of 600 litres and is based on an annual Dose Limit of 1 mSv (i.e. ALI/20) on the premise that it is not necessary as part of a worker's employment that he or she should imbibe contaminated drinking water. All derived limits have been rounded up or down to the nearest one significant figure.

(3) Data on doserate at 1 metre (sometimes called the *specific gamma ray constant, Γ*) have been provided by Amersham International plc, and are for guidance only; these doserates do not take account of β or low energy (< 20 keV) X/τ emissions.

(4) In practice, the main contribution to the γ doserate from a well shielded Kr-81m generator is from the Rb-82m contaminant ($t_{\frac{1}{2}}$ = 6.47 h); this will be present in a proportion which depends on the production technique and which increases with time since production, but typically the Rb-82m/Rb-81 ratio at the end of batch production might be 25%. Although Rb-82m emits a multitude of γ energies from 0.554–1.475 MeV, the principal contribution from a shielded generator is at 0.777 MeV (82% unattenuated).

(5) Secondary limits for inert gases have not been published in ICRP-61. The value shown for the DAC for Xe-133 is therefore the previously published value from ICRP-30; this is based on the external dose from total submersion in radioactive gas and should therefore be unaffected by the changes in organ weighting factors. If the limiting dose is the β dose to the skin, the dose limit (and therefore the DAC) will be unchanged; if the limiting dose is the dose to the lens of the eye (300 mSv under ICRP-30, but now 150 mSv under ICRP-60/61), then the DAC should not be reduced by more than a factor of 2.

Appendix IV   Radionuclide shielding data

Radio-nuclide	principal emissions $E_{\beta max}$ MeV	E_γ MeV	γ attenuation 1st TVL[1] mm Pb	max. range of β particles[2] mm water
Au-198	0.961	0.412	12	4.1
C-14	0.156	–	–	0.30
Ca-45	0.257	–	–	0.66
Ca-47	1.99	1.297	46	9.7
Cl-36	0.709	–	–	2.8
Co-57	EC	0.122	≈0.7	–
Co-58	β^+ 0.475	0.811	28	(1.6)
Cr-51	EC	0.320	7.1	–
Fe-59	0.467	1.099; 1.292	44	1.6
Ga-67	EC	0.093; 0.185	5.3	–
H-3	0.0186	–	–	0.007
I-123	EC	0.027; 0.159	1.2	–
I-125	EC	0.35; ≈0.030	≈0.06[3]	–
I-131	0.606	0.364	11	2.3
In-111	EC	0.171; 0.245	2.5	–
In-113m	IT	0.392	9.5	–
K-42	3.520	1.525	53	18
K-43	0.825	0.373; 0.618	18.2	3.5
Mo-99*	1.232	0.740; 0.141	20	5.6
Na-22	β^+ 0.546	1.275	37	(2.0)
Na-24	1.392	1.369; 2.754	59	6.4
P-32	1.709	–	–	8.2
Rb-81*[4]	β^+ 1.05	0.190; 0.446	15[4]	(4.6)
Rb-82m[4]	β^+ 0.80	0.554; 0.777	?	(3.3)
S-35	0.167	–	–	0.33
Se-75	EC	0.136; 0.265	5.1	–
Sn-113*	EC	≈0.026; 0.393	≤0.5	–
Sr-85	EC	≈0.014; 0.514	16	–
Sr-89	1.463	–	–	6.8
Tc-99m	IT	0.141	0.9	–
Tl-201	EC	0.167; ≈0.075	≤0.9	–
Xe-133	0.346	0.081; ≈0.033	≤0.7	1.0
Y-90	2.274	–	–	11
Zn-65	EC	1.115; ≈0.009	42	–

* *assumed to be in equilibrium with shorter-lived daughter.*

(1) γ attenuation data are derived from tables published by Amersham International plc and are for guidance only; they do not take account of low energy (<20 keV) X/γ emissions. Values quoted are for the first Tenth Value Layer (TVL) in lead; due to filtration of lower energy emissions, subsequent TVL's may be greater than the values quoted. The TVL refers to attenuation of *doserate* not absolute γ flux.

(2) Values for the maximum range of β particles in water are derived from graphical data published in the *Handbook of Radiological Protection Part 1: Data* (1971, HMSO London). β particle ranges in tissue and most plastics will be similar though slightly shorter. Values quoted in parentheses for β^+ emissions assume the same dependence as for β^- particles.

(3) The TVL for I-125 is derived from the mass attenuation coefficient for Pb at 30 keV published in Kaye GWC and Laby TH *Tables of Physical and Chemical Constants* (13th edition 1966, Longman, London).

(4) In practice, the main contribution to the γ doserate from a well shielded Kr-81m generator is from the Rb-82m contaminant ($t_{\frac{1}{2}} = 6.47$ h); this will be present in a proportion which depends on the production technique and which increases with time since production, but typically the Rb-82m/Rb-81 ratio at the end of batch production might be 25%. Although Rb-82m emits a multitude of γ energies from 0.554–1.475 MeV, the principal contribution from a shielded generator is at 0.777 MeV (82% unattenuated). The attenuation of the doserate from such a (shielded) generator will therefore vary with time as the relative intensities of the emitted γ rays change; a typical attenuation coefficient for the doserate from a shielded generator at $2\frac{1}{2}$ hours after production might be 0.4 cm^{-1}, equivalent to a TVL of about 60 mm.

Appendix V Statutorily defined limits

Radio-nuclide	IRR 1985 Schedule 2 col. 2 notification MBq	col. 4 contamination Bq cm^{-2}	col. 5 total activity MBq	IRR Schedule 6 Part I §2 50 MBq MeV[1] MBq	IAEA 1985 Safety Series No 6 A$_2$ TBq[2]
Au-198	0.5	6×10^3	500	120	0.5
C-14	0.5	1×10^4	900	β	2
Ca-45	0.5	7×10^3	300	β	0.9
Ca-47	0.5	4×10^3	300	40	0.5
Cl-36	0.5	7×10^3	90	β	0.5
Co-57	0.5	2×10^4	200	400	8
Co-58	0.5	6×10^3	300	60	1
Cr-51	5	1×10^5	7000	1500	30
Fe-59	0.5	4×10^3	100	40	0.8
Ga-67	0.5	4×10^4	3000	300	6
H-3	5	4×10^6	3×10^4	β	40[3]
I-123	0.5	1×10^4	1000	300	6
I-125	0.05	1×10^2	10	1100	2
I-131	0.05	1×10^2	10	130	0.5
In-111	0.5	2×10^4	2000	120	2
In-113m	5	2×10^5	2×10^4	190	4
K-42	0.5	2×10^4	2000	180	0.2
K-43	0.5	2×10^4	2000	50	0.5
Mo-99*	0.5	5×10^3	400	210	0.5
Na-22	0.5	2×10^3	200	20	0.5
Na-24	0.5	1×10^4	1000	10	0.2
P-32	0.5	2×10^3	100	β	0.3
Rb-81*[4]	5	1×10^5	1×10^4	210	0.9
Rb-82m[4]	5	5×10^4	4000	20	0.02[5]
S-35	5	2×10^4	800	β	2
Se-75	0.5	2×10^3	200	120	3
Sn-113*	0.5	5×10^3	200	190	4
Sr-85	0.5	1×10^4	600	90	2
Sr-89	0.5	2×10^3	50	β	0.5
Tc-99m	5	4×10^5	3×10^4	400	8
Tl-201	5	7×10^4	6000	540	10
Xe-133	5	gas	5×10^5	1100	20
Y-90	0.5	2×10^3	200	β	0.2
Zn-65	0.5	1×10^3	100	80	2

* *assumed to be in equilibrium with shorter-lived daughter.*

(1) Calculated from published data on γ emissions and rounded down to the nearest 10 MBq.

(2) 1 TBq (tera-becquerel) = 10^6 MBq.

(3) and, for liquids only, a concentration $\leqslant 1$ TBq l^{-1}.

(4) In practice, the main contribution to the γ doserate from a well shielded Kr-81m generator is from the Rb-82m contaminant ($t_\frac{1}{2}$ = 6.47 h); this will be present in a proportion which depends on the production technique and which increases with time since production, but typically the Rb-82m/Rb-81 ratio at the end of batch production might be 25%. Although Rb-82m emits a multitude of γ energies from 0.554–1.475 MeV, the principal contribution from a shielded generator is at 0.777 MeV (82% unattenuated).

(5) This is the general A$_2$ value (IAEA 1985 §306), as no individual value is specified for Rb-82m.

Appendix VI Derived Limits for Surface Contamination

Surface	Levels of contamination that should not be exceeded (Bq cm^{-2})*		
	Class III	Class IV	Class V
Surfaces of the interior and contents of glove boxes and fume cupboards	The minimum reasonably achievable		
Other surfaces in Controlled Areas including equipment therein	30	300	3000
Supervised and public areas, clothing, bedding, body surfaces	3	30	300

Class III radionuclides are not alpha emitters and not in classes IV or V.

Class IV radionuclides are C-14, S-35, Mn-54, Co-57, Zn-65, Ga-67, Se-75, Br-77, Sr-85, Tc-99m, Cd-198, I-123, I-125, Cs-129, Hg-197, Tl-201.

Class V radionuclides are H-3, Cr-51, Fe-55, Ni-63, Cs-131.

* Measurements averaged over areas not exceeding 1000 cm^2 for floors, walls, ceilings, 100 cm^2 for body surfaces and 300 cm^2 for other surfaces.

Appendix VII   Addresses and contact points for advice or emergencies.

1. ARSAC Secretariat,
   Department of Health,
   Division HSIA,
   Room 515/6,
   Eileen House,
   88–94 Newington Causeway,
   London SE1 6EF.
   tel: 01-972 2718

   Applications for ARSAC certificates, advice on nuclear medicine procedures and research.

2. Health & Safety Executive,
   Baynards House,
   1 Chepstow Place,
   London W2 4TF.
   tel: 01-243 600

   Health and safety, Ionising Radiations Regulations 1985; communication normally to the local office.

3. Department of Economic Development,
   Health & Safety Division,
   83 Ladas Drive,
   Belfast BT6 9FJ.
   tel: 0232 701444

   Health and safety, Ionising Radiations Regulations (Northern Ireland) 1985.

4. HM Inspectorate of Pollution,
   Department of the Environment,
   Romney House,
   43 Marsham Street,
   London SW1P 3PY.

   Radiochemical matters, radioactive waste disposal, accidental loss or dispersal of radioactivity in England.

   tel: 01-276 0990 (ask for the Senior Radiochemical Inspector);
   outside normal hours, contact Resident Clerk, 01-276 5999.

   Northern Regional Office:
   HM Inspectorate of Pollution,
   Department of the Environment,
   1st Floor, Stockdale House,
   Headingley Business Park,
   8 Victoria Road,
   Headingly,
   Leeds LS6 1PF.
   tel: 0532 786636

   Lancaster Office:
   HM Inspectorate of Pollution,
   Mitre House,
   Church Street,
   Lancaster LA1 1BG.
   tel: 0524 382100

5.	HM Industrial Pollution Inspectorate for Scotland, Scottish Development Department, 27 Perth Street, Edinburgh EH3 5RB. tel: 031-556 8400	Radiochemical matters, etc. in Scotland.
6.	Water and Environmental Protection Division, Welsh Office, Cathays Park, Cardiff CF1 3NQ. tel: 0222 825111	Radiochemical matters, etc. in Wales.
7.	Department of the Environment for Northern Ireland, Alkali and Radiochemical Inspectorate, Calvert House, 23 Castle Place, Belfast BT1 1FY. tel: 0232 230560 outside normal hours, contact Duty Officer, 0232 757414.	Radiochemical matters and transport of radioactive material in Northern Ireland.
8.	The Transport Radiological Adviser, Department of Transport, Radioactive Materials Transport Division, 2 Marsham Street, London SW1P 3EB. tel: 01-276 5050	Transport of radioactive materials in Great Britain.
9.	Radiation Protection Adviser, Health and Safety Unit, British Rail, 23 Hartley House, Railway Technical Centre, London Road, Derby DE2 8UP. tel: 0332 42442	Transport of radioactive materials by rail.
10.	Royal Mail Parcels Marketing, Post Office Headquarters, Headquarters Buildings, 33 Grosvenor Place, London SW1X 1PX. tel: 01-245 7454	Transport of radioactive materials by post.
11.	National Radiological Protection Board, Chilton, Didcot, Oxon OX11 0RQ. tel: 0235 831600	General radiation protection advice in the south of England and Wales.

National Radiological Protection Board,
Hospital Lane,
Cookridge,
Leeds LS16 6RW.
tel: 0532 679041

General radiation
protection advice in the
north of England and
Wales.

National Radiological Protection Board,
155 Hardgate Road,
Glasgow GS1 4LS.
tel: 041-440 2201

General radiation
protection advice in
Scotland.

12. Northern Ireland Radiation Protection
Service,
Forster Green Hospital,
110 Saintfield Road,
Belfast BT8 4ND.
tel: 0232 793681

General radiation
protection advice in
Northern Ireland.